THE EARTH AND ITS PEOPLES

General Editors

J. M. PARRISH, M.A. (Oxon.)
JOHN R. CROSSLAND, F.R.G.S.

THE EARTH IN HER MAJESTY.

Rakaposhi (25,000 ft.) in the Himalayan system, seen from a distance of 10 miles. This is probably the only view in the world of a sheer height of 19,000 ft. seen from such close quarters.

G. P. Skrine.

THE EARTH AND ITS PEOPLES

GEOLOGY : GEOGRAPHY : ETHNOLOGY
ARCHAEOLOGY : ANTHROPOLOGY
COMPARATIVE RELIGION

Advisory Editor
SIR ARTHUR SMITH WOODWARD
F.R.S., LL.D., *lately Keeper of the*
Geological Department, British Museum

Edited by
H. A. T. CHILD, B.A. (Cantab.)
Geology and Geography Master at
Bedales School

ODHAMS PRESS LIMITED
LONG ACRE, LONDON, W.C.2

INTRODUCTION

Is "All the world a stage"? Are all the men and women in it "merely players"? Is it true to say that we are just puppets, moved by the invisible strings of the forces which the world around exerts on us, or have we the power to control our own destinies? This book is an attempt, not to answer that most difficult of all questions, but to indicate to the ordinary man who is interested in life some of the ways in which this great world stage of ours seems to influence the growth and development of man, and some of the ways in which we seem to control that world stage ourselves.

Its aim is twofold : first, to give as clear and concise a description as is possible of the world as the home of man, of its history from the early beginnings, of the slow but immense changes it has undergone, and of the great variety of conditions which are now found on the surface of the globe. The second aim is to trace the process of man's struggle towards civilisation ; the story of the slow process of trial and error in the making of tools, of rules of conduct and of life, by which we have arrived at our present stage of development.

HOW THE BOOK IS ARRANGED

The book is divided into five sections and, though these sections together make a connected whole, if the reader's interest lies in one particular part it can be read separately without reference to the others.

The first section—Geology—deals with the earth's crust and the story of its formation. It describes the materials of which the crust is made, the ways in which the materials are formed, and how they have been changed and altered, as millions of years have passed, into the continents and oceans as we know them to-day. It tells of the ways in which this crust may be investigated, and of how we may attempt to piece together its history, and even sometimes to date the great events in its distant past.

The second section—Geography—is a description of the earth's surface as it now is ; of the great variety of lands and climates that are to be found at the present time, and of the ways in which man has arranged his way of living so as to suit each variety. It tells how man in each part of the world has altered in appearance, dress, and customs, and describes the methods by which he is slowly gaining control over his surroundings, removing the barrier of distance from his neighbours, making barren regions bear fruit, and encircling the world with his thread-like routes of trade.

The third section—Archæology—becomes more historical in its outlook. Here the theme is the traces which early human beings have left behind them in the shape of their tools, weapons, houses, and burial-places, and the story of their lives, which we may construct from these traces. It is an account of very slow improvement in ways of living, and leads naturally to a comparison with the ways of living of modern primitive peoples. This is the subject of the next section—Anthropology—the " Study of Man " ; that is to say, the study of the customs, laws, and rules by which he regulates his relations with the world and his fellows. The marriage laws, family laws, taboos, magic, and religious beliefs of primitive folk are all of interest to us, for many of our own customs and laws have their roots in the ways of thought of our own primitive ancestors.

Finally, the last section concerns itself with the reaching out of man's thoughts and emotions towards what is beyond, and, as the study of Comparative Religion, it traces the rise and development of the great religious systems of the world out of the contact of primitive man with the supernatural. This section points out the similarities and differences in the great faiths such as Islam, Hinduism, Buddhism, and Christianity.

For the help of the reader whose interest is aroused by the subjects dealt with, there is a list of books suitable for further reading placed at the end of each section. There will also be found at the end of each section a brief account of the practical applications of the subject, and of the way in which training in it can be obtained.

CONTENTS

A WORLD BORN OF FIRE AND SCULPTURED BY TIME

by H. A. T. CHILD, B.A. (Cantab.)

FEW people are indifferent to scenery; there is something very deep-rooted in man which responds to beautiful or imposing natural surroundings, and from which he acquires a sense of peace and security which stands him in good stead against the nerve-shaking hustle of modern civilisation. This being so, the more he cultivates his appreciation of scenery, the greater will be the happiness and the well-being which he will derive from it; yet few people make any attempt to deepen their feeling for scenery, although in their appreciation of other things they are seldom so narrow-minded. A beautiful old building excites their curiosity as to its history; a famous picture leads them to discover the " schools " that have influenced it and the technique that has helped to make it famous; and in each case what they learn of history and of painting helps them to appreciate the building or the picture much more than they would have done otherwise.

This should be their attitude towards scenery. For, although a man can like or dislike scenery without knowing anything about it, a knowledge of the causes and of the history of scenery will give him a keener feeling for what he sees in the countryside, so that his interest is heightened and his pleasure in it vastly increased.

For scenery is always changing; indeed, all scenery owes its particular characteristics to the changes through which it has gone in the past, that is, to its history. This history is so sensational, and involves such enormous forces and such vast periods of time, that its scientific study—geology—is one of the most fascinating of all studies, and the picture it gives of the slow evolution of scenery is a very great help to man in his feeling for the countryside, the stage on which he erects his own small scenes of fields and towns and on which he plays his little part. The man who understands geology, however little, has a deeper feeling for what he sees as he travels about his earth, and a fuller appreciation of his own significance, than has a man who just likes what he sees but does not understand it.

Of course, geology has a broader aspect than that of the mere study of scenery, for we find that we cannot make clear the origin of land-shapes until we know a great deal of what underlies the surface of the earth and so we have to investigate as deep as we can. Unfortunately, we cannot with certainty go very far. Also other aspects of scenery, such as its covering of vegetation, come within the province of geography, so that perhaps a better way of defining geology would be to call it the science of the structure and history of the earth's crust. But since the structure and history of the crust in any particular place largely governs the scenery of that place, geology and scenery are very closely connected. As an illustration, let us take two strongly contrasted districts in the British Isles and see how geology explains the peculiar characteristics of each place.

VOLCANIC ACTIVITY THAT MADE THE LOVELY HIGHLANDS

ALONG the north-west coasts of the Scottish Highlands stretches a region famed for its beauty, its barrenness, and its isolation. Here are numerous islands, most of them mountainous, craggy cliffs, long arms of the sea stretching inland between purple heather-covered hills, thousands of lakes lying in hollows in the peaty and boggy moor, and swift streams running down the desolate glens. People are few ; here and there is a little village of stone houses where the Highlanders contrive to get a living by keeping sheep or by growing what crops the cool, wet climate will allow them, while others are driven by the inhospitable land to get a living by fishing in the stormy and dangerous seas. All this " character " of the region, apart from the climate, is largely due to the underlying rock, for here is one of the oldest parts of the earth's crust.

Many hundreds of millions of years ago the North-West Highlands were the scene of a vast outburst of volcanic activity, and the whole country is seamed with injections of once liquid rock. So numerous are these injections that the whole mass must have been like a big sponge filled with melted lava, and earlier still the mass, into which the lava was injected, was possibly itself in a liquid state. Gradually the mass cooled and solidified into very hard crystalline rock which forms the underlying foundation of the region. Later, an enormous amount of broken-up rock material was brought down by torrential streams from some mountainous area, about which we know nothing. The mountains must have been subjected to very severe weather conditions which quickly split and cracked their surfaces into fragments that were carried away by the violent streams and deposited in the hollows where the waters lost their force. These fragments have now been hardened and consolidated into a coarse red " sandstone " which is in places over twenty thousand feet thick.

All this happened so many million years ago that there was then no life on the earth to leave its remains behind in the form of fossils. Gradually the region, once probably very mountainous, was broken to pieces and worn down by the weather, so that by now the hills are only a very small remnant of what they must once have been. The wearing-down process was also much increased by the fact that recently—recently, that is, when compared with the enormous age of the rocks—the whole district was covered by a large mass of ice which, moving over the rocky surface, ground away much of the material, rounding off the hills and eating away hollows in which many of the lakes now lie. Long arms of ice descended to the sea, forming deep glens, and a still later sinking of the land allowed the sea to invade many of these glens, forming the long " sea-lochs " which are so characteristic of the Western Highlands.

Thus we see that a combination of natural forces, such as volcanic activity on a huge scale, the action of weather over an enormous period of time and great changes of climate, have gradually combined to mould and shape the North-West Highlands very slowly, but very surely, into the lovely scenery which we find there at the present day.

THE STORY OF THE FENLANDS : WHERE RIVERS MUST BE HELPED ALONG

THE most recent part of Great Britain to be formed which is of any size is the Fen District of eastern England. Here the history is of a very different nature from that of Scotland and so, consequently, is the appearance of the country. Instead of rolling hills and moors, the Fens stretch for miles in a flat series of fields of black, highly cultivated soil. Here and there are low banks bordering the long straight drainage ditches which slowly empty their almost stagnant waters into the Wash, where the sea exposes at every low tide miles of " flats " of mud and sand. Flatness is the most striking feature of this land. Except for a few slight rises in the ground, usually occupied by a village, the whole country has the appearance of being planed down to a geometrically horizontal surface, over which the rivers from the Midlands have great difficulty in finding their way to the sea, so that they have to be helped by artificial channels and by sluice-gates to keep the high tides from flowing inland, while much of the rain that falls on the Fens has to be pumped from the fields into the ditches.

The history of the Fenland does not go back so far into the dim past as does the history of the Scottish Highlands, nor does the story tell of such violent changes. It is more a tale of slow and gentle submergence by, and emergence from, the sea, and may be said to have begun a few million years ago when the region was under the sea and a series of clays was deposited on the sea floor. Later, a deposit of another kind was formed on the clays, when there was no longer any mud in the waters. This is the chalk, and it was formed from the shells of marine animals which slowly accumulated on the bottom until they formed a considerable thickness. Then occurred a slight elevation so that these deposits became land, and after they had been slightly tilted and worn down by the weather, a broad belt of clay was left on the west, and another belt of chalk on the east, as in the diagram.

Through this region a river made its way to the North Sea, cutting with its waters a gap in the chalk, and forming a broad flat valley in the softer clays. Then a slight sinking of the land allowed the sea to flood part of the river-valley, forming the present-day Wash. Then, as in the case of Scotland, came the ice-age, covering the region with a sheet of ice which left behind when it melted a series of clays and boulders over which the rivers again had to find their way to the sea. In the marshes and meres, moisture-loving plants grew and filled up some of the areas with peat, so that now the flat plains of the Fens are formed of various materials : marine-muds, river-muds, ice-formed clays, or peat. The rivers flow so sluggishly that the silt they carry is soon deposited, and the Wash, once much larger, is steadily decreasing in size. Measurements indicate that the whole of the Wash will become land in ten thousand years;

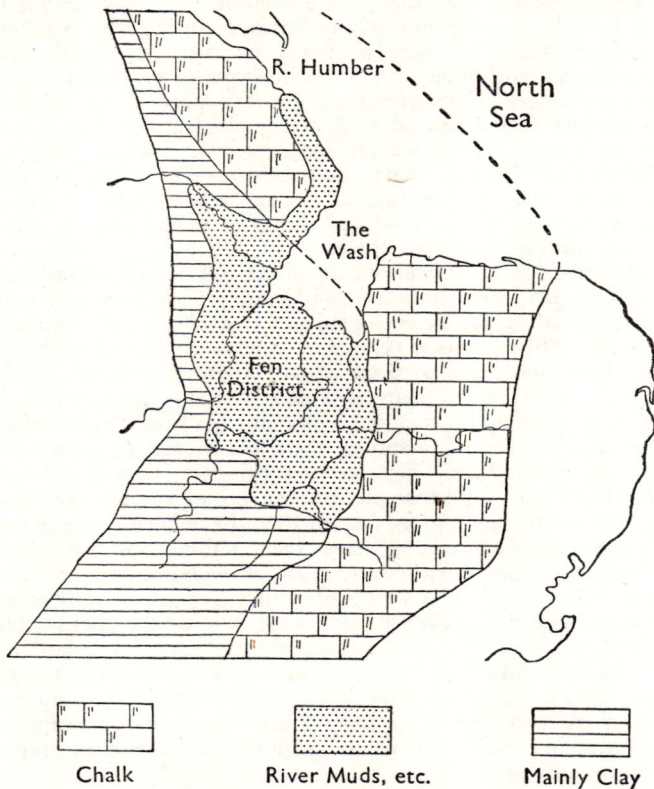

1. A STORY OF SLOW AND GENTLE CHANGE

During the few million years of its formation, the Fenland was slowly submerged by the sea, when first the clay and then the chalk were deposited. Then slowly these deposits became land again. The Wash is now steadily shrinking in size. The dotted line marks the former continuation of the chalk.

and man, by building dykes and drains, is doing a considerable amount to aid the process of nature.

THE HISTORY OF LAND REVEALED IN ITS FACE

THUS we can see that the appearance of any region is largely a reflection of its history during the millions of years that have slowly passed by since the earth first became a solid globe. It is the business of geology to trace these changes. By investigating every part of the earth's crust wherever it can be seen, the geologist picks up a clue to its history here and there and, gradually piecing together these clues, he can construct the history of a region and account, to a certain extent, for its appearance. He may even be able to forecast something as to its future, many thousands of years from now.

During his investigations he finds out many astonishing things. He learns how the solid land everywhere—not only in Scotland or the Fens—is subject to a process of continual change. True, it is a very slow change compared with the short life of a man, or even when compared with the whole time of existence of man as a race, but slow though it is, it is very sure, and if we give them enough time the so-called " everlasting hills " disprove their name, for they will inevitably disappear. The very continents themselves are found not to be permanent, for the geologist discovers that the rocks forming a great part of them have been made under the sea ; some regions have been submerged not once, but many times. Moreover, there is evidence of the existence of other continents long since disappeared. Many other things does the geologist find as he studies the rocks. He learns of the origin of the rocks themselves ; how they are slowly built up into great thicknesses ; of the origin of metals and minerals ; of the mechanism whereby the mountains are made and unmade ; and of the thousands of forms of life which have been evolved and which have disappeared before our time.

THE HIGH ROADS AND BY-ROADS OF GEOLOGY

GEOLOGY has, of course, a wider scope than that of the study of the history of the earth's crust. There are many different branches of the science, some of which involve pure geology only, and others which involve a knowledge of other sciences such as physics and chemistry, and which lead us gradually towards those sciences. The main part of geology is, perhaps, a description of the types of rocks to be met with in a particular place, including their arrangement in that place, together with an account of their relative ages and an attempt at their history. This is called stratigraphy—that is, a description of the " strata," or layers of rock. Then there is the study of the rocks themselves, describing the different classes of rocks found all over the world and their mode of origin. This is petrology. There is also mineralogy : the study of the materials of which rocks are made.

Palæontology is the science of the forms of life, or fossils, found buried in the rocks, and there are other branches such as the study of the movements of the earth, involving much physics, and the study of the changes which rocks undergo when exposed on the surface, which is largely physical geography. Some of these branches of geology have become so large and complicated that they are separate sciences in themselves ; mineralogy, for instance, usually has a separate department in the universities ; but we have to consider all of them in order to get a really complete knowledge of the history of the earth on which we live.

GETTING UNDER THE SKIN OF MOTHER EARTH

THE first thing that a geologist has to do is to inspect the structure of the earth wherever he can see that structure exposed, and at once he finds himself faced with difficulties. The first of these is the enormous area with which he has to deal. The total land surface of the globe amounts to about fifty-five thousand million square miles, so that to inspect it all thoroughly and to determine all the varieties of surface to be seen involves a very large amount of work. Indeed, comparatively little of the earth's surface has been investigated in detail. Much of Europe has been well inspected and some of North America ; parts here and there in the other continents are well known ; but the difficulties of travel in such places as Central Asia, Central Africa, and South America, and the lack of a civilised population in these parts and many others, makes the work of geology necessarily slow and expensive, so that in many cases it is only the main features of the surface that are known.

It will be a very long time before the details are all worked out and fitted into a complete general scheme. The work is, of course, being pushed on as fast as time and money permit. Most of the European countries, for instance, maintain in their numerous colonies a geological survey department, and some Eastern countries employ European geologists to investigate their territories; but, even so, the vast areas to be covered demand a long period of time in which to be thoroughly investigated.

The second difficulty is due to the fact that the greater part of the earth's surface is overlaid by a covering which effectively hides the true nature of the crust. This covering is of two kinds—vegetable and mineral. The vegetable covering, or vegetation, exists nearly everywhere. We know that in Great Britain forests, grass or moorland vegetation cover the country for miles, leaving no space where we can see what is underneath. Even where the plough or the spade has left the surface free from its usual covering of plants, again we are no nearer to a view of the true structure of the earth's crust, for these implements of cultivation expose only the second—mineral—covering on which plants depend for their lives—the soil.

SOIL-MAKING : THE WEATHER AT WORK

Most people accept the existence of soil without question, and do not realise that it has to be made from some sort of material, and in some places does not exist. Soil is simply the result of exposing the true materials of the earth's crust to the atmosphere. Buildings, when exposed to the weather for a long period of time (especially, but not necessarily, in cities where smoke and soot help the process), will eventually show signs of decomposition on their stone surfaces. In the same way the materials of the earth's crust, of whatever kind, when exposed to the weather, gradually break up into small fragments, and since the earth's surface lies horizontally, and not vertically as do the stones in the walls of a building, these broken-up fragments lie where they are formed. The roots of plants, growing in the fragments and penetrating downwards as far as they can go, greatly assist the breaking-up process, and finally the remains of plants which die on the soil surface get mixed up with the fragments, forming a dark coloured substance called humus.

Soil, then, consists of a mixture of finely broken-up rock material and vegetable matter, or humus. The type of soil will obviously depend, to a certain extent, on the underlying material, but it seems that the climate of a particular district also has an important effect on the nature of the soil.

Thus, over a large part of the earth's surface, there exists this covering, of immense importance to man, indeed to all life, but a severe handicap to geological investigation. Its thickness varies from a few inches to several feet, but, however thin it may be, it effectively hides the real nature of the underlying crust. The geologist therefore has to look for places where this covering is absent in order to understand the true structure of the earth.

WHEN "ROCK" MEANS EVERY KIND OF SURFACE

IN a general sense the word "rock" is taken to mean a hard, mineral substance, usually of a grey or brown colour, which is to be found in mountains, cliffs, and steep places; but in geology its meaning is much wider. When discussing the earth's crust it is essential to have a term which can be taken to denote any kind of material which helps to form this crust, without

2. TWO VEILS WHICH HIDE THE EARTH'S CRUST

Vegetation and soil form two coverings which make it difficult to investigate the earth's crust. Soil is itself rock, broken down by the action of time, weather, and the roots of plants.

implying anything as to its nature. For this, geologists use "rock" in the sense of anything which helps to form the earth's crust, whether a hard mineral substance like slate or granite, or whether a soft mineral substance like clay or sand. If the reader will remember this enlarged scope of the word " rock "—its meaning being extended to include absolutely anything which helps to form the earth's crust—much confusion and waste of time will be avoided.

We have seen how the geologist, in order to investigate the rocks, is forced to look for places where the covering of soil and vegetation is absent. Such places, which are known as " exposures," are of various kinds and fall into two main classes : natural exposures and artificial exposures.

Natural exposures will occur where for some reason or other the covering of the soil has been removed by natural means. This will always happen where the slope of the land surface is so steep that the soil cannot stay on it, and rolls or is washed down by rain to the bottom of the slope. The roots of the vegetation-covering will, of course, help to hold the soil to a steep slope but, as a general rule, if the slope is sufficiently steep, neither soil nor vegetation can remain on it, except in a few cracks and crannies, and the result is a bare face of true rock. Mountainous regions consequently show much more of their structure to a geologist than do plains.

Another important type of exposure is that which occurs where the sea, battering away with its waves at the land, has cut a steep face or " cliff." Cliffs afford valuable views of the crust to the geologist, but they do not occur on every coast, for in some places the sea is busy piling material on to the land, covering up such exposures as there may be with sand-dunes. Just as the sea cuts into the land and gives us a view of the rocks, so do rivers help us. The action of running water, as will be explained later, is usually to wear away the land surface over which it flows, so that rivers, especially in mountainous districts where they flow swiftly, often expose along their channels the rocks over which they flow.

The second class of exposures—artificial exposures—are often extremely useful but, unfortunately, being made by the hand of man they occur only where man is particularly active, where, for instance, there is some valuable mineral in the earth crust. In the coal-mining districts of Britain, for example, the thousands of galleries and tunnels in the collieries enable the geologist to get a very good picture of rocks in which they are made, but elsewhere, as in southern England, there are very few mines to help him, and he has to rely on other artificial exposures, such as quarries, chalk-pits, railway and road cuttings, or even the banks on the sides of sunken lanes. Another class of artificial exposures is that of wells and borings for oil or water, but these, like railway or road cuttings, must be observed while they are being made, before they are bricked up or, in the case of cuttings, overgrown with vegetation. Borings sometimes are very helpful, as the drill, which is usually hollow, brings up a central core of the rocks which can be examined carefully.

HOW DEEP DOES OUR KNOWLEDGE GO ?

THE consideration of exposures, such as mines and boring, leads to the question of how deep into the crust our knowledge extends. We are, of course, severely limited in this way. The great majority of exposures are on or near the surface, and mines and borings go only a comparatively short distance into the crust ; they occur, moreover, only in a few places. The deepest mines in the world—the Rand gold-mines in South Africa—merely penetrate the crust to a depth of eight thousand feet, and the deepest oil borings have reached ten thousand feet, whereas the distance from the surface of the earth to the centre is four thousand miles. Consequently our knowledge of places where such mines or borings occur reaches less than one two-thousandth of the total way, and elsewhere is limited to a very small depth.

Apart from a very thin outer layer, the structure of the earth is still hidden in mystery, and we can only guess at what is inside. There are a few indications of what there may be inside the earth, but they are nothing more than indications. For example, it seems possible that the interior is very hot, for measurements in mines show that there is an average increase of temperature as we go down of 1° F. for every sixty-four feet, though the figure varies in different parts of the world ; nor can we be sure, of course, that we should find this increase continuing if we could go deeper.

Again, we know that the earth is comparatively heavy. It is possible to measure the actual weight of the earth by experiment, and such experiments show that the earth is more than twice as heavy as it would be if it were made of such rocks as occur near the surface. This fact, coupled with our knowledge that the earth is a huge magnet, seems to point to the suggestion that the interior is largely made of some heavy metal such as iron ; but beyond the mere suggestion we cannot yet go.

WE have seen above how the rocks which the geologist wishes to study are not to be observed everywhere; it is only in small, isolated patches here and there, at the surface or sometimes below it, that they may be seen in their place, and the construction of the earth between these exposures can be dealt with only by guesswork. The distance between exposures varies from a few yards to many miles, and consequently the task of interpreting the geological structure of a region varies very much in difficulty, though in all cases the principle is the same. A careful study is made of the rocks disclosed at each exposure, and though, of course, specimens may be taken away to the laboratory for further examination, the essential thing is to get as clear an idea as possible of the structure of the rocks as they lie in place.

From this it is sometimes possible to guess at the probable nature of the next exposure and, if this is confirmed by observation, the procedure may be further extended, and so on. If, on the other hand, the second exposure is found to contradict what is suggested by the first, the work has to wait for further evidence. This study of structure must, of course, be based on a thorough knowledge of the kinds of rocks which are normally to be met with in any area, and to this we must now turn our attention.

ROCKS THAT WERE BUILT BY FIRE AND WATER

A COLLECTION of specimens taken from the geological exposures of a country or a region reveals an astonishing variety of rocks. They are of all kinds—hard and soft, heavy and light—and are made of many different kinds of rock-building materials, which we call minerals. These minerals, the essential materials of the crust, are chemical compounds of various substances, some of the most important of which are the elements silicon, oxygen, and aluminium. Rocks are formed of various mixtures of minerals. The study of minerals—mineralogy—is itself a very complex science, and it must necessarily be omitted from this section. It is sufficient here to recognise that all rocks are formed of minerals of many kinds, most of which are hard crystalline bodies.

The study of the many varieties of rocks which are known to occur has led to several ways in which they can be classified, one of the simplest of which is according to their mode of origin. There are two main ways in which rocks can be formed ; one is due to the action of heat, and the other to the action of water.

THE CRYSTAL GRANITE THAT WAS BORN OF FIRE

IF, as is often supposed, the earth as a whole originally cooled from a gaseous to a liquid, and finally to a solid state, the ultimate origin of all rocks must have been a consolidation from a state of fusion, but only one of the two great classes of rocks has this origin. These are the igneous (" fiery ") rocks. There are many varieties of igneous rocks, but they all show the essential characteristics of a once-melted mass of minerals. If such a melted mass is allowed to cool, the various minerals in it begin to crystallise, just as melted sugar will do, and each mineral crystal will grow, as the mass gets cooler and cooler, until it meets other crystals growing in the same way, and finally the mass sets solid. An igneous rock, therefore, consists essentially of a mass of interlocking crystals of various kinds of minerals, and it is usually possible to distinguish the different crystals in such a rock by their colour and shape, although sometimes they are too small to be seen with the naked eye.

A good example of a coarsely crystalline igneous rock is granite, polished surfaces of which are often used for ornamental purposes since the large, differently coloured crystals sometimes have a striking effect. In a normal granite one can usually distinguish three main minerals by their crystals : glassy crystals show the presence of quartz; white or pink milky crystals the presence of felspar ; and black crystals that of mica.

The second great class of rocks is derived originally from the first class by a series of processes which will be described later, but which may be briefly outlined here. Whenever a mass of rocks is exposed to the weather, very slow but certain decomposition sets in. The rock slowly crumbles away at the surface, and the broken-up material is carried down to the sea by the rivers, eventually to be deposited on the ocean floor. When the rivers, carrying this rock material, or sediment, reach the sea, the coarser material drops to the bottom first, while the finer mineral particles travel farther with the currents before they reach the ocean floor, so that a certain amount of sorting takes place. Also rivers and currents sometimes change direction, so that different kinds of material are deposited on top of each other in different places ; the final result is a series of layers of the different kinds, rather like the layers in a cake. These layers are called beds or strata and vary considerably in thickness, from a few inches to thousands of feet and, of course, they take many thousands of years to accumulate.

When a considerable thickness of the layers has been reached, the weight of the upper beds compresses and con-solidates the lower ones and, finally, by a mechanism which will be outlined later on, these beds of sedimentary rock, as they are called, are raised again to form new land, perhaps to be worn down again in their turn. A further consolida-tion may take place on the new land by the action of per-colating water which deposits cementing material between the particles or mineral grains which form the beds.

Igneous and sedimentary rocks can, therefore, usually be easily distinguished. Igneous rocks, owing to their origin, often show a hard interlocking mass of crystals. They seldom, if ever, occur in beds. Sedimentary rocks, on the other hand, nearly always occur in beds, are usually softer than igneous rocks, the constituent mineral grains being loosely packed, often of a very similar size, and sometimes cemented together by some other mineral deposited by percolating water.

HOW FAST DID THE ROCKS COOL ?

THESE two great divisions of igneous and sedimentary rocks can be further classified in various ways. Here it is necessary to mention only one or two of the main types. Igneous rocks vary largely according to the minerals which are found, or not found, in them, and they also vary largely in the size of their crystals. This last variation depends on the depths at which they have solidified. If the rock has cooled at a great depth, the heat will only have escaped slowly, and the crystallisation will have proceeded correspondingly slowly, thus allowing the crystals to attain a comparatively large size before the whole mass became solid. On the other hand, rocks which were formed as liquids on or near the surface, cool quickly, and crystallisation occurs at numerous centres close together, so that the solid result has very small crystals, often too small to be seen by the eye. Cooling may even take place so quickly as to prevent crystallisation altogether, and so produce a glass, such as obsidian.

Sedimentary rocks fall into four main types according to their constituent particles. These four types are arenaceous (sand), argillaceous (clay), calcareous (lime), and carbonaceous (coal) rocks. The first two classes differ not so much in the kind of material that forms them as in its coarseness. The arenaceous or sandy rocks are formed of larger-sized particles than the argillaceous or " clayey " rocks, and in the former rocks the degree of coarseness may vary from a fine sand-grain to large blocks of material. Most of us are familiar with the kind of rock called sandstone and, as its name implies, it is made up of sand-grains which are simply mineral particles roughly of the same size but often of different minerals, though there is usually a predominance of the very common mineral—quartz—which gives sands and sandstones their usual light colour.

Under a microscope, the sand-grains forming a sandstone may be seen to have the spaces between them filled in with a cementing material. This material consists of minerals in solution deposited by water which has soaked through the rock. This cementing material is sometimes of quartz, like many of the grains themselves, sometimes of calcite (calcium carbonate), and occasionally of other minerals, such as iron-ore, and the extent to which it binds the grains together varies considerably. Sometimes a sandstone is soft enough to be crumbled in the hand ; at other times it is hard enough to be used for grindstones.

Rocks made of larger materials than sand-grains are usually called " grits " and " conglomerates," but in them also there are the same constituents of fragments and cementing material. In some conglomerates the pieces are actually pebbles, and there are some rocks made of materials so coarse that they can only be described as boulders. A good example of a conglomerate is a rock which occurs in Hertfordshire, where it is known as " puddingstone." It consists of small rounded pebbles of black flint, surrounded by a white cementing material, and it looks exactly like a raisin pudding.

" STICKY " ROCKS THAT DEFY THE WATER

Turning now to the rocks made of finer material—the argillaceous or " clayey " rocks—we find again a considerable variation. Rocks which are made of material slightly finer than sand-grains are called flags and mudstones, and there is also the very large class of clays proper, in which the materials are so fine that it is often impossible to identify them under the microscope. It is this fineness of material which makes clays impervious to water, so that they are sticky, and form soft boggy land. There is one interesting alteration which clays undergo when they have been subjected to great pressure, either by the weight of a great thickness of rock on top of them, or by some other means. When tremendous force has been exerted on them in this way they become hardened and may be easily split in thin layers in a direction at right angles to that in which the pressure was exerted. These hardened clays or " slates " are, of course, economically useful wherever thin slabs of stone are required.

The third great class of sedimentary rocks—the calcareous or " limey " rocks—have a quite different origin. Although all round the shores of any land mass, enormous quantities of sediment are brought down by the rivers and dropped on the sea floor every year, there are much larger areas—in the middle of oceans, for example—where very little sediment can be deposited, for it has all reached the bottom before it can travel so far. In such areas the only sediments that can be formed are those derived from dust in the air which settles in the water, and from the organisms which live in the water. The first kind of sediment cannot be very great in quantity, but the second kind sometimes builds up enormous thicknesses of rock.

Every one is familiar with chalk, or calcium carbonate, as the chemist calls it, but every one is not aware that it is essential for many forms of life. Chalk is slightly—very slightly—soluble in water, and sea water always contains a small amount of chalk in solution. Most forms of life in the sea which have hard parts, such as bones or shells, have the power of extracting this chalk from solution in the water and of building it up into their skeletons. In the same way, land animals extract the chalk from the water they drink in order to build up their hard parts. In the sea, whenever marine animals die, their skeletons or shells sink to the bottom, and in places where no other sediment is being deposited these remains will gradually form a deposit consisting almost entirely of chalk. The process is, of course, extremely slow. It is almost impossible to grasp the immense length of time involved in the deposition of many feet of calcareous rock, but such rocks are known to exist many thousands of feet thick.

The softer calcareous rock is called chalk, and the harder kind, limestone. In appearance the chalk rock is a white or greyish rock which can be scratched with a knife, and it is often crowded with the shells and hard parts of animals. Corals are among the most important limestone-forming organisms, but the remains of thousands of kinds of animals are to be found in limestones, and they are a happy hunting-ground for the expert on fossils. Under the microscope, chalk or limestone is seen to consist of fragments of shells, etc., embedded in a matrix of finer material—largely calcium carbonate also—which may be simply finely-powdered shell fragments or, as has been suggested, it may be deposited actually from solution in sea-water, as the cementing material of a sandstone is deposited by water percolating through the pores of a rock.

THE NURSERIES OF OUR COAL SUPPLIES

THE last of the four great classes of sedimentary rocks, is much less common than the other three, and is not important as a building material for the earth's crust, but it is, nevertheless, extremely important to our modern civilisation, based as it is so largely on the use of coal. As their name implies, these rocks are formed largely of carbon and are derived almost entirely from plants, which are the only organisms capable of extracting the carbon from the gas, carbon dioxide which is found in the air, and of building it up into their tissues. It is not often that plant-remains are preserved to such an extent that they form a rock and, consequently, coal deposits are much rarer than other rocks.

The necessary conditions for the formation of coal seem to be, first, a rapid and continuous growth of a thick cover of vegetation on the earth's surface, such as happens in wet tropical regions; and, secondly, this dense vegetation must be covered by a layer of other rock—sand or mud—before it can be completely decomposed and removed by the weather. Such conditions can occur only occasionally, and probably there is nothing exactly like them to be seen operating in the world at the present day. Coal deposits do not occur everywhere, and the coal in them, as may be imagined, is found only in layers, or seams, a few feet thick. It is not surprising that we are using up our coal supplies at a rate a thousand times greater than that of their formation.

THE GREAT ARTISTS OF SCENERY : ROCKS AND THE WEATHER

WE have seen that the rocks which form the crust of the earth show a very large variety. They vary in hardness from rocks which are some of the hardest bodies known, to loose, unconsolidated sands, and they vary also in their solidity —that is to say, in the extent to which they are cracked and fissured. Scenery, as we shall see later, is largely the result of the action of the weather, particularly water, in wearing away the rocks, and it is clear that the different kinds of rocks will " weather " at very different rates and in very different ways. As a rule, the harder the rock, the more slowly will it be worn away, and it will, therefore, tend to stand up as hills compared with the softer rock round it. In addition to this, as has been explained above, rocks are decomposed at the surface into soil, and the kind of underlying rock will influence the kind of soil on it. This, in turn, will influence the kind of vegetation which grows on the soil, so that we can see that the rocks are one of the most fundamental factors in influencing the scenery of the country in which we live.

Let us take a few examples of the way in which rocks influence the scenery of a region. To begin with, most hard rocks form hilly country ; the action of weather must have been going on for a long time in the region of hard rock which is flat. The Highlands of Scotland, for example, are largely formed of granite and of a very old hard rock called gneiss. These rocks weather into a particularly infertile soil, in which little can be grown besides the characteristic tough moorland plants such as heather and wiry grass. The mountains of Wales are largely of slate and sandstone, though here and there are some volcanic masses, and though the Welsh slates and sandstones are of a hard type, they afford, on the whole, a more fertile soil than is found in the Highlands, and the pasture, from the point of view of sheep, is better, as it is also in the Southern Uplands of Scotland, which are formed of similar rocks to those of Wales.

WHERE WATER BURROWS: A HOME IN THE ROCKS

THE Pennine Highlands, " the backbone of England," are an example of a different kind of formation. Here the predominant rock is limestone, which has in places an upper layer of harder rock, called the millstone grit, which gives to many of the prominent hills of the Pennines their curious flat-topped appearance. Limestone often gives rise to peculiar country owing to its porous nature and its comparatively high solubility in water. Water often soaks into it instead of running over the surface, and one frequently comes across streams that have found their way into some crack which they have enlarged, and down which they disappear. Such "pot-holes," as they are called, are common in the Pennines, as are also caves formed by some underground stream which has altered its course. Another characteristic of limestone is the very thin poor soil which forms on its surface, so that the vegetation is poor and scanty like that of granite or gneiss. In some parts of Yorkshire and Lancashire the rain has washed away this soil altogether, leaving large bare patches of white rock called "clints," looking like snow in the distance, on which nothing grows except a few ferns in the crannies.

Another good example of the effects of weathering on hard rock surrounded by softer material is that of Dartmoor. It is a familiar sight to tourists, this bare, barren area of hilly moorland, surrounded by the fertile vales of Devon, and it owes its existence to volcanic activity of the past. Millions of years ago the Devonshire region suffered the intrusion from underground of a large mass of liquid granite which pushed its way into the layers of sedimentary rock, lifting them up into an arch over it. There it solidified, and, by the action of the weather through millions of years, the sedimentary cover has been worn off the top, and the country all round considerably lowered, so that the moor stands up over the surrounding vales.

The well-known Downs of the south of England are a further example of the action of weather. They are formed of chalk, a soft limestone which is even more porous than the Pennine limestone, so that water soaks into it very readily and wears the surface down slowly. The absence of streams is a noticeable feature of the chalk country, which has a thin soil, as in the Pennines, so that trees are uncommon except for a few thorny types and the lime-loving yew and juniper. Occasionally beech trees are found on sunny slopes and on the top of the Downs where patches of clay retain the moisture, but the characteristic bold, bare outline of the chalk hills is largely due to the underlying rock.

KNOWLEDGE THAT ADDS TO THE PLEASURE OF SCENERY

THESE paragraphs above have shown very briefly how the main features of scenery are due, to a very large extent, to the underlying structure of the earth's crust. There are other factors which will be discussed further on, but without a knowledge of the nature of the rocks of a region it is impossible to penetrate very far into the mysteries of its origin. In places it is possible to get a clear idea of the kind of rock that makes a country, but elsewhere it may involve years of patient work on the part of the geologist. Fortunately for us, the whole of the British Isles has been carefully examined and mapped by members of the Geological Survey of Great Britain and by others. Any one who uses an ordinary map on his walks and holidays will find a new occupation for his leisure times if he takes with him also a geological map of the same area, and perhaps, helped by the Survey's " Memoirs " and other books mentioned at the end of this section, he will find a hobby which may become a strong and abiding pleasure.

EARTH HEAT AND SUN HEAT ERECT THE MOUNTAINS

ASTRONOMY tells us that the earth possibly owes its birth to the approach of a star so near to the sun that a tidal wave was produced in the sun, causing a filament of the sun's " matter " to be drawn out from it. This filament is then supposed to have gradually cooled and condensed into the planets, of which our earth is one. Presumably, therefore, our earth originally cooled from a gaseous state through a liquid to a solid state and, consequently, the first crust was formed by cooling round a still hot and liquid interior.

Whether any parts of this crust are still to be found on the surface, we cannot say for certain ; possibly some of the oldest rocks known are of this kind, but most of the surface rocks of the present day are of a later date. They are either tongues of liquid rock pushed up from underneath, cooling when they reach the surface or get near to it, and forming igneous rock, or they are sedimentary rocks formed by the breaking-up of older material, which may have been either igneous or sedimentary in character. In either case, however, the process of forming rocks is due to the energy derived from the heat of the sun, for the interior heat of the earth—the cause of volcanic activity—is simply a part of the sun's heat, since the earth is supposed to have been originally part of the sun. The sedimentary rocks owe their existence to the action of weather in various forms, and since weather is simply the result of the sun's heat on the atmosphere, again we derive the energy for their formation from the sun. Just as all forms of life, animal or vegetable, get their energy from the sun, either directly or through the food they eat, so does even the earth's surface owe its present shape and all the changes it has undergone, or will undergo, to the all-embracing solar energy.

STOREHOUSES OF DESTRUCTION : THE VOLCANOES

MEASUREMENTS of temperature in mines and underground workings show that there is a rise in temperature of the rocks the farther we go down. This varies in different places, but in general the rise amounts to 1° F. for every 64 feet of descent. We cannot say for certain that this increase goes on indefinitely until the centre of the earth is reached (if it did, the temperature there would be about 33,000° F.), but we do know that in places the temperature of the earth is above the melting-point of the rocks, and that in places these melted rocks find their way to the surface, forming those startling features of the landscape—volcanoes.

Volcanoes seem to occur usually where there are lines of weakness in the crust, and along such lines of weakness we sometimes (but not always) find rows of vents through which the liquid rock occasionally escapes, together with a large volume of steam and other gases derived from the liquid materials. The rocks cool very quickly when they reach the surface so that, as a rule, they do not flow far before they solidify, forming a vast mound of lava, as it is called, round the vent. In some volcanoes the lava becomes solid before it reaches the outside, and it is blown out of the vent by the increasing pressure from underneath, falling round the aperture as small fragments known as volcanic ashes. Vesuvius has ejected at times both liquid lava and solid ashes, sometimes with very violent explosions, such as that which buried Pompeii in A.D. 79, when a large part of the mountain was blown into the air ; while Stromboli, an island volcano in the Mediterranean, which is, perhaps, connected with the same line of weakness as that on which Vesuvius stands, erupts regularly with a mild explosion every ten minutes.

Some volcanoes are more or less continuously active,

others only erupt at long intervals, lying dormant for many years, while there are many more extinct volcanoes than active ones. Extinct volcanoes can be found in many parts of the world, including the British Isles. Part of the island of Mull in the Hebrides, for instance, has been made out to be the much weathered remains of an old volcano, while much of the county of Antrim in Ulster consists of a vast series of lava-flows, in which the rivers have cut the famous " glens."

"THE RING OF FIRE": VOLCANOES THAT ENCIRCLE THE EARTH

A NOTICEABLE fact about the distribution of volcanoes, especially of active ones, is that a large majority of them occur around the coasts of the Pacific, or form islands in that ocean. All the way along the West Coast of the Americas are to be found numerous large and often extremely active volcanoes, such as Cotopaxi, in South America, and Mt. Wrangel in Alaska. The " Ring of Fire," as it is called, is continued in the volcanoes of Japan and the East Indies, where Krakatoa, the biggest known active volcano in the world, exploded in 1883—with such violence that the noise was heard two thousand miles away—and further still into the volcanic district of New Zealand where the hot springs indicate a late stage of activity. The " Ring " is almost completed by the active volcanoes of the Antarctic continent, where Mt. Erebus reaches a height of over thirteen thousand feet. This tremendous circle of cones would seem to indicate that there is some special line of weakness in the crust which has influenced the shape of the Pacific coasts, but suggestions as to its cause are at present very speculative.

Although the surface accumulations of volcanic activity sometimes form series of rocks of vast dimensions, still greater are the subterranean intrusions of liquid material which go on in all volcanic districts, for the liquid rock, as it is under great pressure, forces its way along any weak line that it can find, sometimes upward, sometimes horizontally between beds of sedimentary rock, and sometimes accumulating in large masses. The result is that underneath a volcanic area the whole crust is seamed with veins and masses of igneous rock, some of which may be later exposed by the wearing away of the surface. The granite mass of Dartmoor has been already noted as an example, and there are other such masses to be found in the British Isles, particularly in the Scottish Highlands.

A good example of underground intrusion is the Great Whin Sill of the Pennine moorland, a horizontal sheet of igneous rock covering hundreds of square miles, which has been pushed between t e beds of limestone of which the Pennines are chiefly formed. In other parts of the British Isles more or less vertical sheets of intruded rock are to be found, called dykes, sometimes occurring to the extent of hundreds in a few miles. Incidentally it is in connection with these intrusions of igneous rock that most deposits of valuable metals are found.

HAMMERED AND CHISELLED BY THE WEATHER: HOW ROCKS GET THEIR SHAPES

IT now becomes necessary to understand the means by which the weather breaks up any rocks already formed into material suitable for making new sedimentary rock. The process is called " weathering," and any of the factors which make up what we call " weather," such as heat, cold, rain, snow, and wind—all ultimately due to the sun's heat—help to break up the rocks wherever they are exposed.

Heat and cold play a large part in breaking up the rocks. Nearly all substances, including mineral substances, expand slightly when heated, and contract similarly when cooled, so that the changes of temperature which occur between night and day and between winter and summer will cause the rocks to expand and contract, setting up strains and stresses which give rise to numerous cracks which can usually be seen in any rock surface. These cracks are further enlarged and deepened by the action of frost, or rather of frozen water, which expands as it freezes, sometimes exerting enormous forces, tending to thrust apart the walls of rock in which it is imprisoned. The rugged and splintered appearance of the rocks in cold mountainous regions is largely due to this disruptive action of frost.

The weathering action of rain and snow is of a different kind, and consists mainly of a solvent action on the rocks. Even though rocks are only minutely soluble in water, a period of millions of years will ultimately allow the rain to carry away many tons of material from the land surface, which may be deposited again if the water is evaporated, or which may remain in solution. The salt of the sea is largely due to the slight amount which all rivers bring with them in solution,

2

and since the sun evaporates the water from the sea's surface, leaving the salt behind, the sea is gradually becoming more and more salty. Lakes in desert regions, where the evaporation is intense, are often extremely salt, as is the Dead Sea in Palestine ; and they may dry up altogether, leaving behind a thick crust of solid salt. Most of the salt deposits of the world which are economically important are buried dried-up lakes of this kind ; sometimes other substances are found as well, such as the valuable saltpetre of Chile, which is used as a fertiliser : but ordinary salt is much the most common mineral to be formed in this way.

The action of wind in breaking up rocks is only well marked in desert regions where other weathering agents, such as rain, are absent or rare. Wind, by picking up sand-grains and blowing them against rock surfaces, acts as a polisher, sometimes giving rocks quite a smooth, shiny surface and, after a long time, wearing them down considerably.

HOW THE ROCKS GO DOWN TO THE SEA

ALL these processes are, of course, extremely slow. But slow though they may be, they are in continuous operation wherever a land surface is exposed to the weather, so that in sufficient time, which may be measurable only in millions of years, whole mountains may be entirely broken up into small fragments and carried by the rivers to the sea. But the action is not so slow that we cannot sometimes observe its more powerful effects : landslides and heavy floods may in a few hours materially alter the appearance of a district ; and when it is realised that such a small river as the Thames carries down with it to the sea *every year* between one and two million tons of rock material, we can realise that Great Britain is in a steady process of disintegration.

As soon as a rock surface is broken up into small enough fragments, the pieces are liable to be carried away to the sea. This may not happen immediately ; possibly the fragments may help for many years to form a soil covering, or they may find their way to the bottom of a lake for a time ; but their ultimate destination will almost certainly be the sea. The process by which they reach the sea is called " transport," and is due to much the same agencies as those which cause weathering, but operates in a different form.

In mountainous districts where the slopes are steep, probably the first transporting agent is gravity. As soon as a rock fragment is thoroughly loosened from its parent mass, it falls and rolls down a mountain slope until brought to rest. In very mountainous districts the noise of falling stones and boulders may sometimes be almost continuous, especially in warm weather, when the rocks are not held together by ice. As a result, at the foot of steep slopes we usually find a piled-up mass of broken rock, called " scree," awaiting further transport. The famous screes of Wastwater, in the Lake District, are a fine example of the extent of weathering and transport in this way ; and Wastwater will eventually be filled up by scree material unless the water succeeds in carrying it away.

HOW THE RIVERS RUN AWAY WITH THE EARTH

PROBABLY the most important transporting agents are the rivers. All rivers, even when flowing slowly, carry with them in suspension little particles of rock, such as mud, and the swifter they flow the more they can carry. Any one who has seen a stream in full flood, and has noticed its brown colour, will realise that an enormous amount of material must be carried in this way ; and the figures given for the Thames indicate that even a small stream is capable of moving many tons of material every year. The total amount of rock waste which is annually poured into the sea by all the rivers of the world has been roughly estimated at eight thousand million tons [1]—an almost incredible figure !

There is another action of rivers which is very important in altering the surface features of the land. In addition to carrying fine material in suspension, rivers are able, especially in flood-time, to roll much larger pieces of rock along their channels, and these pieces act as hammers and chisels, knocking other pieces out of the river-bed which are carried along in their turn. By this means, rivers are continually deepening their channels, so that an originally flat surface will eventually be carved into a series of steep-sided valleys wherever the raindrops have collected into streams. Moreover, down the steep sides of these valleys the rain causes new tributary streams to flow, and these in turn cut their way downwards, so that the action of the streams, combined with the action of the tributaries which they cause, is first to make a valley, and then to deepen and widen it continuously. The great majority of valleys are formed by streams in this way.

[1] Holmes, *The Age of the Earth.*

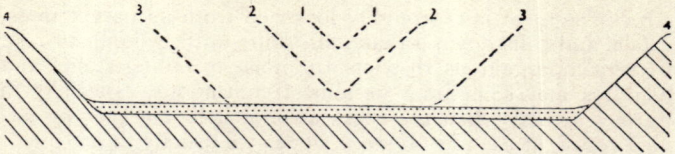

3a. FROM " YOUNG " VALLEY TO " OLD "

A section through a river valley, showing how the early, swift-running river (1) cuts sharply into its bed, the valley gradually deepening (2) and broadening by the action of tributaries (3). When a level nearer that of the sea is reached, the river may wander sideways, eating out slowly a wide, flat basin (4).

"NO THOROUGHFARE": A PROBLEM FOR THE STREAM AND RIVER

THE only place where a stream cannot cut its way down in this manner is at its mouth. Here, instead of cutting down, the stream may often flow so slowly as to deposit some of the mud brought down by the swifter current from higher up, and so wide mud-flats are formed, such as those of the Thames estuary. Moreover, a short way back from the mouth the river will soon cut down to a level where further action is impossible, so that the lower courses of most streams, if they have been in action for some time, are at or very near to sea-level. Here the stream can only wander sideways, forming curves and loops, eating away the banks a little in one place and depositing mud on the bank in another, so that eventually it is wandering over a wide, very flat valley formed largely of its own mud. Such a region is often liable to flooding, since the river is always threatening to choke up its own course, but it may be also a region of great fertility and lush pastures if well drained.

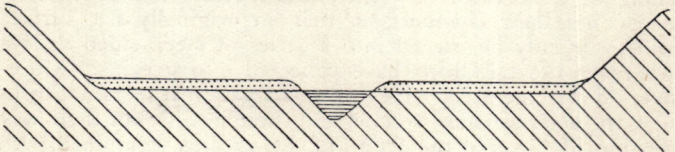

3b. THE RIVER CUTS A NEW PATH

Should an uplift occur in the land, the river becomes once more swiftly running and begins to form a new valley within the old.

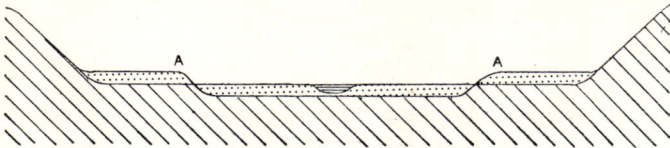

3c. THE FIRST TERRACE IS FORMED

Once more down to its old level, the slow, winding river broadens the new valley, leaving the unreached edges of the old valley as the terraces at " A."

Thus we see that most rivers show in their upper courses— in the hills—valleys still in the process of rapid formation, with steep sides and a swiftly flowing stream, still actively cutting its way down, while in their lower courses they usually have a " mature," wide, flat-floored valley covered with river mud over which the stream finds its sluggish way in loops and curves. How much of these two types of valley there may be depends on the length of time the river has been in existence ; a young river will be swiftly flowing and actively cutting down along most of its course, while an old river will for most of its length occupy a wide valley through which it slowly finds its way. We can find many examples of both types in the British Isles where the mountainous districts, such as Wales, show the first type, while the slow moving rivers of the Midlands illustrate the second type.

Ultimately, of course, if a land surface is exposed to the action of rivers for a sufficient length of time, it will be worn down and destroyed until it is nearly flat. Some of the big plains of the world owe their existence to rivers in this way, though it often happens that other things, such as an uplift

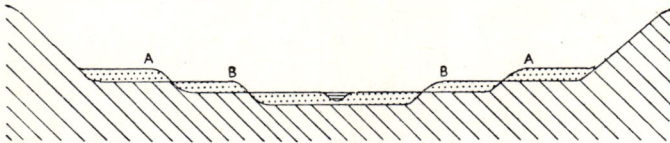

3d. A SECOND UPLIFT AND DOUBLE TERRACES

Here the process has been exactly repeated, and two series of terraces, A and B, have been formed. With some English rivers, such as the Thames, three such terraces exist, and serve to indicate three changes in land level.

in the land, intervene before the rivers reach their final stage. If this should happen, a river which has already formed a wide flat-floored valley will start cutting downwards once more, and will leave on the sides of its valley a series of " terraces," as they are called (see Fig. 3). Then it may widen its new valley and suffer a second uplift, leaving another series of terraces, and so on. In some of the English rivers, such as the Thames, three such terraces are to be observed, indicating three changes in the level of the land compared with the sea.

ICE, THE CARRIER AND CARVER OF LAND

ANOTHER important agent, both for wearing away the land and for transport of the material, is ice. Ice action occurs wherever the average yearly temperature is so cold that snow accumulates faster than it melts ; thus the Polar regions and the high mountain districts of the world are those which feel the action most, although many other parts of the world—the British Isles, for instance—have in the past been subjected to such a cold climate that ice has played a large part in the formation of their scenery. Great Britain, especially in its northern parts, shows evidence of having been largely covered by a huge sheet of ice.

One of the properties of snow is that when it is compressed it changes into ice ; thus, wherever snow accumulates to a sufficient depth, the lower layers are gradually changed into ice—the ice from which glaciers and icebergs are formed. Although ice is a solid substance, it possesses the property of melting at any point on which pressure is applied, and of freezing as soon as this pressure is released. It is this which makes ice so slippery, for there is always a film of water between ice and the surface on which it rests, due to the pressure. It is also this which allows the big icefields in high mountain districts gradually to squeeze out huge tongues of ice which descend the slopes of the mountains until they reach a place where they melt as fast as they move, when the ice is replaced by a stream of water.

This downward movement of glaciers is, of course, very slow when compared with the movement of rivers—the movement of glaciers has been measured in many places and varies from twenty inches to a hundred inches per day [1]—but, even so, they have considerable erosive power,

[1] Lake, *Physical Geography*.

for they carry with them a large amount of rock material which either falls on to the ice from the mountains above and then sinks in or is torn away by the ice from the surface over which it moves. As these boulders and stones are pushed along under the enormous weight of the ice, they are pressed down against the rock floor and act as cutting tools, producing long grooves and scratches, tearing away other pieces of rock and being themselves reduced in size, sometimes to powder, as they move along.

As a result of this process, a glacier becomes so charged with rock material that at its lower end it sometimes has the appearance of being made more of rock than of ice. When it melts, the rocks and boulders, now much reduced in size, rounded off and covered with scratches, are left in a semi-circular mound, called a " terminal moraine." Since this moraine is partly derived from the bed of the glacier, it can be seen that glaciers cut their way down into the rocks just as rivers do, so that they move down a steep-sided valley.

ROCKS ENGRAVED AND SCULPTURED BY ICE

IN the mountainous districts of Great Britain we can find many signs of the past action of glaciers. In the Scottish Highlands, the Lake District, and Wales, we can see rock surfaces which have been smoothed and scratched by ice, and we can trace old glacier valleys in the hills, often with morainic mounds at their ends. Many lakes (Lake Windermere, for instance) owe their existence to the fact that they occupy an old glacier valley which has been dammed at its end by a moraine of boulders, sand, and gravel, left by the old glacier.

By studying all the evidence of past ice action, geologists have been able to work out the history of the well-known "ice age," and have been able to see that at the time of the ice age all the high ground in the north and west of the British Isles was covered with an ice-sheet of great thickness, through which the higher peaks projected, and from which were sent out large tongues of ice, carrying with them many boulders over the lower country. For example, rounded and scratched boulders of a peculiar type of granite known only in Galloway, in south Scotland, are found on the surface of the Cheshire plains and in North Wales, showing that an ice-sheet must have moved southwards from Galloway across the Irish Sea and on to the North Wales coast. Rocks from the Lake District are found also in Cheshire, while the granites of Shap Fell, just to the east of the Lake District, have been pushed by the ice over the Pennines as far as the Yorkshire coast.

At the height of the ice age the various glaciers spreading out from the hills seem to have combined to form one continuous sheet which covered most of the British Isles as far south as the Thames Valley. This enormous sheet, besides bringing with it material from the higher ground, has torn up the underlying rock and ground much of it into fine fragments. When the ice melted, these ground-up fragments were left behind, forming a layer of sticky clay in which are embedded numbers of rounded and scratched boulders of all sizes. These boulder clays are of great importance in determining the character of the soils in various parts of the country.

One interesting feature is that among the boulder clays of the Fen District and Cambridgeshire are found occasionally rocks of a very peculiar kind, which are known to exist only in southern Norway. We know that at this time, not only England but the whole of northern Europe was largely covered by a huge ice-sheet, the centre of which was approximately where the Baltic Sea now is, and which has left behind similar traces in the shape of boulder clays, displaced boulders, and so on, so that it is possible that ice, carrying with it rocks from Norway, moved right across the North Sea and piled itself on the shores of Britain, though there are some difficulties in the way of this explanation.

FOOD FOR THE EVER-HUNGRY SEA

Besides water and ice, wind and sea carry out a certain amount of transport. In desert regions, sand can be carried long distances by the wind, and the sand-grains are polished and rounded in the process. The sea also attacks our coasts with its waves and, like rivers and glaciers, it picks up pebbles and rocks, using them as battering-rams to break away the land, cutting a deep notch with steep, sometimes vertical, cliffs, and a wave-cut platform on which the broken-up material forms a beach. If the tides, waves, and currents can carry enough material away to deep water, this cutting action can go on indefinitely, and the sea will gradually eat into the land, but it often happens that the accumulation of beach material becomes so thick that it acts as a natural break-water, and the waves seldom reach the base of the cliffs.

Groynes and breakwaters are sometimes built in order to assist the piling-up of sand and shingle and so to prevent our coasts from being eaten away, though they are not always effective. Off the shores of Holderness, north of the Humber, for example, lie several villages under the sea which are mentioned in *Domesday Book*. Here the coast is particularly soft, and erosion is rapid. Where the rocks are harder the process is slower ; in certain places the currents and tides may actually pile material up on to the land, and with the help of the prevailing wind sand-dunes are formed, which may advance over the land and bury fertile ground in spite of efforts to stem their forward movement by planting trees. On the whole, however, the sea is eating away the land much faster than it is building it up.

Thus we see that the forces of weather are continuously breaking up our land surfaces and carrying them away to form fresh rock in the depths of the ocean. Professor Holmes estimates that the British Isles are being worn away at the rate of one foot in three thousand years on the average. This is extremely slow, but it is also extremely sure. The hills are slowly but surely crumbling away, and gradually the whole land surface is becoming lower and flatter, and were it not for the intervention of other forces, to be considered in the next section, the continents would become nothing but a series of flat marshy plains at or near sea-level.

THE UNDERGROUND FORCES AT WORK

WE have seen how the ultimate condition of the continents, if left to weather alone, would be that of a flat or nearly flat plain. It is consequently somewhat surprising to find that parts of the earth are still remarkably mountainous, while others that have been mountainous are so no longer. We can only suppose that the highly mountainous areas of to-day are of comparatively recent formation—that is, that the earth's crust is capable of movement. Actually we have plenty of evidence that the crust is by no means in a stable state, for measurements by accurate machines show that it is always vibrating at intervals, and occasionally, as we all know, these vibrations become very intense, causing the collapse of buildings and sometimes disastrous loss of life.

Earthquakes, as these intense vibrations are called, tend to occur in certain localities only. The smaller vibrations, which are recorded by instruments, but do no damage on the surface, occur nearly everywhere, and they are often only the dim echo

2 *

of the intenser kind, coming from far away, although sometimes they may be due to some small local disturbance of the
crust. Fortunately the record made by the seismograph, or
vibration recorder, enables us to determine the direction and
distance of earthquakes, and observations seem to show that
the point of origin of most earthquakes is some line of weakness in the crust. It is a very significant fact that many of
the most severe earthquakes tend to occur along the coast of
the Pacific Ocean, or among the islands bordering that coast,
and that it is here that we have many of the highest mountain
ranges, and, as has been already noted, most of the active
volcanoes.

But earthquakes sometimes show evidence of kinds of
movement other than that of vibrations alone. For example,
after the famous earthquake of 1822 in Chile, the sea coast
was found to have been raised by three to four feet, and
similarly after the Alaskan earthquake of 1899 some parts of
the coast were found to be raised forty feet, as shown by the
barnacles still attached to the rocks. During the earthquake
at Napier, New Zealand, in 1931, the harbour shallowed so
rapidly that boats had to put to sea in order to save themselves. Thus it is quite possible to see that in a region where
earthquakes have been repeatedly occurring for centuries, a
considerable amount of elevation or sinking may have taken
place.

HOW THE COAST-LINE ROSE AND FELL

THERE is plenty of evidence of elevation, and of sinking,
even in places where earthquakes are not known to occur.
One of the features of the British Isles shown on a map is
that the western coasts have a strongly irregular and indented
coast-line, while the eastern and southern coasts run in smooth
curves, except where the river-mouths enter the sea. Surveys
of the thousands of inlets of the western coasts show that the
features of the land are often continued under the sea. For
instance, in the long bays of south-western Ireland it is
possible to trace the river-channels continuing under the
water ; in fact, most of these bays and the " sea-lochs " of
western Scotland are drowned river or glacier valleys, showing
that the whole coast has sunk under the sea.

On other parts of the coasts, on the other hand, there is
evidence that the land has risen from the sea. We have seen
how the waves cut cliffs and form beaches wherever they beat
against the shore. In places it is possible to trace old beaches

and cliffs, above the present beach-level, now out of the action of the waves, and at various places on the coast of the British Isles at least four marked beaches have been made out, one at about a hundred feet, another at fifty feet, another at twenty-five feet, and a fourth at ten feet above the present sea-level, although, of course, they have been destroyed in many places, and their height also varies considerably. They seem to indicate that at one time the land was a hundred feet lower than at present, and that it stood at this level long enough for the sea to cut a cliff and platform ; and it seems to have oscillated between these levels, with pauses at each height corresponding to the raised beaches.

Actually it has been possible to determine that the ten-foot beach is the oldest, and the twenty-five-foot beach the youngest of the three, so that it seems likely that at first the sea stood ten feet higher than at present ; then rose to the hundred-foot level ; formed a beach there ; sank to below its present level, forming submerged forests ; rose to the twenty-five-foot level, forming another beach ; and finally sank still farther until it reached its present height. But there are many difficulties in the interpretation of the meaning of these raised beaches since they do not occur everywhere, and not always together, so that we have to be very careful as to the conclusions we draw from them. It should be noted also that we may talk of the " sea sinking " or the " land rising " indifferently, as we have no means of distinguishing the one from the other.

THE TESTIMONY OF THE TERRACES

A FURTHER piece of evidence as to changes in level of land and sea is sometimes to be found in river valleys. We have seen how rivers, when they have nearly reached sea-level, form a broad, flat valley, being unable to cut their way downwards any farther, and we have seen how, if the land rises compared with the sea, " rejuvenation " takes place and " terraces " are formed. The presence of terraces indicates that the sea stood at the terrace level for some time, so that the river could form a " mature " valley, and consequently the presence in the Thames Valley of three series of terraces seems to indicate three periods when the sea was at quite a different level from that which it has now. This suggests a movement of the land from one level to another.

In addition to this evidence of changes of level, actual

measurements have been made. Here the difficulty is that the rising and sinking of the land is extremely slow, but in Sweden measurements by tide-gauges have been made for two hundred years, and there it has been found that the North coast of Sweden is rising from the sea at the rate of two-fifths of an inch in a year. In the extreme south of Sweden, on the other hand, a slight sinking seems to be going on. Similarly, in Japan, some areas are sinking at a rate of rather more than one fifth of an inch a year, while others are rising as fast as nearly an inch a year. At this rate the coast will be eighty feet higher in a thousand years' time.

FORCES THAT HAVE SPLIT THE LAND

TURNING now to the evidence of the actual rocks themselves, we find that they often show signs of having been considerably disturbed. In many places there occur what can only

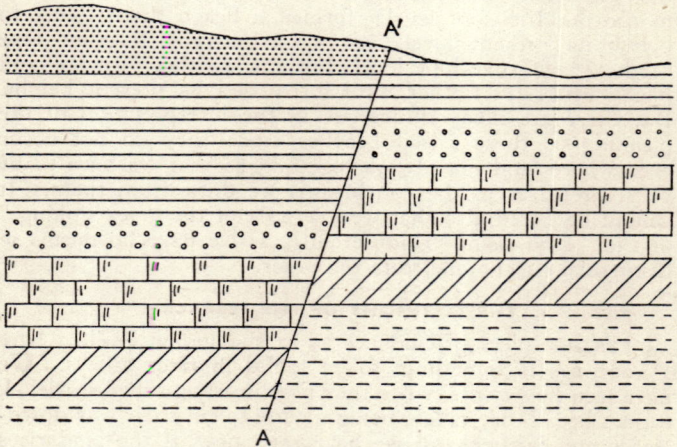

4a. A " FAULT " IN THE EARTH'S CRUST

The fault has occurred at A-A and let down the beds on the left. Note how the layers have slipped.

be described as cracks in the crust. The deposits formed under water occur, as we have seen, in layers of different kinds of rocks one upon the other, and we often find that the layers on one side of these cracks or " faults " are much lower than on the other, as in the Fig. 4a.

Faults may sometimes be seen running across the face of a cliff or quarry; in some districts they are very numerous, hundreds occurring in every mile, while in others they are rare. The difference in level on the two sides of a fault varies from a few inches to thousands of feet. Occasionally two big faults have let down a narrow strip of country between them, forming a long, narrow valley, called a rift-valley (Fig. 4b). The most startling example of this is the Great Rift Valley of Africa, which stretches from Lake Nyasa in the south of East Africa through Tanganyika, Kenya, and Abyssinia to the Red Sea. The Red Sea itself seems to be part of this rift-valley, which continues into Palestine, where the Dead Sea and the river Jordan mark its northward limit, some three thousand miles from Lake Nyasa. In places this huge

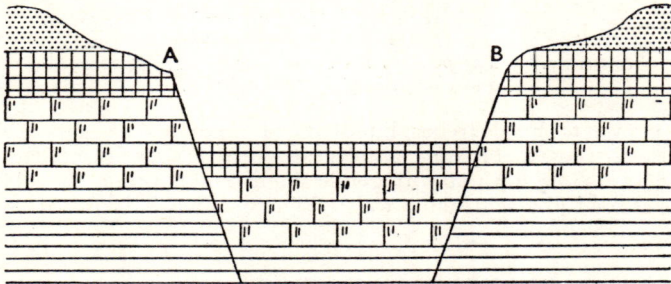

4b. HOW A " RIFT-VALLEY " IS FORMED

Two cracks or "faults" (A and B) have occurred close together, and the land between them has fallen to a lower level, in this way forming a " rift-valley."

system of cracks forms a well-marked trench, with steep sides thousands of feet high along the faults, while elsewhere it is obscured by lava-flows and ashes from the volcanoes which occur along these lines of weakness.

ONSLAUGHTS THAT TURNED MOUNTAINS UPSIDE DOWN

BEDS of rock also show another kind of disturbance which is even more striking. Instead of lying horizontally upon one another, they are sometimes found to be folded—that is, bent into a series of ridges and furrows, as though they have been subjected to a horizontal pressure (Fig. 5). One can get an idea of how this may be done by taking a fairly large sheet of paper and holding each edge between the fingers. Then, on moving the hands towards each other, the paper will be arched upwards and downwards in the same kind of way. Rock-folds are found of all sizes from very small ridges and

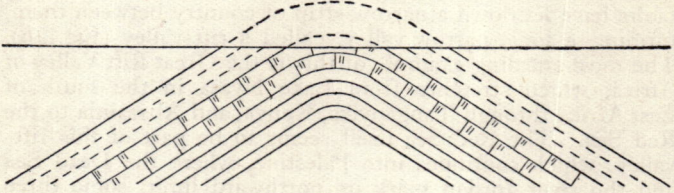

5a. A SIMPLE "ARCH" FOLD IN THE ROCK BED

A section through a rock bed which has been forced upwards or folded (probably by pressure from each end), forming an "anticline." The peak of the curve will in time be crumbled and worn away by the weather.

furrows to huge arches hundreds of miles across, and the intensity of the folding also varies greatly; *e.g.* sometimes there is a low, flat arch with gentle slopes, and at others the fold is shaped like a breaking wave (Fig. 5c) when it is called an

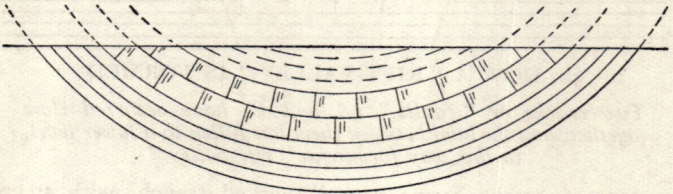

5b. A "TROUGH" FOLD IN THE ROCK BED

Here the rock beds have curved downwards instead of upwards, forming a "syncline." The exposed layers of rock will in time be worn away by the weather.

overfold. Simple arches are called "anticlines," and simple troughs "synclines."

Most very mountainous areas are highly folded areas, since the rocks are squeezed upwards by the folding process, and some ranges of mountains are simply long anticlines, though it does not always follow that anticlines are mountains, and that synclines are valleys, for the weathering process often wears down the original up-folds faster than the down-folds, and river-valleys make many alterations in the original fold arrangement of the rocks. In highly mountainous areas, such as the Alps, Rockies, or Himalayas, the rocks are formed by a mass of extremely complicated and intense folds, both large and small; in fact, it is almost impossible to realise the enormous forces which must have been exerted to squeeze and crumple the rocks into such a contorted mass as they now are. Some parts of these mountains are upside down, and it has been

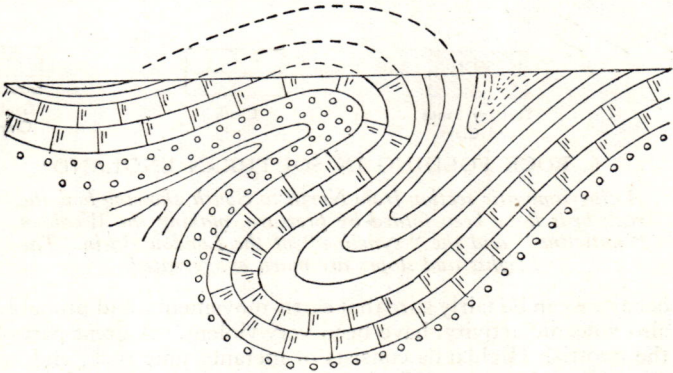

5c. THE RESULT OF A MIGHTY SQUEEZE

Such intense pressure has been applied to these beds of rock that they have folded right over upon themselves, forming an "overfolded anticline and syncline."

estimated that the squeezing-up of the Alps has reduced the original width of the beds by some one hundred and fifty to two hundred miles.

It is, of course, extremely difficult to understand the structure of these complex mountains, and the interpretation of highly folded regions is made more difficult still by the fact that the pressure and heat produced during the folding movements have often so altered the rocks that their original condition is hardly recognisable; they are sometimes entirely recrystallised. The highly altered rocks of such regions are often regarded as a separate class — the " metamorphic " or ' changed " rocks—and wherever such metamorphic rocks

THE WEALD

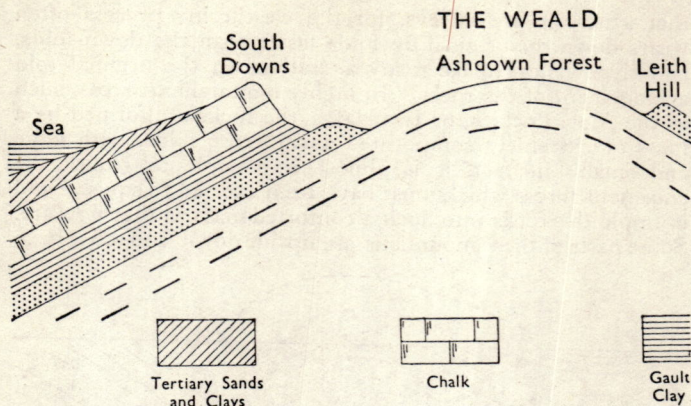

6. ROCK-FOLDING IN SOUTHERN ENGLAND:

A diagrammatic section from North to South, showing how the rock beds have been folded by pressure, making the Wealden "anticline" and the "syncline" of the London Basin. The heights and slopes are much exaggerated.

occur we can be fairly sure that earth-movements, and probably also volcanic activity, have been very violent. A great part of the Scottish Highlands consists of metamorphic rock, and, as we might expect, we can find there very intense folding and distortion of the rocks. In places even large masses of country have been pushed up and made to slide over other parts along what are called " thrust-planes." This violent activity, however, took place a very long time ago, and the original high mountains have been acted upon by the weather for so long that most of them have been worn away, and only the stumps remain to show us what a mountainous country it must once have been.

TUCKS THAT WERE TAKEN IN SUSSEX AND KENT

As an illustration of folding on a less violent scale, let us consider the Weald of Sussex and Kent. In the Weald the rocks consist of fairly recent sands and clays, surrounded both on the north and south by the famous chalk hills of the North and South Downs, both of which present a steep face towards the Weald in the centre and a gentler slope north and south away from it. Originally these rocks were all formed

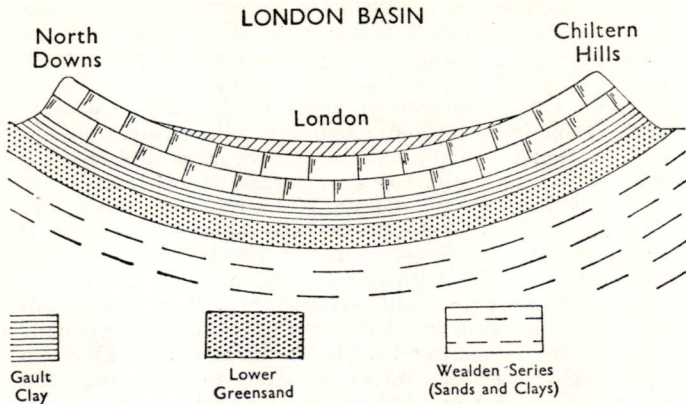

THE WEALD AND THE LONDON BASIN

In the Weald as it is to-day, the top beds of Tertiary sands and clays, chalk, clay, and lower greensand, seen in the section through the London Basin, have been worn away, leaving the rock at the bottom—the Wealden Series—exposed.

as horizontal beds of sediment, the Wealden series underneath, and the chalk above it. Then folding occurred, and the whole was ridged up into an anticline running from east to west, probably at the same time as that of the folding which produced the Alps. This produced a range of mountains several thousand feet high, across the Weald, and the higher parts of the fairly soft chalk were rapidly weathered away and removed by the rivers which ran down on either side of the anticline. The Wealden series was even softer than the chalk, so that when the whole of the chalk had been removed from the centre, the rivers cut away material still quicker, forming the basin-shaped weald, and leaving the chalk ridge on either side, through which they cut gaps for themselves to the Thames or the sea, such as the gaps at Arundel and at Guildford (Fig. 6).

When one stands on the steep chalk " scarp " overlooking the Weald, it is interesting to realise that the chalk continued right across the country to meet the Downs on the other side, probably forming high mountains in the middle, before it was washed away. In a similar fashion, the chalk continues as a syncline under London, coming out again in the Chiltern Hills.

It is, of course, very difficult to understand exactly how these folds occur. Most rocks, especially the older rocks, are extremely rigid, and break under a strain much more easily than they bend ; and yet we find such rocks in folded areas with the appearance of being twisted and bent very sharply, sometimes without much sign of fracture. In this case, as in most geological problems, we have once more to bring in the conception of slow forces acting through an enormously long period of time. The rocks are not folded suddenly : it takes thousands, perhaps millions, of years. If we take a stick of sealing-wax in our hands we find we can easily snap it in two with our fingers, for sealing-wax is a rigid, brittle substance ; but if a stick of sealing-wax is supported at either end and left for some weeks, it gradually develops a sag in the middle. In the same way, rocks which are subjected to sudden forces are likely to be crushed and shattered, but if subjected to a compressional force for a very long time—thousands and thousands of years—they may be gradually bent and contorted into folds. Moreover, if they are buried at a great depth underground the enormous pressure will help to keep them from fracturing.

THE PERENNIAL PUZZLE : HOW DID THE FOLDS GET THERE ?

THE actual cause of the great pressures which bring about these movements has still to be found. The earliest suggestion was that the crumpling was due to the contraction caused by the earth's cooling, but this contraction is not enough to account for what is observed. Many causes of folding have been suggested, such as tidal forces generated in the crust, or forces due to the heat given out by the radium in the crust, but there is not space to consider them here. There is one theory, however, which may be mentioned, as it is now considered to be well established, and it may lead to a complete explanation of folding. This theory suggests that the continents are masses of rock which, if they cannot be said to be actually floating, are at least lighter than the substratum of rock on which they rest. As the continents are weathered away, they become lighter still ; their equilibrium is disturbed, and forces are set up by which the weaker parts are compressed, while others are stretched. Isostasy may also help to explain another theory—that of Wegener, who supposes that the continents were once joined together and have since split up and drifted apart ; but here again we are on such controversial ground that we are beyond the scope of this section.

Not only is large-scale folding confined to certain regions of the crust, it has also tended to occur at certain times and not at others. Some periods of the earth's history have been times of intense folding activity ; others have seemed to be times of comparative quiet, when nothing but the steady wearing away of the rocks has occurred. Geologists have been able to work out the relative ages of these mountain-building periods, and in their investigations a large amount of evidence has come to light which tends to show that many of the mountains began their history by a sinking movement along a narrow trough, called a " geosyncline." This trough was flooded by the sea, which deposited sediments in it, and then later the more solid and rigid blocks of country on either side seem to have compressed the new, soft sediments between them, and squeezed them up into mountain ranges following the long, narrow line of the trough. In some mountain districts, such as those of the Alps and the Western Uplands of the British Isles, this " geosynclinal " evolution has been fairly clearly made out, but other regions still await further investigation.

HOW THE SEA HELPS TO BUILD THE MOUNTAINS

THE realisation that mountain-building tends to occur at certain times, between which are periods of quiet, has led to the conception of what is known as the " Cycle of Erosion." During the quiet periods, the continents are steadily worn away by the weather, and their material is deposited in the sea, forming thick layers of sediment. If the quiet period were long enough, the continents would be entirely worn down to low-lying country, but usually before that happens everywhere a mountain-building period intervenes, and the sea-formed sediments are folded up to form new land on which the weather starts its work again. Thus there is a continuous cycle of rock material from land to sea and back again which seems to have gone on all through the ages.

Of the oldest mountain-building periods we as yet know but little, partly because they seem to be so extensive, and partly because these very old areas of folding have also been the scenes of later movements, and it is often difficult to distinguish between them, but much of the oldest rock of the coast is highly folded and altered by heat and pressure. The whole series of very early movements is the " Pre-Cambrian " series, and covers a vast amount of time, probably including several distinct mountain-building periods. In America some geologists claim three such Pre-Cambrian periods.

A later mountain-building period, about which much more is known, is the " Caledonian " period, so called because the classic example of the folding is in the North-West Highlands of Scotland. Many of the upland areas of the British Isles, such as Wales, the Lake District, and the Scottish Highlands owe their existence largely to this folding, and they were once probably continuous with the mountainous peninsula of Norway and Sweden where the folds are of the same age. The majority of the folds of this system run from north-north-east to south-south-west.

Another folding period, of still later age, is that which is known as the " Variscan " system. Variscan folds run across Europe roughly from east to west, but the mountains which they form have been very much broken up and even incorporated in a still more recent folding period—the " Alpine "—so that only isolated blocks of mountains of Variscan age remain. Such blocks are those of the Vosges, Black Forest, Bohemia, and the Central Plateau of France, while in the British Isles the Mendip Hills, Cornwall, and south-west Ireland were folded in Variscan times.

SOME " MODERN " EXAMPLES OF MOUNTAIN BUILDING

THE " Alpine " movement—the last great period of mountain-building—occurred so recently that the folded regions still form most of the high mountains of the world, and its recent date enables us to know more of its structure and history than we do of any of the other periods. The Alps themselves, the Pyrenees, the Apennines, and the Carpathians, are all part of this system, which can be traced from Europe into Asia where the great ranges of the Kuen Lun and Himalaya bear witness to the enormous forces which produced the folding.

The islands of the East Indies are partly submerged chains of Alpine mountains ; Japan is also partly of this age, while in the Americas, the Andes and the Rockies continue the system, making it seem one of the biggest we know, although there is no reason to suppose that the earlier systems were any smaller. It is only the slow process of decay with time which makes these earlier systems take a minor place as features on the surface of the earth.

THE FOSSILS : FROZEN PICTURES OF THE ANCIENT PAST

IN the earlier sections the age of rocks has sometimes been mentioned ; some distinction has been made between older rocks and newer rocks, and this implies that there must be methods of determining the difference. One method which is applicable to all sedimentary rocks is by the law of super-position, which implies that of two beds of sedimentary rock the lower bed is older than the upper one. This is obvious when one considers the origin of sedimentary rocks, but it is actually not universally true. In a highly folded region, for example, the beds may be upside down. The other main method is by means of fossils, without the help of which geology would still be in an extremely chaotic state.

A fossil is any form of life which has been in some manner preserved after its death. Ever since life began on this earth, plants and animals have been dying, and occasionally the conditions have been such that parts of these plants and animals have been prevented from total destruction and have been buried in the rocks, to await future discovery. It is only occasionally that this happens, and it is only occasionally that the whole plant or animal is preserved, as, for instance, the mammoth found frozen into the ice in Siberia. Generally it is only the hard parts of a living thing which remain, and these are seldom in their original state. Moreover, land animals and land plants are much less often preserved than are sea animals and sea plants, for, in the first place, the majority of sedimentary rocks are formed under the sea, and, in the second place, the chances of a land animal or plant being covered up and preserved before it is entirely decom-posed are very small. It is only where the land conditions are peculiarly favourable that terrestrial forms of life are found in any abundance ; for instance, the peculiar conditions necessary for the formation of coal have made the " Coal Measures " famous for their plant-remains.

HOW THE LAND TAKES PATTERNS OF SHELLS AND BONES

IN the sea, on the other hand, the forms of life generally sink to the bottom when they die, and are often covered up by the sediment which settles down with them. Their soft parts are usually decomposed, but the hard parts—shells, bones, scales, etc.—remain buried in the newly-formed rock. Sometimes these hard parts remain practically unchanged; at other times percolating water gradually dissolves the shell or skeleton away, depositing some other mineral in its place, often preserving the original structure in the minutest detail, so that we get a shell or a bone formed of some other mineral substance. The commonest minerals which replace the original substance are calcium carbonate (though many fossils are originally made of this), silica (like flint), and iron pyrites, a brassy-looking substance. Iron oxide also often replaces the original material of the fossil.

Replacement does not always occur. Some fossils are entirely renewed by the slow solvent action of water, and others are entirely removed, but sometimes even though the fossil has gone, it is possible to see signs of its past existence. A bivalve, or two-shelled animal, for instance, may have its interior filled with sand or mud after its death, and then this may become consolidated so that after the fossil has been buried and its shells removed, the interior or " cast " is left in a hollow space, preserving perfectly the shape of the inside of the shell. It is usually possible to identify the species which these " casts " represent.

There is another type of fossil which, although not strictly due to the remains of animals or plants, may be classed as a fossil, since it is due to fossil agency. These are footprints and tracks. A sandy shore, particularly if it is wet, receives imprints very readily, and if these imprints are covered up with more sand before they are destroyed they may be beautifully preserved by further consolidation of the material. Sandstones and mudstones, when taken from quarries and split into slabs, sometimes show on the newly-exposed surface beautiful footprints of animals which have been dead for millions of years. Worm casts and tracks are also found in this way, and although not strictly fossil, the ripple-marks seen on most beaches are often preserved. Old paving-stones sometimes have this wavy ripple-marked surface.

FOSSILS THAT TELL THE AGE OF THEIR HOSTS

ALTHOUGH the law of superposition can be used for distinguishing between rocks of a different age in a particular area, it is of little or no use for comparing rocks of two different areas. For if, for example, we are studying a sandstone in one place, it does not follow that a sandstone was being formed everywhere else during the same time. In fact, a sandstone may have been formed in one place while a limestone was being formed in another, a clay in another, and so on, so that to correlate rocks in different areas requires more help than is given by their appearance or by the law of superposition. It is here that fossils are so essential, and their value depends on the law first enunciated by William Smith, a canal engineer, who, as a result of his studies of the rocks in which his canals were dug, showed that each group of beds was characterised by a certain set of fossils.

Smith's "Strata identified by Organised Fossils" was brought forward before Darwin had stated his theory of evolution, and until then the origin of fossils was a subject of wild and fantastic guesswork—they were supposed by some to be the remains of all the animals which did not get into the Ark and so were destroyed by the Flood—but once the theory of evolution was established, Smith's "Law" naturally followed. For evolution implies that every species of plant and animal lives only for a certain period of time, after which it dies out, and never occurs again, so that rocks of a particular age contain an assemblage of fossil-remains characteristic of that age and of no other. Evolution also implies that the older a rock may be, the more primitive will be the fossil assemblage, and this we find on the whole to be the case.

There are certain difficulties in identifying rocks by means of fossils. In the first place, one cannot establish the contemporaneity of two beds because they contain the same *single* species of fossil. A single species may have existed for a very long time, through several series of beds, and it did not necessarily live in one place while it was living in another. Thus, fossils which had a long range in time, but which were strictly confined to one district, are not of great use in correlating rocks ; the most useful fossil is one which existed for a very short time and over a wide area. Even so, it is a risky business to use one fossil only to identify a rock series, and so for the identification of beds, geologists always take the whole fossil assemblage. If two beds of rock in different places and with different appearance contain the same, or nearly the same, *assemblage* of fossils, then it may be assumed with almost complete confidence that they were formed at the same time.

By this means the rocks of the British Isles and of most parts of the world have been divided into a number of main " eras." These eras are further subdivided into smaller units, which are also fairly well known throughout the world, and which are known by their fossil assemblages to be contemporaneous. These subdivisions are called " periods " or " systems," and they are further subdivided into smaller " stages " and still smaller " zones." The extent to which these smaller subdivisions are made out depends on the degree to which the district concerned is known, and also to the abundance of fossils which can be found in the district under consideration. In some cases the smallest divisions are hundreds or thousands of feet thick (especially in the oldest rocks, where fossils are often few or even absent); in others, as in the Lias series of England, fossils are so numerous that the series has been divided up into zones and sub-zones only a few inches thick in some cases.

THE FOSSILS' PLACE IN THE STORY OF LIFE

APART from their value in identifying rocks, fossils are of extremely great interest because of the light they throw on the problems of evolution. The whole process of evolutionary changes—by whatever means they may be supposed to come about—demands an enormous length of time. Thus a study of the life of the present day gives only half a picture of the reality, and such experiments in breeding as can be carried out have to be done chiefly with quickly reproducing forms of life, such as flies or sweet-peas ; even so, these experiments represent only a tiny fraction of the time during which natural evolution has been working itself out.

Fortunately, fossils provide us with a record of the changes which life has undergone for millions of years past. It is true that it is a broken and fragmentary record—as we have seen, it is only a very few of the living things which existed that are ever preserved—but, even so, the fossil record provides us with an astonishingly detailed account of the history of life on this earth. As we trace the fossil assemblages through the rocks from the older series to the newer, we find thousands of species which arrived on the scene, developed and branched into new species or subspecies, and finally died out, sometimes leaving a higher form which carried on the main type of plant or animal, but often just ceasing to exist altogether.

Era.	System.	Important Fossils.
Cainozoic (Tertiary).	Quaternary .	Ice Age : Development of Man to present day.
	Neogene . .	Advent of Man ?
	Palæogene. .	Recent forms of life begin.
Mesozoic (Secondary)	Cretaceous .	Reptiles. Sea-urchins. Lamellibranchs. Abundant sponges. Ammonites at first abundant, then die out.
	Jurassic . .	" Age of Reptiles." Rapid evolution of many forms, such as ammonites, bivalves, corals, sea-urchins.
	Triassic . .	First mammals.
Palæozoic (Primary)	Permian . .	Trilobites disappear.
	Carboniferous .	Plants abundant. Insects. Amphibians.
	Devonian . .	" Age of Fishes." First-known plants.
	Silurian . .	Fishes become abundant. Graptolites.
	Ordovician .	First fishes. Bivalves develop.
	Cambrian . .	First-known Trilobites. Brachiopods, primitive corals, and sponges, etc.
Pre-Cam-brian		Primitive forms of life. Fossils very rare or absent.

7. THE GEOLOGICAL DIVISIONS OF PRE-HISTORY

In this chart of the Geological Eras and Systems the period nearest our own time is shown at the top of the page.

The number of extinct forms of life as revealed by the rocks seems almost incalculable.

By piecing together the parts of the picture which fossils thus present to us, we gradually make out a vast genealogical tree, not only for man, but one embracing all the present main forms of life. For some branches the tree is still very incomplete—there are many missing links, especially among the plants—but in some cases we have established a fairly complete line of descent. The horse's ancestors, for instance, have been traced back to the time when they had four toes and were animals the size of a small dog, and many lower forms of life have been linked up with their ancestors found in the rocks.

In addition to this picture of the history of life on the earth, fossils have afforded a great deal of information as to the actual mechanism of evolution, for we can trace gradual and minute changes of life-forms through the rocks as the conditions of life changed, and we can thus get an idea of how variations in species are produced.

WHEN PALM AND FIG TREE FLOURISHED IN ENGLAND

To a certain extent, fossils may be used to give us a picture of the conditions under which they lived, though it is not always possible to say much with certainty. For example, modern corals are found only in waters which are not more than fifty fathoms deep and in which the temperature does not go below 68° F., and it might be argued from this that rocks containing abundant corals must have been formed in water under these conditions. But though this may be true, there is no reason to suppose that the corals which existed in the past were limited by these conditions.

However, when we consider that modern corals flourish only in clear water, and argue from this, we are on surer ground, for we find that the corals of the past are nearly always found in limestones, which can be formed only in clear water; and when we find that a whole assemblage of fossils is of a warmth-loving type, it is perhaps safe to assume that the climate was a warm one. As an example of this, we may suggest the London clay, which contains remains of palms, figs, magnolias, turtles, crocodiles, and snakes, so that the climate in England at the time the clay was formed seems to have been a tropical or subtropical one.

There are other indications of conditions which are given

by fossils. Those which lived in fresh water can usually be distinguished from those which lived in the sea, and they thus give us evidence of the formation of sediments in large lakes, which would not be obvious otherwise. The rocks of the Sussex Weald are of this type. Similarly, if a sandstone contains nothing but land types of animal, the chances are that it is a desert sand which was not formed under the sea, as are most rocks.

PATIENCE AND A HAMMER: THE FOSSIL HUNTER'S GOOD COMPANIONS

Fossil-hunting is an easy, fascinating, and often exasperating occupation. All that is needed is a geological hammer and a store of patience. Some people seem to have a " nose " for fossils, and after a few minutes' search in a quarry will find a rare and valuable specimen ; others may search all day, only to find something they have found before. Even so, the element of excitement in not knowing what one may come across the next minute makes it a fascinating business.

Any geological exposure which is not in igneous rock may possibly contain fossils, but different kinds and ages of rock vary enormously in the abundance of fossils they contain. In general, the newer the rock the more abundant are the fossils in it, but this is not always so ; some quite recent rocks are completely barren, while some very old limestones are packed with fossils. Limestones and chalk are in general good for fossils, so are some clays and shales ; sandstones tend to be rather barren, but are not always so.

Here are one or two precepts a fossil-hunter should observe :

1. If a fossil will not come out easily, do not risk breaking it to bits with a hammer. Chip away the whole block of rock in which it is embedded, take it home, and get it out gently at your leisure.

2. Do not take a fossil away from an exposure without noting carefully the " horizon " at which it occurs. A specimen " from a pit in Hampshire " means very little. The exact stratum *in* the pit should be noted.

3. Do not start digging in a pit of soft sandstone under a mass of overhanging rock. This seems obvious, but is sometimes forgotten.

THE OLDEST ROCKS OF ALL

W E are now in a position to consider the branch of geology known as stratigraphy—that is, the description of the rocks as they actually occur in place. For this purpose, we must confine ourselves to the British Isles, where fortunately there is an extraordinarily complete sequence of rock formations from the oldest types to the newest. In general, the oldest British rocks occur in the north and west, and these are buried beneath newer and newer series as we proceed to the south and east, though there are many local disturbances in this arrangement which have been produced by earth-move-

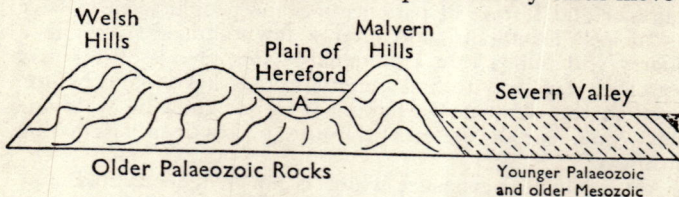

Welsh Hills   Malvern Hills   Plain of Hereford   Severn Valley
A
Older Palaeozoic Rocks   Younger Palaeozoic and older Mesozoic

8. FROM OLD TO NEW ACROSS BRITAIN :

A simplified section taken from West to East, showing the main kinds of rock underlying the surface soil. The older kinds of rock are found in the West and North. For clearness, the heights and slopes are much exaggerated.

ments. The generalised section across England indicates very roughly the order of the rocks (Fig. 8). It is impossible here to show in much detail how this arrangement of rocks has been worked out, and how the conditions and history of the various periods has been understood ; one of the many books on stratigraphy must be consulted for this.[1] Here we can indicate only the general matters involved in the history of the British Isles, and give an outline of the formations as they exist to-day.

Perhaps the most incomplete part of the record of the rocks is that which deals with the earliest formations of all. There are several reasons for this. In the first place, being older than any other, the Pre-Cambrian group is liable to be covered to a great extent by newer material ; it is only here and there that the Pre-Cambrian crust projects through the

[1] See p. 84.

many other layers, though it probably underlies much of the present surface at some depth. Secondly, owing to their very great age, Pre-Cambrian rocks are more likely than any others to be altered by earth-movements and volcanic activity, so that it is often extremely difficult to determine their original condition, and also to recognise rocks of the same origin in different places. Thirdly, owing again to their enormous age, fossils are extremely rare. At one time it was thought these rocks were formed before there was any life on the earth, but a few doubtful fossil forms are now known, and there are other indications of the presence of organic life, but they are so rare as to be quite useless for the purpose of classifying these ancient rocks.

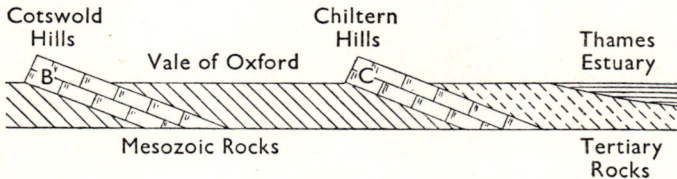

THE ROCKS OF WALES AND THE THAMES VALLEY

The old red sandstone deposited in Devonian times is shown at A. The oölitic limestone of the Jurassic period at B, and the fold in the chalk of the Cretaceous period once continued further West, but has now been worn away.

SCOTLAND'S TESTIMONY TO THE VOLCANOES' FURY

IN the Pre-Cambrian formations it is possible to recognise three different types—definite sediments, definite igneous rocks, and highly altered or metamorphosed rocks—which may have been originally either sedimentary or igneous. They occur in various patches in different parts of the country, the largest area, as we have already said, being in the North-West Highlands of Scotland.

In the North-West Highlands the underlying Pre-Cambrian rock is known as the *Lewisian Gneiss* (named from the island of Lewis). This is a hard, crystalline, highly metamorphic rock, often banded with black-and-white layers of minerals, and it seems to have been originally an igneous rock. The whole " complex " is riddled with a series of dykes of other igneous rock which were injected after the main mass had cooled, and it is also crushed and folded to an enormous extent. During its formation this area must have been the scene of volcanic and mechanical activity on a huge scale, but later it seems to have calmed down and helped to form a land-mass which was rapidly weathered away.

The material produced by the weathering was washed down into the valleys and hollows where it now forms a series of coarse sediments, over twenty thousand feet thick, filling up the low parts of the Lewisian Gneiss and even overtopping some of the Gneissic hills. This is the second great Pre-Cambrian deposit of Scotland, and is known as the *Torridon Sandstone*, from Loch Torridon in the North-West Highlands. It is a very coarse red sandstone, made up of grains of quartz and felspar. These may have been derived from the Lewisian Gneiss, but they seem also to have had another source of origin which was perhaps outside the British Isles. In some of the coarsest beds are pebbles which have been cut and polished by the wind, and this, together with the prevailing red colour, seems to point to the fact that the weathering took place under desert conditions, but the region was probably subject to occasional violent downpours of torrential rain which washed the scree material down into the valleys, eventually filling some of them up.

In England and Wales, Pre-Cambrian rocks appear in a series of small areas pushing through the newer rocks which lie above them. One of the largest of these areas is the island of Anglesey, two-thirds of which is occupied by a compli-cated series of lavas, granites, volcanic ashes, gneisses, and jaspers, all highly folded and metamorphosed. This is one of the most famous of the regions of oldest rock, for it was here that Greenly, after a most careful and elaborate study, was able to make out a complete succession of the different types of rock, and to show, by the fact that in places the strata were upside down, the presence in the region of great over-folds. Another interesting patch of Pre-Cambrian rocks is in Shropshire where lavas and ashes form such hills as the Wrekin and Caer Caradoc. The wild moorland district, known as the Longmynd, nearby is formed of very ancient sediments, in part resembling the Torridon Sandstone of Scotland.

In the Midlands there are one or two areas where these old rocks appear. Gneiss forms the centre of the Malvern Hills; the Lickey Hills, near Birmingham, and the Nuneaton ridge are of Pre-Cambrian volcanic rocks, and the little isolated moorland area, known as Charnwood Forest, consists of both volcanic rocks and sediments. In most of these cases, although the actual age of these rocks is not absolutely certain, the fact that they are overlain by rocks of the next succeeding age—the Cambrian—implies that they belong to the same era as the rocks of the Scottish Highlands.

WAS PREHISTORIC WEATHER LIKE OUR OWN?

A QUESTION of great interest concerning these ancient formations is whether the conditions under which they were formed were the same as those which prevail at the present day, or whether there were other forces in operation which we do not now have. For example, the enormous thicknesses of the Pre-Cambrian rocks in parts of the world (at least 180,000 feet) supposes an enormous period of time for their formation, that is if the processes of weathering and so on continued at the same rate as they do to-day. It is generally assumed that the time required for the formation of the Pre-Cambrian group is at least as long as that required for the formation of all the other groups put together, but it is possible that weathering, igneous activity, and so on, took place at a much greater rate and in a much more violent way than they do now. It is impossible to say for certain whether this is so or not, but the form and appearance of the later Pre-Cambrian rocks suggest that these processes were fairly similar, if not in intensity, at least in kind, and without such a supposition it is impossible to form any coherent plan for the mode of origin of these extremely obscure and complicated rocks.

THE EARTH'S SECOND LAYER

SUCCEEDING these oldest rocks of all comes a group of systems (from Cambrian to Permian in the table) which are known as the Palæozoic or Primary Group. Palæozoic means literally " old-life," and although they are very old, these systems are very much younger than their predecessors. Even the lowest of the Palæozoic systems—the Cambrian, is very different from the Pre-Cambrian, and there must have been a very long period of time between the latest Pre-Cambrian rocks and the first of the succeeding system, for, as we have seen, fossils are extremely rare in the Pre-Cambrian, whereas they are comparatively common in the Cambrian system. Moreover, these fossils are by no means primitive in their development. The animal kingdom had already developed its main branches except that of the vertebrates, and representatives of each branch are to be found in the Cambrian rocks, and from this we must suppose that the interval of time was enormously long.

The chief characteristic of the earlier parts of the Palæozoic system (Cambrian to Devonian) is that it presents a complete " cycle of erosion." [1] In Cambrian times the first event was the gradual sinking of the old much worn down pre-Cambrian continent, so that it was flooded by the sea along a long, narrow trough running from the north-east to the south-west right across the British Isles, and extending up to Scandinavia. Most of Scotland, the Lake District, Wales, and Ireland were eventually submerged in this trough, or geosyncline, and the sea deposited sediments in all these areas. To the north-west, part of the old pre-Cambrian area remained land (called " Atlantis " by the geologists), and there was probably another land-mass to the south-east, but about this we know little as it is now covered by more recent sediments.

The sediments formed in this trough varied considerably. At certain times and in certain places the water was shallow, with swift currents, so that only the coarser kinds of sediment were deposited ; at other times it was deep and still, so that fine muds settled on the bottom. These are now shales and slates, whereas the former type are sandstones and quartzites. Each type is, moreover, accompanied by a characteristic set of fossils. In general, the shallow-water type tends to occur near the shore-lines of the trough, as in North-West Scotland, while the deep-water type tends to occur in the middle (roughly in the Lake District and Isle of Man), though there seem at times to have been islands in the trough. Occasionally, as the geosyncline sank, there were outbursts of volcanic activity, producing beds of lava and volcanic ashes.

Towards the end of Silurian times, the geosyncline seems to have been almost entirely filled up with sediments, and then begins the second half of its history,[1] when the two land-masses on either side squeezed the sediments into a great mountain range. This is the Caledonian mountain range

[1] See p. 51.

already mentioned, and it was completed by the end of Devonian times, when nearly the whole region had become a land-mass once more.

At the bottom of most exposures of Cambrian rocks is a bed of white quartzite, representing the original coarse sandy sediment produced when the trough was first beginning to form. Later Cambrian beds are mainly sandstones and shales, indicating the gradual deepening of the water, but in Scotland the later Cambrian consists of a limestone (the Durness Limestone) which perhaps represents the remains of a reef which extended on the clear waters along the northern coast of the trough. The best-known area of Cambrian rocks in the British Isles is in North Wales, where the anticline known as the Harlech dome exposes a fairly large area of these rocks. The most common kinds of fossils found in the Cambrian are those known as the trilobites and the brachiopods. Many of the former give their name to the beds which they characterise.

THE FIERY BIRTH OF THE WELSH MOUNTAINS

PERHAPS the first indications of the squeezing-up of the geosyncline are to be found in the succeeding system —the Ordovician (Ordovices, an ancient Welsh tribe), for during these times there was a very great outburst of volcanic activity, which poured out lava and ashes on the sea floor. These Ordovician igneous rocks now form some of the hills of North Wales, such as Snowdon and Cader Idris. The other deposits are both shallow and deep-water sediments, as in the Cambrian, though the fossils, of course, are different ; for instance, true corals, and a few fish make their appearance.

The succeeding Silurian period has also the same main types of rock, though volcanic activity was not so common, and there tended to be more shallow-water than deep-water sediments since the trough was filling up. Coral reefs also occurred, forming beds of limestone, such as the Wenlock Limestone. In the Silurian period, graptolites are very important as fossils, and fishes become abundant.

In Devonian times the whole region, except in the south-west of England, had become land, and was ridged up into a series of great mountains. Between the mountain ranges were long, narrow basins, partly occupied by lakes, into which the weathered rock material was poured to form great thick-

3

nesses of sandstone (Old Red Sandstone) in a way which recalls the formation of the Torridon Sandstone. Since there was probably no actual sea in the areas now covered with Old Red Sandstone, the fossil-remains are rare, and, except for some fish, consist of land-forms, among which are a few specimens of the earliest known plants. The climate of Devonian times seems to have been very dry ; possibly the mountains cut off most of the rain, except for occasional violent showers.

HOW THE LATER SYSTEMS WERE FORMED

THE two last systems of the Primary group—the Carboniferous and the Permian—seem to repeat this erosion cycle, though perhaps not on such an extensive scale. The Carboniferous period begins, like the Cambrian, with a sinking of the now much worn-down Devonian continent and an invasion by the sea, but perhaps owing to the dry climate and the consequent lack of rivers, this sea was free from sediment, and in it hundreds of feet of limestone were formed. Soon after its formation this Carboniferous Limestone became land, and now constitutes much of the Pennine Highlands. Over this land, which was at low level, a large river wandered down from the north, bringing with it much sediment with which it formed a delta, covering much of northern England.

These deltaic deposits are known as the Millstone Grit, and it was on the millstone grit that there grew the dense swamp vegetation which later was to become coal. The Millstone Grit delta seems to have oscillated in level to a certain extent so that parts of it were at times dry land, while parts were swamp, and in other places it was submerged. While it was a swamp the climate allowed a dense mat of vegetation to grow, and this was occasionally submerged, and covered with mud or sand by the sea or the river, so that the " Coal Measures," as the top of the Carboniferous is called, consist of an alternating series of shales and sandstones, with the comparatively thin but extremely valuable seams of coal.

At the close of the Carboniferous period we have a return of earth-movements—the Variscan or Hercynian movements —and again a return of land and desert conditions, during which the Permian deposits of almost unfossiliferous sandstones were formed, although the sea then covered northeast England and caused the formation of the Magnesian Limestone there.

THE " MIDDLE AGE " OF GIANT REPTILES

THE *Mesozoic* ("Middle Life") or Secondary rocks occur on a far less extensive scale than do the primary rocks. The total thickness of the sediments and the time required for their formation are both much less, and many of the fossils can be seen to be ancestors of groups that are living to-day. The previous era ended with widespread desert conditions in this country, and these conditions are continued in the first period of the Mesozoic—the Triassic Period. Great Britain seems then to have been a dry and barren region of scree-covered mountains and plains, partly covered with sand-dunes, and with here and there a salt lake. Occasional rainstorms spread the sands and screes farther over the plains, and later, in Triassic times, violent storms may have flooded the plains for a period, leaving behind them a thin layer of fine red mud, which eventually accumulated to form a thick bed of red " marls " which actually stretches from the British Isles to Bavaria.

Between these infrequent floods the country seems to have been nothing but a barren sun-baked plain with occasional hills of older rock here and there. Some of these old hills can still be traced, with the Triassic marls banked up against them, and the surface of the old rock is often seen to be rounded and polished by the sand-grains which the wind blew against it so long ago. Some of the salt lakes of these desert times dried up and crystallised, leaving beds of salt which were covered up by the marl, and which now form valuable salt supplies in Cheshire and elsewhere.

The Triassic period was brought to an end by another submergence, during which the sea covered most of the south-east and the midlands of England, but much of the old mountains of the Scottish Highlands, Wales, and Ireland remained land, and have probably been land ever since, receiving no further deposits. In this *Jurassic* sea, which gets its name from the Jura Mountains of France and Switzerland, there was an abundant fauna, among the most important groups of which were the ammonites and the bivalves, but it is also interesting from the fact that the reptiles first began to flourish, and achieved an abundance and a size which they have never equalled since. It is in the Jurassic and the succeeding Cretaceous times that we find fossil skeletons of the giants of the reptile world like *Iguanodon*, the flying reptiles like *Pterodactylus*, and the swimming reptiles like *Plesiosaurus*.

The Jurassic sea varied considerably in character from time to time. Sometimes it was a muddy sea in which blue clays and shales were laid down, such as the Lias shales, the Oxford clay or the Kimmeridge clay ; at other times the sea seems to have been clearer, and limestones were formed, some of which are probably of coral-reef formation, such as the beds which are known as the Corallian, in which corals, brachiopods, and sea-urchins abound.

THE " EGG-STONE " : STRANGE TRICKS PLAYED ON ROCKS BY THE SEA

LIMESTONES occur at intervals all the way through the Jurassic, and they often show a peculiar formation known as *oolitic* from its resemblance to the roe of a fish (Greek *oolith*=egg-stone). These oolitic limestones have the appearance of being made up of hundreds of little round grains, and under the microscope are seen to consist of concentric layers of calcium carbonate, often formed round a nucleus such as a grain of sand or a shell-fragment. The calcium carbonate was probably actually deposited by precipitation from the sea, and formed round these nuclei as they were rolled about by the waves and currents, so that the presence of oolitic limestone is generally taken to indicate shallow waters. There is other evidence of shallow water in the Jurassic rocks, for we find in the *Estuarine beds* a series of sandstones, shales, and even thin coals, the fossils of which clearly show the presence of the conditions of a river-estuary.

The thicker limestone beds of the Jurassic, such as the *Great Oolite series*, form one of the most prominent features of south-eastern England, stretching in a long series of turf-covered uplands from the Yorkshire Moors to the Dorset coast. The Cotswold Hills are part of this formation, which provides much of the best building-stone of the country, such as the famous Bath and Portland stones. Both of these stones are oolitic.

Jurassic limestone country can usually be easily distinguished by its stone walls and grey or yellow houses built of blocks of limestone, with roofs made from easily split slabs of the same material.

THE LAKE THAT STRETCHED FROM KENT TO FRANCE

At the end of Jurassic times a great deal of Britain became land, and the succeeding period was one of slow submergence. The first deposits were therefore of a shallow-water type, consisting of sandstones, which are characterised by a peculiar greenish tint due to a mineral called glauconite. These are the *Lower Greensand* series of rocks, and they are followed by a deposit of blue clay, known as the *Gault*, which in turn is succeeded by the *Upper Greensand* and then by the *Chalk*, one of the most important formations in England. These three successive deposits probably indicate a continuously deepening sea, but in southern England they were all preceded by a peculiar series of clays and sandstones which are known as the Wealden series, since they occur in the Weald of Kent and Sussex. The fossils of the Wealden series indicate that it is the deposit of a *freshwater* lake, and this Wealden Lake stretched across the Channel to France, Belgium, and as far as Hanover, as is evidenced by the deposits there.

The most characteristic deposit of Cretaceous times is the Chalk. Chalk consists almost entirely of Calcium Carbonate —in some cases it is over 98 per cent. pure—and the sea must have been extraordinarily free from sediment for chalk to be formed. It is suggested that the neighbouring land had been worn down during chalk times to a very low level, and that a desert climate also prevailed, so that there were no rivers to bring sediment down to the sea.

The " Alpine " earth-movements, as we have seen, folded the chalk country, after it had been raised from the sea, into a series of gentle anticlines and synclines, and weathering has now reduced the chalk outcrop to long lines of very characteristic " down " country, such as the North and South Downs, the Chiltern Hills, and the Yorkshire Wolds. The presence of nodules of flint (Silica) in the chalk, deposited from solution by percolating water, and the open nature of the country due to the thin soil on the chalk, made the Downs one of the most habitable places for early human beings.

In Cretaceous times, as in the Jurassic, forms of life were very abundant, and reptiles flourished exceedingly. A very important group are the sea-urchins, but the ammonites which were so abundant in the Jurassic become gradually less so.

Although the reverse might be expected, corals are not abundant in the chalk, which possibly was formed at too great a depth for them.

THE EDIFICE COMPLETED : THE EARTH'S TOP LAYER

THE last great group of rocks is the *Cainozoic* (" Recent Life ") or Tertiary group. This is divided into three smaller periods—the *Palæogene*, *Neogene*, and *Quaternary*— but these are very small periods compared with earlier ones ; in fact, the whole of the Cainozoic group of systems is perhaps as small as a single system of early rocks such as the Cambrian or Ordovician. This group is sometimes divided into the five series : *Eocene*, *Oligocene*, *Miocene*, *Pliocene*, and *Pleistocene*.

There is a considerable gap in time between the Cretaceous system and the first system of the Tertiary. This is well shown by the fauna, for not only does not a single species survive between the Cretaceous and the first Tertiary rocks, but whole groups of animals died out. The great marine reptiles disappeared, as did also the last of the ammonites, and the higher types of mammal made their first appearance. (The *earliest* mammal is found as far back as in the Trias.)

During this gap at the end of the Cretaceous, considerable earth-movements seem to have raised what is now western Europe into a land-mass, from which the upper layers of chalk were weathered away. Then a slight subsidence enabled the sea to gain access to a basin-shaped area covering south-eastern England and north-west France. This *Anglo-Parisian Cuvette*, as it is called, was shallow, and at times was connected with a southern ocean and at times with a northern one. Two large rivers emptied themselves into it, one from the west in Devonshire, the other from the south somewhere near Paris.

Slight changes in level resulted either in the sea enlarging the basin, or in the rivers building out their deltas, so that we get (*e.g.* in the Palæogene Period) an alternating series of marine sands and clays with estuarine or even freshwater deposits. When communication with the southern ocean was opened, fossils from that area made their appearance, such as the Nummulite, a primitive animal with a disc-shaped shell which helps to build up limestones in some places.

During Neogene times the great Alpine mountains rose, and, as we have seen, this region was folded into gentle anticlines and synclines by the " Alpine " movements. It was then that the London Basin and the Wealden uplift were formed, and owing to these movements the Anglo-Parisian Cuvette became land in which were a few large lakes ; the largest depression, which was again flooded by the sea later, eventually became the North Sea. In fact, towards the end of the Neogene times, the distribution of land and sea becomes the same as it is now, the last main change being that East Anglia was submerged for a time and received some deposits of shelly sands known as " crags."

The Palæogene and Neogene deposits of alternating sands and clays now cover two areas in England. These areas—the London and Hampshire Basins—occupy two synclines in the chalk and are characterised by gently undulating country, in which the clay belts are usually regions of woods and pastures, while the sandy belts form many of the heaths, such as the New Forest and the numerous commons of Surrey. The fossils of the earlier part of the period, such as those of the London clay, seem to indicate a warm, if not tropical, climate, and as we study the fauna of the succeeding beds of the group we find that more and more temperate types appear. Finally, in the most recent Cainozoic deposits, there is evidence of a considerable oscillation of climate between cold and warm periods, but this finally culminates, as is evidenced by Arctic types of fossils, in a very cold period, and we come to the Ice Age.

THE GREAT ICE AGE AND THE COMING OF MAN

THE cooling down of the climate at the end of the Cainozoic era eventually reached such a stage that the whole of north-west Europe was covered with an enormous sheet of ice. The centre of this ice-sheet was roughly where the Baltic Sea is to-day, and from this centre it stretched in all directions. When it was at its maximum extent nearly the whole of the British Isles was covered, except the country south of the Thames. The closest parallels to this vast extent of ice are now only to be found in Greenland and Antarctica, where the conditions seem to be fairly similar to those of the ice age, or Pleistocene epoch.

Such a mass of ice, moving slowly outwards from its centre like a huge glacier, must, of course, have altered the face of the country. The higher ground must have been considerably worn away, and we find that much of the lower ground is now covered with material which the ice brought with it from the hills. These deposits are known as "drifts," and they are of various kinds, one of the commonest being boulder clay. This is a very variable kind of clay, usually containing boulders and ice-worn pebbles of rocks, which have been brought long distances from their original source by the ice. Boulder clay covers large areas of the plains in the central parts of both England and Ireland.

Gravels and sands are also found in many places as a result of the ice age. Most of these drift deposits were probably formed along the edge of the ice-sheet; some are actual moraines, while others seem to be deposits caused by the numerous streams which came out from the edge of the ice and which were, of course, full of sediment which was quickly deposited.

AN "ICE AGE" THAT WAS SOMETIMES WARM

DURING the whole ice age the climate was not perpetually cold. There seem to have been considerable changes during the period, and the types of deposit found, together with fossils in them, show that as well as cold conditions like those of the Arctic tundras, there were times of extreme, dry climates like those of the present Russian steppes, and also times (at least in the Alps) when the climate was a warm, temperate one. In the Alps four climatic oscillations can be recognised. In the British Isles the evidence is not so clear, but the study of plant-remains from certain peat deposits seems to show that there were some temperate kinds of vegetation during parts of the ice age.

Some southern animals are also found, such as the hippopotamus and rhinoceros, whereas in the deposits of the colder periods the fossils are all of a cold loving type, such as the mammoth, the woolly rhinoceros (both covered with long hair), the reindeer and the musk-ox (now known only in Greenland and in northern Canada); while the plant-remains consist of mosses, lichens, and small shrubs, such as the dwarf birch and Arctic willow, which are characteristic of the modern tundra.

When the ice finally disappeared, the country must have presented a very different appearance from that which it had before Pleistocene times, and although in the main the features were the same—the old highlands still remaining as highlands, for instance—there must have been a considerable alteration in detailed appearance. The rivers, for example, had to find new courses for themselves, their old channels being often blocked by drift deposits. The many old river-channels which can be found here and there owe their lack of rivers largely to this cause.

Another effect of the ice was to cause changes in level of land and sea. We have seen[1] how the theory of isostasy supposes that land-masses are in a way " floating " on heavier rock, and consequently the enormous weight of the ice is supposed to have depressed the land considerably, and it is suggested that it has not even yet recovered completely from this movement. This " isostatic depression " provides us with a possible cause for the raised beaches and river-terraces which we have already noted, and which were formed towards the end of the ice age, or sometimes after it had finished.

These glacial times, with their rapid and extreme changes of climate, must have been very trying for the animals which lived then, and it is surprising to find that it is just in these times that man first begins to flourish. Human beings possibly began just before the ice age, but it is only then, in the river-terraces and glacial gravels, that his remains, in the form of bones, stone tools, etc., are found in any abundance.

TRYING TO TELL THE AGE OF THE EARTH [2]

THE age of the earth has always been a fascinating subject for thought, just as the idea of its creation has puzzled and stimulated mankind through the ages. One of the first great controversies which modern geology had to win was over this question, about which a fierce quarrel was waged rather more than a century ago. For it was then that geologists were at last beginning to realise that in order to understand geological processes they had to suppose vast periods of time for their operation, and in consequence they

[1] See p. 50.
[2] For many of the figures given in this section, I am indebted to Professor Arthur Holmes's *The Age of the Earth*.

3*

found themselves in opposition to established thought which was based on the literal interpretation of the Old Testament.

An estimate of the age of the earth, based on the story of genealogical descent in the Old Testament from the creation of Adam and Eve onwards, gave about four thousand years as the maximum time. The geologists found this to be quite inadequate, and they were in consequence in danger of being branded as heretics, and some of them could only reconcile their geology with their belief in the literal truth of the Old Testament by supposing the occurrence of great world catastrophes which made up for the loss of time. However, these suppositions had eventually to be given up, and a uniform process of nature over a vast period of time was generally accepted.

There are many methods of attempting to determine the age of the rocks, and it is only recently that they have begun to show any agreement; it is also only recently that they can be said to be at all accurate, but it should be remembered that "accuracy" in this connection has a very wide meaning. We cannot yet measure the exact number of years during which a rock has existed; it can only be stated at best in round millions of years, and when we consider the age of the whole earth we have to be more cautious still, for it is just the oldest times of the earth about which we know least.

FIXING THE AGE OF THE EARTH BY THE STARS

THE recent gains in our knowledge with regard to the stars, in particular of their evolution, has enabled us to make a rough estimate of their ages. It is now generally believed that a star derives the enormous amount of heat and energy which it pours out from the actual destruction of the matter which forms it, so that as a star continues to shine it loses matter. On this hypothesis a star will "weigh" less and less the older it grows. It is possible to calculate the rate of loss of mass with time, and by this method Sir James Jeans estimates the time necessary for a star to change from the biggest to the smallest kind to be 200 million million years, while our sun seems to have reached a stage when it is about 7,800,000 million years old. There are other methods of estimating the approximate age of the universe, and they agree with the above in being of the order of millions of millions of years.

The earth is a member of the solar system, which is generally supposed to have been formed from the sun by the tidal attraction of another star which at one time came very near the sun, thus pulling off a filament of gaseous matter which eventually condensed into the planets. Our earth thus has an ancestry going back for the enormous period of time mentioned above, but it is also possible to make an estimate of the time of the birth of the solar system. The newly-born planets are supposed to have had originally to force their way through a gaseous medium which has since nearly disappeared, and this gas had the effect of reducing the elliptical nature of the paths of the planets, making them more nearly circular.

By taking the present eccentricity of the orbit of Mercury and comparing it with its early eccentricity, which can be calculated, Jeffreys has estimated that the time taken for Mercury to achieve its present path is between a thousand million and ten thousand million years, and these figures we perhaps may take as an upper and lower limit for the age of the Solar System, including our earth. From other considerations, Jeffreys suggests that the earth cooled down from a gaseous to a liquid state within five thousand years, and took not more than ten thousand years after that to become mainly solid.

THE SEA HELPS TO SOLVE THE AGE PROBLEM

TURNING now to the actual surface of the earth itself, we find that there are several ways in which it has been affected by the passage of time since its formation, and that the changes thus produced can be used to find the amount of time which has elapsed.

Ever since rivers first were formed—and they presumably began very soon after the earth became solid—they have steadily poured both particles of sediment and substance in solution into the sea. The sun has evaporated the water from the oceans, and the winds have carried the water vapour over the land, where it had descended as rain. The rain has dissolved more soluble substances out of the rocks, which the rivers have again carried to the sea, and so the process has been continuously repeated, more and more soluble material being carried down to the sea, to remain in solution in the ocean. It is a gradual concentration on a huge scale, and as a result sea-water is salt, for the most abundant substance in it is common salt (sodium chloride), though there are many others, such as magnesium chloride and sulphate, calcium carbonate, etc.

These chemical compounds are supposedly derived from the rocks ; common salt, for instance, is often found in rocks, and consequently rivers, even though they are called "fresh," have a small percentage of salt in them, though it is now much less than the percentage in the sea. Therefore, if we assume that the sea was originally fresh, the amount of salt in it will give us an idea of the time it has existed, provided that we know the rate at which the rivers are bringing salt into it.

Analyses of specimens of sea-water, combined with estimates of the total volume of the sea based on surveys, give a figure for the amount of salt in all the seas of over 12,600 million million tons. Similar methods of survey and calculation show that the amount of salt which is brought into the sea by the rivers every year is about 156 million tons, and from these figures we find that the amount of time required for the weight of salt to reach its present huge value is about eighty-one million years.

This is a surprisingly low figure. It is, however, open to some serious objections, for it is based on considerable assumptions. It is assumed, for instance, that the rivers have always brought down annually the same amount of sodium as they do now, which may quite likely not have been the case ; river analyses, too, are open to some suspicion, since the amount of salt in fresh water is extremely small, and the possibility of errors correspondingly great. Allowances made for this factor and for many other possibilities of error bring the number of years up to a considerably higher figure, but, even so, the chances of being mistaken are so many that this method of estimating the earth's age cannot be regarded as at all satisfactory.

WHAT THE ROCK MEASUREMENTS TELL US

A SOMEWHAT similar method of judging the earth's age is by means of the solid matter which the rivers carry down to the sea. We have seen how all land surfaces are subject to denudation, and how the material forms beds of sediment in the sea which may later become land again. From this we can see that by finding the thickness of the whole "column" of sedimentary deposits we can get an idea of how long the process has been going on.

Estimates of thickness are actually very difficult to make. As we know, we can scarcely ever observe a section through one of the bigger systems from the top to the bottom, for it is only here and there that parts are exposed. One or two special places, such as the Grand Canyon of the Colorado river, cut right through a large number of systems (in the Grand Canyon they reach from Pre-Cambrian to Carboniferous), but, even so, we are not sure that in these places the *maximum* thickness of the rocks is exposed. Moreover, it is very difficult to take account of the gaps or " unconformities " that occur in the succession of the rocks, which represent a period of emergence above the sea when no deposition would take place.

However, with the detailed knowledge now at our disposal, we can make some estimate of the total thickness of the rocks. Professor Arthur Holmes gives the maximum known thicknesses of the main groups as follows :

					Feet
Cainozoic Era .	.	.	.	.	73,000
Mesozoic Era .	.	.	.	.	91,000
Palæozoic Era .	.	.	.	.	185,000
Pre-Cambrian Era	.	.	.	.	180,000
Total thickness of deposits at least				.	529,000

When we consider the immense slowness of the processes of weathering and deposition, the time required to form a total thickness of deposits of over one hundred miles is almost inconceivable. But beyond showing us that an enormous length of time is required for their formation, these figures can tell us very little, for we cannot estimate the rate at which the beds were deposited. Some beds were formed comparatively quickly, others extremely slowly, and it is quite likely that during the formation of many beds the process varied considerably, sometimes depositing material, at others removing some before more was laid ; so that the thickness of a bed need bear very little relation to the time taken for its formation. At the most we can say hundreds, perhaps thousands, of millions of years are required.

RADIO-ACTIVITY : MOST ACCURATE CLOCK OF ALL

IT is only during the last forty years that the now familiar radio-active elements have been discovered and investigated. These elements are all peculiar in that they steadily and continuously emit certain rays, which are of three kinds —Alpha particles, Beta particles, and Gamma rays. Alpha particles are known to be the nuclei of helium atoms, or, put in another way, they are electrically charged helium atoms ; Beta particles are electrons, or very small negative charges of electricity ; while the Gamma rays are not particles at all, but are radiations like X-rays. The important point is that when a radio-active element gives off these particles and rays it is itself changed into a different element, so that we get one radio-active element continuously splitting up into another element, and into helium atoms. The new element may be itself radio-active, and may split up again into another, and so on, so that we can get a chain of these radio-active elements beginning with uranium and thorium at one end and finishing with the stable element—lead—at the other. A given amount of uranium will eventually produce a given amount of lead and helium, and also we can determine the rate at which uranium breaks down.

These facts give us another method of determining the age of the earth, for fortunately there are many rocks which contain, or which originally contained, uranium, together with lead which has been formed from it ; so that by analysing a mineral and determining the proportions of uranium and lead in it we can determine the length of time during which the breaking down of the uranium has been taking place. The difficulty in this estimation is that some ordinary lead may have been originally present in the rock, but fortunately the lead derived from the breaking down of uranium is slightly different from ordinary lead, and the two kinds can be distinguished, though they cannot be separated by chemical means.

There are one or two objections to this theory. We must be sure, for instance, that none of the lead has been removed from the rock, or added to it, since it was formed, and there is also the doubt as to whether in earlier times the transformation process took place at the same rate as it does now ; but on the whole the most accurate measure we have of the age of the rocks is that derived from this source. Actual estimates from specimens of rock vary to a certain extent, but there is more general agreement in estimates by this method than in any of the other methods we have considered. The age of the oldest types of Pre-Cambrian rock according to Professor Holmes, is, by this method, about 1200 million years ; while late Palæozoic rocks appear to be from 200 to 300 million years old, and Tertiary rocks have an age of about 30 to 60 million years.

It should be remembered that, very approximate as these figures are, there was quite possibly a very long period in he earth's history between the times of its birth and the formation of the earliest known rocks. Possibly from the birth of the earth to the present day, 2000 million years is an average figure to take, but geologists differ very widely in their estimates of these enormous periods of time.

PUTTING GEOLOGY INTO PRACTICE

THE value of any scientific study has two aspects : One is the practical aspect ; the value of this lies in the application of the science to the life of man, helping him to get his daily bread with less effort or in less time than he did before. The other is the philosophical aspect, by means of which man gains a knowledge of the nature of the universe around him, and of his place in it. To a large extent these two aspects are complementary, in that without the first kind man would have little or no leisure in which to study the second, and, on the other hand, without the knowledge gained by a philosophical study of science for its own sake, the practical application of it would have achieved very little.

Geology has, like any other science, both of these aspects. Considering first its practical use, or economic geology, we find that there is a very large field to cover, for one of the first discoveries of man which helped him to rise above the beasts was that of the valuable materials which could be dug out of the earth's crust. Ever since the first tunnels and galleries were made in the chalk for flint, mining has been developed and extended until it has become one of the largest and most important activities of man, and there is no doubt that our modern civilisation depends very largely on the great variety of products which is annually extracted from the crust.

HOW GEOLOGY HELPS THE MINER

IN all mining operations a knowledge of geology, if not always essential, is usually extremely helpful, and it is of use in two ways. The first is in prospecting—that is, in the search for valuable minerals. There are still in parts of the world prospectors whose knowledge of geology is very scanty and who work by means of rough-and-ready tests, relying on their " sixth sense " to tell them whether a piece of country is likely to contain a precious mineral or not, but, on the whole, prospecting is becoming more and more a matter of accurate geological surveys. The country is carefully mapped and explored from a geological point of view, and the underground structure determined as far as possible from the " exposures," after which, by comparing the rocks with other similar and better-known regions, the chances of the occurrence of valuable minerals are estimated. If the chances are good, then the presence or absence of the minerals is determined by putting down bores.

Perhaps the best example of this in the British Isles is the discovery of the new coal-field in east Kent. From a study of the rocks in the Bristol coal-field and in the coal-field of Belgium, geologists suggested that an anticline of carboniferous rock existed along a line between these two areas, buried under newer deposits, but possibly near enough to the surface in places to have coal seams which were economically workable. Subsequent borings in east Kent proved this to be the case, and there are now several collieries working in the district.

The second use of geology in mining is in the actual process of extracting the mineral. Here a knowledge of rock-structure, such as the slope or dip of beds, the arrangement of metallic veins, the size of faults, and so on, is obviously essential in planning the construction of tunnels and workings underground.

Besides being of great use in the search for metallic ores and other minerals, such as coal and oil, and in the extraction of these substances, economic geology has many other applications. The actual constitution and structure of individual kinds of rocks, which are economically useful, often has a bearing on their suitability for certain purposes. The structure of building-stones, for instance, is often of use in determining their strength and their resistance to the smoke of cities. Similarly, it is valuable to know the composition of clays used for making bricks, earthenware, or cement, while the value of geology to agriculture in helping us to understand the nature and the possibilities of different kinds of soil is obvious.

There is also another branch of Economic Geology which

is concerned with human activities applied to the earth's crust that do not involve the extraction of minerals. The most important of these activities is the question of water-supply. A very large proportion of the water we use comes from underground sources, such as springs, wells, or borings, and it is clear that in determining where wells are likely to be successful, if sunk, and in estimating the possible yield of water, geology plays an important part.

Minor uses of geology in this respect are in protecting coasts from sea-erosion, where a knowledge of rock-structure is very helpful, and in the construction of buildings in areas liable to earthquakes, where an understanding of the nature of earthquake vibrations is of great help in building houses which will withstand the shocks.

It is difficult to be precise about the other kind of value of geology—its philosophical value—for here man finds that he is face to face with something so much bigger than himself that it is by no means easy to discuss it. In considering the vast periods of time and the enormous forces which geology presents to us, the mind of man is astonished at its own insignificance, but it is in just these things that the value of geology lies, for it is in forcing these ideas upon us that it has, with the other sciences, changed and widened our point of view about ourselves and the uni-verse around us.

DOORS THAT ARE OPEN TO THE STUDENT

GEOLOGY is a specialised science and, like all specialised branches of knowledge, demands its own course of training from a student who wishes to become qualified in it. Most universities have a course of geology, usually extending over three years before a degree is granted, and since a thorough understanding of geology demands also a certain amount of knowledge of other sciences, such as physics and chemistry, these or similar subjects are usually also taken in the first part of a university course, the later part being devoted more exclusively to geology itself.

But although a certain knowledge of physics and chemistry is necessary and helpful, geology is a science with which an unusual amount of progress can be made with the aid of text-books alone, and there is a surprising number of people who, although they hold no university degrees, are very well-informed geologists, and who derive a large amount of pleasure from their geological excursions and from the periodicals on the subject. The great difficulty of study outside a recognised course is that of obtaining practical work, but here museums, such as the new Geological Museum at South Kensington, help to make up the deficiency, and in them the intending geologist can at least see specimens of everything his text-books mention, though actual practical work with the hands and the microscope is, of course, more difficult to obtain.

There are also societies, such as the Geologists' Association, which by organising research, by conducting expeditions to places of interest, and by issuing reports of their proceedings, do much to foster an interest in the subject.

There is no doubt that even with a comparatively small amount of detailed information, any one with a general knowledge of geological principles can derive much interest from the places he visits, and such an interest, well-founded, will lead him, by research into any literature he can find, to develop his principles towards detailed application. As an accompaniment to his journeys and visits, geology is one of the best hobbies a man can have.

GEOLOGY AS A CAREER

IT is perhaps an indication of the interesting nature of geology that quite a large proportion of undergraduates at the universities study the subject, but this has an unfortunate result : the demand for jobs exceeds the supply. It might be thought that since mining, which is a very large industry, needs geological knowledge, there would be a good demand from this source, but the geology which a mining engineer should know is taught together with engineering in the various schools of mining, so that " pure " geologists have not so much scope in this industry.

There are one or two special types of occupation available to geologists, such as surveying for possible oil deposits and a few other minerals. Apart from industry, the most important posts are as members of the geological surveys which are maintained by most governments. These posts are not, of course, very numerous ; besides these there are only a few others, such as jobs in museums and universities ; and as a consequence they are open only to very highly qualified geologists.

WHAT TO READ NEXT ABOUT GEOLOGY

A GREAT many general and specialist books have been written on geology, but the selection mentioned below will guide the reader in his next steps in penetrating further into the mysteries of the earth's crust. A valuable little book on rocks and their scenery, which is also a very good introduction to geology as a whole, is Professor J. E. Marr's *The Scientific Study of Scenery* (Methuen). Another book forming an excellent introduction is J. W. Gregory's *The Making of the Earth* (Home University Library, Thornton Butterworth Limited). A more detailed account of rock-types will be found in the larger text-books of geology, such as Lake and Rastall's (Arnold), and there are also many books on rocks alone, such as *Petrology for Students*, by A. Harker (Cambridge University Press), *The Principles of Petrology*, by G. W. Tyrell (Methuen), and *Volcanoes*, by G. W. Tyrrell (Home University Library, Thornton Butterworth Limited). For a further discussion about the formation of the earth's crust, Professor Marr's and most text-books are useful, while works on physical geography also give interesting accounts of earth-sculpture, volcanic action, transport of material, etc. Professor A. J. Cole's *The Geological Growth of Europe* (Home University Library, Thornton Butterworth Limited) is an interesting account of the later stages of the earth's history. Lake's *Physical Geography* and de Martonne's *Shorter Physical Geography* are particularly clear in their descriptions of this subject.

The study of earth-movements is one of the most recent branches of geology to be thoroughly developed, largely because it had to wait upon a detailed knowledge of the structure of mountain-systems before any comprehensive theories could be applied. It is consequently still a controversial and complicated subject, so that much of the literature concerning it is only to be found in the periodicals of geological societies ; but there are one or two very interesting books which give an account of it.

Earth Lore, by Professor S. J. Shand (Murby), is a short and simplified account of geology, which includes a clear explanation of earth-movements, isostasy, etc., while a more comprehensive work giving detailed descriptions of all the recent theories which have to do with earth-movements is *The Unstable Earth*, by J. A. Steers (Methuen). Two books dealing with special theories of interest are *The Origin of Continents and Oceans*, by Alfred Wegener (Methuen), and *The Surface History of the Earth*, by J. Joly (Oxford University Press). In these books the authors set out their theories, about which much controversy has been raised.

Books on Palæontology may be divided into two classes. First, there are the books which aim mainly at description of fossil types. A small book on these lines is *Palæontology*, by H. Woods (Cambridge University Press), while a very complete and detailed reference book, with numerous illustrations, is Zittel's *Palæontology* (Macmillan), in three volumes— Part I. Invertebrata ; Part II. Fishes to Birds ; Part III. Mammalia. The second class of books are those which deal with the subject more from the point of view of the history and development of life-forms. Books of this type are *Outlines of Palæontology*, by H. H. Swinnerton (Arnold), and *An Introduction to Palæontology*, by A. M. Davies (Murby).

There are many books on stratigraphy, and most of the English text-books on geology give an account of the rocks of the British Isles. Among works of a more specialist nature may be mentioned *An Introduction to Stratigraphy*, by L. D. Stamp (Murby), which gives a short but very clear account of the British rocks, and shows how the past history of the region can be constructed from their evidence. A more recent and larger work, with a strong emphasis on the historical side and on the processes of change, is *The Physiographical Evolution of Britain*, by L. J. Wills (Arnold). An important and very interesting work on ice-action and the Ice Age in Europe and America is W. B Wright's *Quaternary Ice Age* (Macmillan).

A very comprehensive and detailed description of the rocks of the British Isles is contained in the *Handbook of the Geology of Great Britain*, a compilative work edited by Evans and Stubblefield (Murby). Lastly, the detailed stratigraphy of particular areas will be found in the numerous sheet-memoirs of the Geological Survey, issued for the sheets of their geological maps.

There are two chapters dealing with astronomical methods of finding the age of the stars, the solar system, and the earth in *Evolution in the Light of Modern Knowledge* (Blackie). The chapters are by Sir James Jeans and H. Jeffreys. Sir James Jeans's *The Universe Around Us* (Cambridge University Press) also contains an account of these methods while a complete description of all the means of estimating ages, with a comparison of the results, will be found in *The Age of the Earth*, by Professor Arthur Holmes (Benn's Sixpenny Library).

The Elements of Economic Geology, by J. W. Gregory (Methuen), gives an account of the many ways in which geology is applied to practical ends, such as the extraction of valuable minerals, including the metals and mineral fuels, water-supply, and soil.

Finally, there are two geological periodicals which may be mentioned here. They are : *The Proceedings of the Geologists' Association*, published usually four times a year, by E. Stanford, and *The Geological Magazine*, published monthly by Dulau and Co.

MAN LOOKS AT HIS WORLD

by *A. R. B. SIMPSON, M.A. (Cantab.), B.Sc. (Edin.),
F.R.S.E., Diploma in Geography (Edin.), and
BARBARA SIMPSON, B.A. (Cantab.)*

MANY hundreds of years before the Christian era,
geography existed in some form or another. It has
had a chequered career. Just as there are stages in
the development of a butterfly, so it has been with geography.
The caterpillar represents the first stage: it is capable of
progression, but in a limited sphere. Geography in the hands
of the Ancients made great headway, but was ever bounded
by the limits of the then known world. The caterpillar
keeps moving, eating, and growing, until quite suddenly it
undertakes a change and forms a chrysalis which appears
lifeless save for a few vague twitchings.

Geography, which had occupied the minds of thinkers and
scholars throughout the centuries, was allowed to stagnate
during the Dark Ages; indeed, it was kept alive only by the
sporadic, and often inaccurate, efforts of the monks. The
analogy can be carried further, for, just as the chrysalis
is transformed into the glowing butterfly, so geography was
reborn, through the discoveries of explorers and the epoch-
making work of Darwin, to develop into one of the foremost
sciences of to-day.

IS THE WORLD ROUND ?

THE problem of the shape of the earth has always
arrested attention. From the earliest times philosophers seem to have realised that the horizon was roughly
circular in shape, and to have connected it in some degree
with the shape of the earth. Early Babylonian theories
suggested that the earth was a flat disc and that the oceans
were fed with water from the " ocean river " which surrounded the world.

The Greeks made great headway with this branch of
geography, and, as early as the sixth century B.C., Anaximander
had proposed the theory that the earth was a sphere. To
this Pythagoras and various thinkers after him agreed, since
they considered the sphere to be the only perfect body, and

therefore the only fitting form to be the dwelling-place of man. Two centuries later Aristotle proved that the earth must be round from the shadow that it cast on the moon during an eclipse. This marked a tremendous step forward, since it provided a solid foundation upon which to build subsequent knowledge.

The Greek thinkers were also responsible for the first efforts to estimate the position of the earth with regard to the universe, and, as early as the third century B.C., Aristarchus suggested that the earth revolved around the sun. His theory, however, was not accepted ; he was too far ahead of his time, and the more conservative suggestion that the earth was fixed in space held the field, through the writings of Ptolemy, until Copernicus in the Middle Ages proved Aristarchus's theory to be correct. The next milestone in the history of the shape of the earth was provided by Newton in the seventeenth century, who described it as of the same shape as an orange, there being a definite flattening of the surface towards the poles. The question is by no means settled yet, for during the present century other theories as to the shape of the earth have been advanced.

The Greeks did not confine themselves to theories of this sort, but tried, through the systematic collecting and arranging of data, to make an exhaustive geographical study of the *oekumene* or habitable world. Much of this early work has been lost to posterity, but from such writings as are available, we know that Aristotle was conversant with the formation of deltas, coast erosion, the distribution of plants and animals, and similar phenomena. Strabo, who lived at the beginning of the Christian era, compiled a book of travel describing geographically countries bordering the Mediterranean.

Attempts were also made by the Greeks to secure some system of measurement of the habitable world. Their efforts in this respect, together with a summary of all the geographical knowledge amassed by them, are set out in Ptolemy's work of A.D. 150. His greatest contribution was mainly cartographical, and it is largely from maps assigned to this author that we are able to realise the tremendous headway the Greeks had made in the subject of Geography. After the Greeks, geographical knowledge was allowed to stagnate for a period of over a thousand years. Indeed, had it not been for Arab interest in the works of Ptolemy throughout the Middle Ages, it is possible that the pioneer work of the Greeks would have been in vain.

THE FIRST ATTEMPTS TO MAP THE WORLD

WE do not know where the idea of map-making originated, but it is probable that it existed in various forms in many places. With the gradual increase in scientific knowledge and the approach of more advanced civilisation, the process gradually became perfected. The earliest map so far discovered is probably Babylonian. It is made of clay and was unearthed in 'Iraq. It portrays the world as a disc, with Babylon the centre of the land-mass, which is itself surrounded by the ocean river.

As would be expected, it was the Greeks who first made headway with the subject of map-making. In the eight-volume Geography produced by Ptolemy there was one world map which showed that the " then known world " had increased materially in size from the Mediterranean rim. The northern limit included the Shetland Islands, while the British Isles were given both size and shape. Africa was extended south of the equator, and the Indian Ocean represented with an accuracy which suggested that silk traders must have penetrated to the east across it. Besides maps of twenty-six countries, there were six volumes entirely taken up by tabulated latitudes and longitudes of various places. These were often inaccurate, but they marked the first attempt to reduce scattered geographical information to a sound scientific basis.

From the writings of various historical authors, we know that the Romans were also map-makers. To them is assigned the idea of the road map, for they were accustomed to detail a route by means of a map representing a narrow strip of country with the chief features clearly marked each side of the road. Such maps were not drawn to any scale. This idea was carried on by the early Crusaders, who made maps of the route from London to Jerusalem, with crude pictures representing the chief towns through which it was necessary to pass.

After the fall of Rome, such maps as were produced in the western world were drawn chiefly by monks. Religious influence rather than geographical facts tended to be the ruling influence in these maps. Wherever there was a danger of an empty space upon the map, representations

9. HOW THE GREEKS SAW THEIR WORLD: FROM A MAP DRAWN BY PTOLEMY.

of Adam and Eve in the Garden of Eden and Paradise were included. The work of a learned monk, called Cosmas, is typical of this period. He was fettered by the staunch belief that all Biblical stories were facts. " The four corners of the earth " was sufficient proof to him of a flat world. He rejected the idea of a spherical earth, because he said that in the antipodes men would walk upside down, and rain would fall upwards !

While these somewhat retrograde steps were being taken in the western world, the torch which had already been lit by the Greeks was kept alight in the hands of Islam in the East. Arabs trading in China had imported the compass for their own use long before it reached Christendom. Arab maps were concerned chiefly with trade routes and markets, but they also expressed a surprising knowledge of geographical facts, and they were conversant with the use of latitude and longitude. Their work, however, came to a sudden end with the Mongol invasions and subsequent wars, and the flickering torch of geographical learning was left for the western world to grasp.

HOW THE GREEK SAILOR KEPT HIS COURSE

DURING the fourth century the coastwise traffic in the Mediterranean set up a demand for some form of sea chart. The Greeks had invented *Periploi*, or sailing directions, which described all the capes, bays, and promontories to be found along the route, but which, of course, demanded that the user should always keep in sight of land. With the development of shipping, the practice of hugging the coast became distasteful, and this fact, coupled with the invention of the magnetised needle as a means of discovering direction, gave rise to the development of a new form of sea chart called *portolani*.

These charts, which were the ancestors of the modern Admiralty charts, were based upon estimated bearings and distances between the principal ports and capes. They were also characterised by groups of rhumb-lines radiating from common centres, and it was by these that the sailors were able to set their course. Each chart had a scale of " Portolano miles," smaller than the more usual Roman miles, and suggestive of Greek or Oriental origin. Such charts were widely used, so that various " hybrids " were gradually evolved, some being printed on skins and highly ornamented.

During the age of discovery, with an added impetus provided by the introduction of printing from the East, map-making flourished. Gradually, through the voyages of Columbus and Magellan in the fifteenth and sixteenth centuries, the true form or shape of the world became known. Map-makers of this period, however, were still averse from leaving the interiors of the newly-discovered continents blank, so they filled them with the products of their imagination. Cannibal feasts, grotesque half-human figures, with either no heads or faces set in their breasts, men using enlarged feet as umbrellas, people with one enormous eye, all figured in the productions of this period, while the sea was often filled with huge sea-serpents and sad pictures of shipwrecked mariners blown to destruction by a visible wind issuing from a cherub's mouth. Gradually these maps took more scientific form under the guidance of mathematicians, who realised the importance of representing the world drawn to a definite scale. Mercator (1512–94) was the pioneer in turning map-making from an art into a science, and a perfected edition of his method of mapping the world exists in atlases to-day.

PIERCING THE VEIL OF THE UNKNOWN : THE EARLY EXPLORERS

THROUGHOUT the ages, trade has probably provided the greatest stimulus to exploration, although other factors, such as the desire to extend religious and military authority, and the sheer love of adventure, have also played their part. In very early times the Phœnician sailors pierced the veil of the unknown in search of tin and other precious articles. Later, the Greeks, after the famous pioneering journey to India by Alexander, carried on trade with the countries around the Mediterranean.

In mediæval times the stories of the wonders of the East became exaggerated by the traders who returned from thence, with the result that Marco Polo undertook his enormous journey to see for himself " if these things be true." The riches of " Cathay," as China was then called, provided the motive for many expeditions during the Middle Ages which became famous, not by the fulfilment of their goal, but by reason of the new lands they discovered. In this way Columbus, attracted by the possibility of a westerly route to India, discovered the " New World."

The lure of the Spice Islands attracted Portuguese, English, and Dutch explorers into the far-off eastern seas, while the riches of Central America occupied the Spaniards in the West. Competition immediately arose amongst these powers. The love of adventure and an increasing desire to possess foreign territory seized the nations of the world, with the result that fresh discoveries followed in rapid succession until the little world of the Ancients had swollen into the modern world of to-day.

As the comparative inertia of the Dark Ages came to a close, the great period of discovery was heralded by the work of two travellers, one by land and the other by sea. Marco Polo, fired by the desire to see the great Kublai Khan, set out from Venice in 1271 to visit China, a journey which took him " a thousand days." Not only was this expedition a remarkable feat, but its value was greatly enhanced by the fact that Polo was a capable and accurate observer. When he returned to Italy some twenty years later, he was able to supply a considerable geographical account of the lands of the East.

The land route was long and tedious, and the countries, encouraged by the introduction of the mariner's compass, turned their attention to the possibility of a sea route to the East. Prince Henry, " the Navigator," of Portugal, was the pioneer of this work, and under his guidance many expeditions were sent out to attempt a voyage round Africa. Although this was not accomplished during his lifetime, he had taken the important step and laid the foundations for the discovery of a sea route to India.

THE MAN WHO SAILED WEST TO REACH THE EAST

WHILE the Portuguese were thus occupied with the coast of Africa, Christopher Columbus had managed to obtain a hearing for his apparently reckless scheme of sailing into the unknown West in order to reach the East. After a perilous journey of three thousand miles with a mutinous crew, he reached an island of the Bahama group in 1492, and returned thinking he had reached the Spice Islands. In a subsequent voyage, he landed in South America, but died without knowing he had discovered a new continent. It consequently fell to those who followed after him to have the joy that should have been his, the new continent receiving the name America after Amerigo Vespucci, a member of his crew who continued his work.

While Columbus had been thus occupied in the West, the Portuguese were still striving after a route to India via the coast of Africa, and before the close of the century their aim was achieved. Vasco da Gama, with a fleet of four little ships, after a hazardous voyage during which land was not sighted for a period of ninety-six days, eventually landed at Calicut by way of the Cape of Good Hope in the year 1498. The immense value of this voyage could not be appreciated immediately, for it meant that the Venetians, who had hitherto controlled the trade of the East, via the Levant, were to surrender their greatest claim to fame.

The Portuguese now turned their attention westwards, and in 1519 Ferdinand Magellan started in search of a westerly route to the Spice Islands. This voyage was perhaps the bravest and most memorable in history, for, having worked a passage through the narrow channel of Tierra del Fuego, he made a daring voyage across the unknown waters of the Pacific without receiving even the encouragement of striking land of any sort. Eventually he reached the Philippines, where he was murdered in a skirmish with the natives, and was thus robbed of further victory, for his ship continued the voyage and completed the first circumnavigation of the globe.

The foundations had now been laid. The great unknown had to a large extent been conquered by the daring efforts of these early pioneers. As a result of Magellan's triumph, all countries turned their attention to the sea and the discovery of new lands. Before the end of the century, the New World had disclosed her secrets, and Drake had made his famous voyage round the world.

The discovery of the southern continent of Australia came much later. It is assigned to Dirk Hartog, a Dutchman, in the year 1616, although at that time little importance was attached to it, as the land was both unfertile and inhospitable : moreover, the Spice Islands were still magnetic in their appeal. Tasman, in his voyage of 1642, discovered the west coast of New Zealand, and thereby renewed interest in " the great Antarctic Continent," but it was not before the voyage of Cook, as late as 1770, that the mystery of the southern land was solved.

DARWIN : THE INSPIRATION OF MODERN GEOGRAPHERS

DURING the period of great discovery so much geographical data was collected that there was grave danger of geography as a science being buried beneath the jumbled heap of travellers' logs. The task of scholars during the eighteenth century was not one of theorising, so much as that of systematising the enormous mass of knowledge laid haphazard at their disposal. The danger also arose of geography becoming exploded, through the work of specialists, into many component parts, such as climatology, oceanography, and anthropology, with nothing particular to link them together. There seemed to be no reason for facts. Geography had to be learned by rote, lists of capes, bays, mountains, and states in unending succession tending to damp the ardour of any would-be learner.

It was not until the beginning of the nineteenth century that any sort of order came out of this chaos. The work of Humboldt and Ritter stands as a magnificent attempt to find some sort of cement with which to bind together scattered facts and so save the subject from complete dislocation. Humboldt was a wide traveller, who had collected a mass of first-hand information of his own. This he correlated to show that land-forms exercise a determining influence on climate, plants, animals, and even on man himself. Ritter, his contemporary, held the same views, but confined his work chiefly to dealing with the earth as a field of activity for the creature, man.

A great step forward had been taken, but it was not until Charles Darwin, in 1859, published his " Origin of Species " that the character of the required cement was discovered. From the moment that this brilliant scholar set forth his idea of evolution and the influence of environment on every living thing and on its distribution, the solid building of a new and modern geography began. Instead of scattered fact, there was now a unifying principle running throughout the subject.

The work of Darwin can be said to have revolutionised all branches of science so that they have become rearranged and re-orientated around the idea of evolution. The last half-century, therefore, has seen, instead of the death of a geographical bugbear, bristling with inconsequent facts, the birth of modern geography, which is establishing itself more and more effectively as a unifying science. " The study of interrelations " is the desire with which Darwin has fired science. The inevitable result is that instead of each branch of science wishing to develop along lines of its own, each now requires free access to the discoveries of other sciences.

The whole may be compared with a tree. Geography, in that it is responsible for the discovery of the secrets of the earth's surface, forms the roots. Having collected the data, as it were, it is not concerned with the more specialised work of studying each separate subject individually, but leaves it to the anthropologists, biologists, geologists, etc., each to develop their own particular aspect and thus to form the trunk and branches of this tree of science. The geographer again steps in to consider them in relation to man. To do this he links together and utilises the researches of these sciences, and thereby knits together the otherwise scattered branches to form of them foliage and fruit.

MAPS : THE SHORTHAND OF GEOGRAPHY

IN the more civilised parts of the world the tramp or aimless wanderer is in a small minority. Nearly every one wants to get somewhere and as quickly as possible. " Can you tell me the way to ——, please ? " is the only kind of conversation that is likely to occur between any two of these hurrying millions as for an instant their paths cross or meet. A doubt as to direction is a more certain check to a motor's speed than possible danger round a bend of the road.

Direction and distance can both be expressed in words, but the result is a cumbrous catalogue of instructions which are like a tangled skein to be unravelled by the brain step by step until the line is clear. If the same information is expressed in the form of a map, not only one route but the alternatives can be taken in by the eye almost at a glance. It is significant that the Automobile Association's admirable routes for motorists now have strip maps to make the letterpress even more explicit : yet this idea is not new, for two and a half centuries ago an atlas was published showing the main roads of England in the form of strips, including a mile or two of country on either side.

An early eighteenth-century map of Africa indicates in doubtful outline but surprisingly correct position the then unnamed Lake Victoria, accompanied by the remark, " This great lake is placed here by report of negroes." The colouring of these early maps, where it exists at all, is hand-done, though the unwary purchaser should make certain that the colouring is really contemporary and not a twentieth-century afterthought. The maps of to-day, though remarkably similar in outline, are very different in the accuracy of their detail, and hand-colouring (except for a few geological maps) has been entirely replaced by modern printing methods.

THE MAP-MAKER IN DIFFICULTIES

YET this very detail and the magnificent finish of modern maps may give a misleading impression of accuracy, for the map-maker is always struggling against the inexorable fact that he is attempting the impossible. Imagine half the world represented by a melon cut in half. Assume that the interior has been removed and only the rind left, the rind representing the surface of the earth which we wish to map. No matter how we try, we cannot make the rind lie evenly on a flat surface without puckering. In other words, it is impossible to reproduce accurately a curved surface on a flat one without sacrificing something.

Now, imagine the half melon cut into the usual slices, but leave them attached to one another where they are widest. A map can be made by stretching the narrow ends of each slice until the spaces between them are filled up. It will be clear that regions near the equator will be about the right shape and size, but that, as the poles are approached, the countries become greatly swollen in size from east to west ; the poles themselves, which should be points, are turned into straight lines the same length as the equator. If, in addition, the segments are stretched as much lengthwise as they are in breadth, the size of the countries far from the equator will still be greatly exaggerated, but, as they have been enlarged equally in all directions at once, their shape will remain true. This is the principle of the Mercator map of the world, which is probably the most familiar of the many types available. This, besides giving the countries true to shape, is particularly useful for navigators since the direction of any one point from another also remains true.

The Mercator map also makes a brilliant showing when

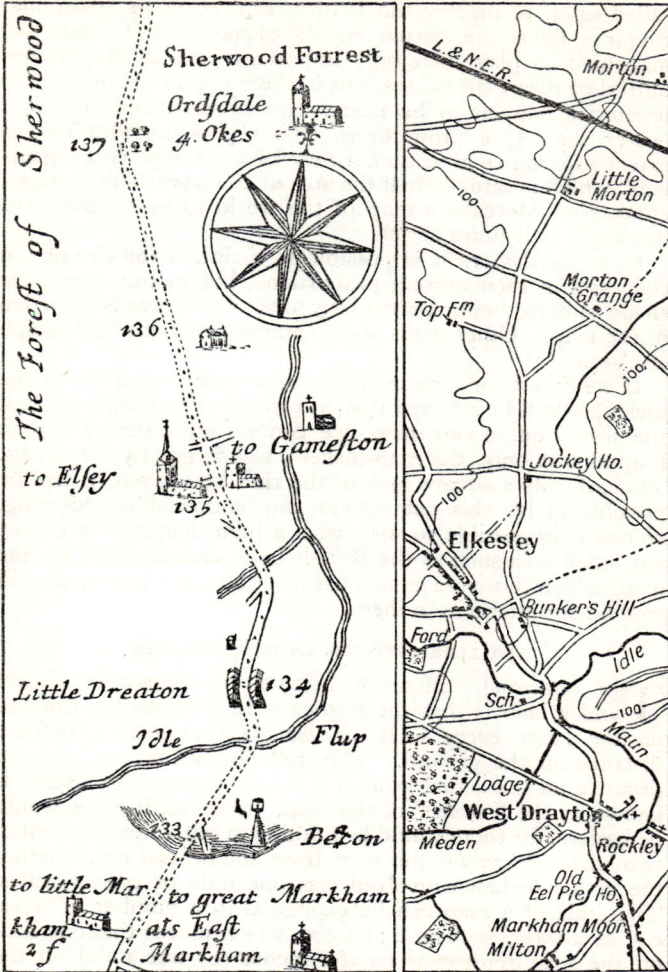

10. MAPS OF YESTERDAY AND TO-DAY.

An early strip map showing a section of the Great North Road, with drawings of the chief landmarks, and a modern road map of the same district.

called upon to display the British Empire in its traditional colour. Then the barren wastes of northern Canada are magnified to play their only important part in the Empire until they dwarf the possessions of the humbler nations whose territories happen to be nearer the equator, and therefore nearer their true proportions. To give some idea of the extent of this magnification, it may be mentioned that Greenland, which is actually half the area of India (without Burma), appears on Mercator's map of the world to be no less than five and a half times larger.

By other devices it is possible to maintain the size of the countries in their correct proportions, but in this case their shape suffers, being particularly distorted towards the edge of the map. Other maps again compromise with both shape and size.

If we revert for a moment to our original metaphor of the melon, it will be realised that, if instead of trying to get half the world on to one map, we confine our interest to one limited area only, the map-maker's task is greatly simplified. Thus, if only a square inch of the rind be cut out, it will be possible to lay this flat without any appreciable puckering. Hence it is possible to map with a high degree of accuracy any small area such as the British Isles, and, as these are the maps which the average man has most occasion to use, we will confine our attention to them.

THE LINK BETWEEN LAND AND PAPER

THE essential difference between a landscape picture and a map is that the former is in perspective, whereas on the latter every inch of distance represents a definite distance on the ground. This ratio of distance on map to distance on the actual ground is a very important one and is known as the " scale " of the map. Without it maps would be useless, for there would be nothing to tell a weary traveller, two inches away on the map from the nearest inn, whether the actual distance involved was one mile or twenty miles. The scale of a map can be expressed in a number of ways, *e.g.* as a ratio, such as 1 : 63,360, which means that one inch on the map represents 63,360 inches (or one mile) on the ground : the scale can also be expressed in line or bar form on the map.

Apart from maps showing the whole of Great Britain at once, the smallest scale available on Ordnance Survey maps (*i.e.* those produced by the British Government) is ten miles to one inch, and the largest twenty-five inches to one mile. Between these extremes the user has the choice of scales of ¼ inch, ½ inch, 1 inch, and 6 inches to one mile. The two largest maps, or " plans," as they are called, are uncoloured, and are chiefly used in connection with ownership of land and building. The chief patrons of the others are the tourists.

Those who have climbed a mountain peak and on its windy summit wished to name the lesser peaks spread out before them ; or those who, within the narrow compass of the seat beside the driver, have tried to trace a by-road where it deserts one sheet for another before the mute but insistent query of the next dividing of the ways, will realise that there is a limit to the useful size of a map. As map sheets, despite ingenious folding schemes, must be strictly limited in size, there is only one variable that remains, namely, the scale. If an airman travelling from, say, London to Edinburgh used the ordinary one-inch-to-one-mile Ordnance Survey maps he would have to change from one sheet to another every quarter of an hour : with the latest edition of the ten-miles-to-one-inch scale, two maps, printed back to back on one sheet, would suffice.

In Norway, those who prefer to see its beauties from the leisurely viewpoint of the hiker are apt to feel a little over-whelmed, if not dissatisfied with their efforts when reckoned in Norwegian miles, one of which equals seven British. In the same way a hiker in Britain who was at all anxious about " covering the ground " might feel depressed by his apparently small progress recorded by the ten-miles-to-an-inch map, whereas a one-mile-to-the-inch sheet would show the results of his exertions in more flattering perspective. Similarly, the touring motorist will probably prefer the quarter-inch to one-mile scale, though the half-inch and even the one-inch-to-the-mile maps will be invaluable for exploring historic sites and choosing picnic places in any one neighbourhood.

THE UNMOURNED DISAPPEARANCE OF THE " CATERPILLAR "

THE earlier maps showed rivers, boundaries, and places as accurately as they could. Later, a conventional drawing for hills appeared and indicated approximately their position, but nothing else. The simplest form of this is the caterpillar method of representing mountain ranges.

This caterpillar belongs to a genus which at the beginning of the present century was widely distributed throughout the civilised world, but is now fortunately almost as extinct as the other more graceful creatures of the geographer's heraldry which used to thrive in tropic seas and distant lands before extermination befell them at the hands of the explorer.

These unmourned caterpillars certainly represented length, and, by an ungainly extension of their limbs, a limited degree of breadth, but height defeated them, and the Himalaya and the Andes shared the trappings of the Pennines or the Mendips. The problem of the plateau remained unanswered. In some maps (e.g. those of the French and Swiss Governments) a more scientific member of the caterpillar family, known as hachures, is used with considerable effect, and in the latest British one-inch-to-one-mile map they are also used to bring out the relief—which is what the geographer calls the differences in level of the landscape. Hachure and shading are, however, only supplementary to contouring, which is the basis of all height representation on modern maps.

Imagine a sand-castle constructed in a bath, which is then filled carefully with slightly soapy water so that the miniature currents do not endanger the model landscape. Now empty the bath by two inches at a time. Each of these successive levels will be recorded on the model relief as a " high-tide " mark. These marks are the contour lines for 2 inches, 4 inches, 6 inches, and so on. Look vertically down at these contours and reproduce them, one inside the other, to any given scale on a piece of paper, and we then have a contour map of the original landscape. The degree of detail depends on the smallness of the " vertical interval " between two contours.

In printing maps the contour lines are usually printed from a separate plate, since such features as roads and buildings require frequent alteration, which would be difficult to make without interfering with the permanent contour lines. Disentangling contour lines from their crowded surroundings on a map and piecing them together to form a mental picture of the relief is, however, a task requiring time and a certain amount of skill. The use of hachures to bring out the contours helps matters, and some good examples of this method can be seen on some of the Ordnance Survey one-inch-to-one-mile sheets of Scotland.

A big step forward was made when the system of layer colouring was introduced. In this method the lowlands are usually coloured green and the higher areas deepening shades of brown, though the map-maker (or cartographer) has frequently to fall back on purple or even white for the highest peaks. As many as seven printings may be necessary to complete these maps, but the great development of motoring, not to mention climbing and walking, has greatly increased the demand for maps and made it possible to produce them at a very moderate price.

Those whose motoring has been confined to British roads do not realise how favoured they are, for outside the British Isles large-scale maps in layer colouring are still rare. There is, however, one exception to this in what is known as the 1 : 1,000,000 International Map. The aim of the sponsors of this map is to persuade all countries to undertake the production of a map of their territory on a uniform scheme and scale. Much progress has already been made, especially in Europe, which is practically complete, and in Africa and South America, which are more than half covered.

TRACING MEN'S OCCUPATIONS ON THE MAP

SUPPOSE we take a portion of the Ordnance Survey one-inch-to-one-mile map of England or Scotland. Unless there are large towns on it, the first thing to catch the eye will be the hills or mountains. If these are over 1500 feet or so we may be pretty sure that the chief occupations will be sheep-farming and sport. A marked absence of streams and other surface water on the hills, especially if the lowlands are well supplied, points to the hills being of porous rock, probably limestone or chalk : on these the soil is usually poor, and sheep-farming therefore the most probable occupation. On the other hand, a flat-bottomed valley, with a river winding along it, is likely to have an impermeable bed, say, of alluvial clay : here the dampness will result in grass growing well, and dairy-farming can be expected. Poor sheep-farming land will show on the map fewer and more scattered farms than will the richer agricultural or dairy-farming areas. Sheep-farming in turn makes us look for woollen mills on streams where water-power is available to turn them.

A further study of the map will reveal much, not only about the present occupation of the land, but also about the past. Prehistoric remains are shown in Old English type,

Roman remains in Egyptian type, and Saxon and later (up to 1688) in Gothic type. Thus tumuli on the forest-free heights, avoiding the marshy lowlands, recall the ancient Britons, and the " camps " and marvellously straight roads of the Romans are a reminder of how widespread their influence once was in Britain.

Place-names, too, sometimes give clues to the past. Thus there is the familiar Chester, Doncaster, etc., derived from the Roman *castra*, a camp. Names ending in *-thorpe* are strongly indicative of Danish settlement, just as *-by* is a more general Scandinavian suffix, while names such as Beaulieu are clearly of Norman origin. Caution must be observed, however, in making deductions from place-names and particularly from isolated instances. Thus it is no more safe to deduce that a single place ending in *-ton* indicates early British settlement than it is safe to choose lodgings for the summer on the strength of the house being called " Seaview." As a further warning may be cited E. D. P. Evans's view that *minster* does not necessarily denote some kind of ecclesiastical foundation, but a " place beside a stream " ; he is thus of the opinion that Westminster is derived from *Gwest*, an inn, and therefore means " the inn beside the river."

Sometimes the reasons for the growth of villages and towns can be gleaned from the map. The first requirement for a settlement is water-supply, though a good defensive position also played an important part in determining the site of many of the older towns. Apart from river sites, a less obvious, but much frequented, choice for a village is on what is called the " spring line." When porous rock rests on impermeable rock, rain will sink through until it reaches the latter, when it will come to the surface in the form of springs. Where such a village is situated at the entrance to a valley it will tend to become a market-town where meet the sheep-farmers from the high land and those of the agricultural or dairy farms of the low land. It will also gain as the crossing-point of two routes, that connecting the villages of the spring line and that joining the lowlands with the highlands.

When a market-town grows sufficiently in size, agricultural industries, such as tanning and especially brewing, are almost certain to grow up, and, as we have already suggested, there may be a small woollen industry as well. A hundred thousand seems, however, to be the present limit of size (Norwich excepted) for an essentially agricultural town, and most of them are much smaller. For growth beyond this figure some additional asset is required, such as coastal position and, above all, proximity to a coal-field.

Only a little imagination is required to conjure up from the map a vivid picture of the pit heads, the stark cones of pit waste, the rows of factories with tall brick chimneys belching forth black smoke, railways crossing and recrossing, interminable agglomerations of small houses set in monotonous rows ; in other words, the uniform landscape of any area which has its roots in coal.

Not only do maps suggest, even where they do not actually portray, the man-made changes in the landscape, but also—to the discerning—some of the more rapid natural changes. Rivers are, perhaps, the most changeable of all natural features, and their waywardness is sometimes betrayed by the map. Thus, Axbridge is no longer to be found on the river Axe, which has changed its channel and deserted the town. Part of the boundary between Derbyshire and Staffordshire coincides closely with the river Dove in its upper courses, but when the valley widens and the river is free to wander, the boundary is seen still describing curves now forsaken by the river of to-day. Aldeburgh is no longer on the Alde, for coastal currents have swept its silt into a long spit so that its present mouth is now some nine miles south of its original exit. Similarly, the Isle of Thanet has been silted into a peninsula.

ANALYSING THE WEATHER CLERK'S PRESCRIPTIONS

ANOTHER map, with which we are becoming increasingly familiar in spite of its rather forbidding scientific appearance, is the weather map. As this, however, has to be accompanied by certain technical terms, it will be better first to try to understand some of the factors which affect the climate (*i.e.* the average weather) of a country.

Hitherto we have been regarding the earth as a detached entity. If this were really the case, life, whether vegetable or animal, would be non-existent. Instead, however, of being a star in space, the earth is a planet revolving round the sun. The heat from the sun strikes the earth more and more obliquely—and consequently less and less effectively— as the poles are approached : hence the equatorial regions are hotter than the polar ones. If the axis of the earth were vertical, there would be no difference between the seasons. In reality, however, the axis is inclined, causing each pole to point for part of the year towards the sun and for the other part away from it. This results in the polar seasons alternating between perpetual day and perpetual night, the limits of these extreme conditions being known as the arctic and antarctic circles. The more nearly the equator is approached, the less marked becomes the change of seasons.

As altitude increases, the temperature falls—to the extent of about $1°$ F. for every 300 feet rise in elevation. The reader may argue that, as some one on a mountain is actually nearer the sun than one lower down, he should be warmer. At high altitudes the sun's rays are undoubtedly stronger, but the atmosphere is more rarified, and heat consequently radiates away more quickly; thus it is possible for those venturing to high altitudes to suffer sunburn on one side and frostbite on the other simultaneously.

Next to distance from the equator and altitude, the remaining important temperature control is distance from the sea. It is a commonplace that, if a saucepan of water be placed on a gas ring, the sides of the pan become hot more quickly than the water it contains; in fact, water takes longer than any other substance to absorb heat and to lose it. Thus the temperature of the oceans varies far less than that of the continents, and the "land-mass" effect of the latter, as it is called, results in extremes of temperature.

Winds reaching land from the sea are felt as warm winds in winter and cool ones in summer: hence the seaboards of the continents enjoy a more equable temperature than their interiors, so much so that in Siberia the north wind in winter from the Arctic Ocean is a "warm" wind. It is not surprising, therefore, to find that the lowest temperature ever recorded ($-90°$ F.) was not at one of the poles, but at Verkhoyansk, three hundred miles from the sea in northeast Siberia, and the highest temperature ($136°$ F.) not at the equator, but at Tripolitania in North Africa.

The geographer is not, however, interested so much in these record temperatures as in the "mean" or average experienced in a place from month to month. To obtain these, a thermometer, four feet from the ground, but protected from the direct rays of the sun, is used, and the highest and lowest temperatures during every twenty-four hours noted. The mean temperature for the day lies half-way between these two readings. Similarly, the mean for the month is the average of these daily means. The July mean for London is 63° F. and that for January 39° F.

A POTENT BUT ERRATIC FACTOR IN MAN'S AFFAIRS : THE RAINFALL

THE other factor in climate is rainfall. Hot air will hold more moisture than cold. Therefore, if moisture-laden air is chilled—as, for example, when air over a hot bath comes in contact with the cold tap—moisture is deposited in the form of rain, fog, snow, or hail, according to the temperature conditions. It is a law of physics that any gas (*e.g.* air) when compressed becomes heated, as any one who has ever blown up a bicycle tyre is aware from the rise of temperature in the lower end of the pump ; conversely, when a gas is allowed to expand it cools, which again can be readily proved by suddenly removing the valve from a blown-up inner tube. If air rises, there is less atmosphere above it ; the pressure is consequently reduced and the air is cooled. Air may be forced to rise by meeting higher ground ; by meeting colder (and therefore heavier) air ; by becoming heated, which makes it less dense. Any of these conditions may result in rain.

It is thus evident that winds will be more likely to bring rain if they have passed over a warm sea (or current) than over a cold one or over land ; if they are blowing from warmer latitudes to cooler ones than *vice versa* ; if they are blowing towards mountains than over a hot plain.

It is, however, insufficient to know the annual rainfall of a place, for 20 inches in Scotland will go very much farther than 20 inches on the much hotter fringes of the Sahara. More important still is its distribution throughout the year. Thus a rainfall of 50 inches would appear sufficient for forest growth almost anywhere ; yet, if there is a marked deficiency during, say, three consecutive months in the year (as there is, for instance, in northern Australia), only vegetation which is either annual or provided with some means of tiding over the dry period can exist. The 20 inches of rain, which is the average over part of the Canadian prairies and southern Russia, would not allow of wheat being grown were it not for the fact that most of it falls when it is most wanted for ripening the grain, namely, in the early summer.

4*

An extreme example is afforded by Cherrapunji (in Assam), which holds the world's record average of 460 inches ; yet 98 inches of this falls in July and only one-quarter of an inch in December. Then, again, rainfall may be too heavy, as in tropical regions, where it may leach the goodness out of the soil or sweep it away in a cataract of mud : where crops such as maize are grown, which do not bind the soil and hold it as grass does, this soil wastage may be as high as 85 tons per acre in one year. Even temperate regions are not entirely immune ; thus, for instance, in August 1933, Washington experienced 7 inches rainfall in a day, which brought business to a standstill, resulted in the loss of forty-seven lives, and caused damage estimated at £2,000,000.

Not only is the seasonal distribution of rainfall important, but also its annual reliability. Rainfall averages are taken over a period of at least thirty-five years wherever records are available for that period. In Great Britain even the driest year on record (1887) was only 23 per cent. below the average. As the equator is approached, however, the rainfall tends to be less reliable ; this is true especially where the rainfall is concentrated rather than evenly distributed. Thus, in the Indo-Gangetic plain, statistics show that the rainfall unre-liability advances from 20 per cent. where the annual fall is 44 inches, to 45 per cent. where it is 12 inches, and 65 per cent. where it is only 6 inches. The caution with which the term "mean rainfall" must be used is well illustrated by the figures for a station in northern Australia, where 29 inches fell in one year and but ½-inch in the following one, although the "average" was 6 inches. Similarly, it is a geographic paradox that a party of early explorers in central Australia nearly lost their lives by drowning, owing to their encountering one of the rare, but extremely heavy, deluges which desert regions occasionally experience.

THE PARALYSING EFFECTS OF DAMP AND MONOTONY

HITHERTO we have considered temperature and rainfall as acting separately, but if thus regarded they may give a misleading answer to the question of habitability. Thus a man may feel incapable of physical exertion in a temperature of 80° F. on the Guinea Coast in West Africa, while farther inland a temperature of over 100° F. may feel quite support-able. The discomfort experienced in the former case is clearly not due to heat alone, but to heat combined with excessive moisture. The degree of saturation of the air at any temperature is called the " relative humidity." Thus a temperature of 80° F. may feel muggy or merely scorching, according to whether the relative humidity is in the region of 80 per cent. or only 50 per cent., just as one of 30° F. may correspondingly feel raw or only pleasantly keen.

Other climatic factors bearing on man's reaction to his surroundings are perhaps more psychological in type. They include the beneficial effect of a climate which enjoys variable, as opposed to monotonous, weather. In this connection it may be instanced that statistics show that inventiveness is much more pronounced in northern than in southern Europe —a fact in which climate doubtless plays a part as well as race and civilisation. In the same category comes the allegation that the intensity of the sunshine in Kenya is inimical to prolonged settlement by white men, in spite of the altitude reducing the temperature to within bearable limits. Perhaps, too, it is a climatic devil which seizes the Malay when he suddenly turns aside from his peaceable everyday life and runs " amok."

There are, however, so many factors, from the laws of science to the whims of the individual, which play their part in determining man's reactions towards his environment, that the geographer must beware of isolating too hastily any one influence. When man settles anywhere, he by implication accepts the climate as being suited to his mode of life. He may shiver in an exceptionally cold winter or complain about an unusually wet summer, but he knows that the extremes will not be such as to be unbearable ; in other words, he takes the climate for granted.

The immediate target for his abuse or praise is not the climate, but the weather. Will the rain hold off long enough for the wheat to be carried, or will it be fine for the Derby ? The angler is equally concerned to know whether there will be enough rain to make his efforts profitable. In an endeavour to answer these and a host of similar questions, the Meteorological Office in London utilises the daily reports of some six hundred stations in western Europe to compile a daily weather map, from which it is possible in some degree to forecast the weather for the next twenty-four hours.

" DEPRESSION OVER ICELAND MOVING SOUTH-EAST "

IF we hit a golf ball, it moves. It does so because the pressure behind it is greater than the pressure in front of it.

The same applies to anything which is free to move, including air. In other words, the whole question of winds, and therefore of weather, is dependent on changes of pressure.

There is, however, another influence at work, and that is the rotation of the earth. This causes winds, moving from regions of high to those of low pressure, to be deflected to the right in the northern hemisphere and to the left in the southern. Hence it comes about that, in the northern hemisphere, if we stand with our backs to the wind, there will be a region of high pressure to our right and one of lower pressure to our left. This is known as Buys-Ballot's Law.

A depression, or to give it its more technical name, a cyclone, is a (usually oval) region of low pressure surrounded by higher pressure, the whole being between fifty and five hundred, or more, miles across. These depressions usually move eastwards at an average speed of between twenty and thirty miles an hour. If Buys-Ballot's Law be borne in mind, it will be realised that in the eastern part of the depression the direction of the wind will be from the south ; in the southern part it will be from the west ; in the western part it will be from the north. This may be checked by examining the weather map published in some of the daily papers. The wind directions are shown by means of arrows, with varying numbers of barbs, according to the strength of the wind. Pressures on these maps are expressed in millibars : 1000 millibars represents approximately the mean atmospheric pressure at the surface of the earth, the ordinary fluctuations experienced in the British Isles ranging from about 970 to 1030.

Consequently, as the heart, or " eye," of a depression passes from, say, Plymouth to Cambridge, the wind at Southampton veers from south or even south-east to south, south-west, west, north-west, and north. As might be expected, when the wind is in the southern quarter, it will be warmer than later on when it is in the north. Steady rain is also common in the forward sector of the depression, and sharp, clearing showers in the rear part. The prevalence of cyclones over the British Isles, particularly in winter, does much to explain the variability of the weather experienced.

If the pressure arrangement of a cyclone is reversed, and the pressure is high in the centre and lower round about it, this distribution is known as an anti-cyclone. Anti-cyclones usually cover much greater areas, such as most of Europe or the whole of Central Asia, and are also much more stable than cyclones. They are frequently associated with long periods of calm or with light winds and may remain stationary for a month or more at a time. In winter they often bring damp, dull weather, but in summer they are responsible for long spells of bright, sunny weather. During an anti-cyclone the barometer, which is simply an instrument for measuring pressure, remains steady, while, as a cyclone approaches, the " glass " drops and then begins to rise again after the eye of the cyclone has passed. It should be noted, however, that, while a falling barometer usually implies wind, this does not necessarily bring rain.

SOME TERRIBLE EXPLOITS OF WIND AND WATER

WHEN the pressure differences between the outer edge of a cyclone and its centre are not spread over four or five hundred miles, but confined within only five miles or even considerably less, the resulting winds are enormously stronger. The cyclone then becomes a hurricane, as it is called in the West Indies ; in the United States of America and West Africa they are known as tornadoes, and in the China seas as typhoons. These rarely occur outside latitudes 10–40° N. and S., and are usually local in their effect, but cause an immense amount of concentrated damage.

In one week in November 1932 at least two million banana trees were destroyed in Jamaica ; another hurricane, travelling at 125 miles per hour, swept Cuba, killing about 2000 people ; and a typhoon in Japan destroyed several hundreds of houses in Tokyo and resulted in 35,000 others being flooded. In September 1933, Tampico, the East Mexican oil port, with a population of 76,000, was virtually obliterated by a hurricane which blew for twelve hours with a velocity ranging from 80 to 106 miles per hour. In September 1931 a formidable hurricane struck Belize, the capital of British Honduras, which normally lies to the south of the hurricane tracks ; the wind began to blow violently from the north-west about 1.45 p.m. and continued with increasing severity until 3 p.m., when a lull occurred ; at 3.45 p.m. the wind recommenced with even greater violence than before, but from the south-east, thus working on exactly the same principle that we have already noted in connection with an ordinary cyclone ; the death-roll was estimated at 1000 out of a total population of 15,000. Every year one or more parts of the world are visited by these destructive storms, so this list could be extended almost indefinitely.

Waterspouts are due to the same causes operating over water and within very limited areas. While common in tropical seas, they are fortunately rare elsewhere. Nevertheless, in 1930, a waterspout destroyed several thousands of acres of vines on the northern shores of the Lake of Geneva ; in 1932 a tidal wave, accompanied by a waterspout, flooded Cannes on the Riviera, causing some £400,000's worth of damage, while a small one the following year on one of the Italian lakes resulted in a rain of fish on the shore !

Hail-storms are another local, but intense, agent of destruction. These are most severe during the summer months in the temperate regions where the land-mass effect is most pronounced. In these circumstances the ascending current of air in the heart of a cyclone may rise rapidly and high enough for the condensed drops of moisture to be frozen and fall as hail. The hailstones are frequently as large as pigeons' eggs, and cause great havoc to fruit-trees, crops, and stock, and may even penetrate corrugated-iron roofing. In June 1930 an exceptionally severe onset struck a village in the east of Newfoundland, blocks of ice estimated to weigh ten pounds each falling and destroying the roofs of many of the houses. In July of the same year it is estimated that half a million acres of wheat were destroyed by a hail-storm which swept over the Canadian prairies, while some children were killed and three mosques almost destroyed in southern Siberia. The tea companies of Assam (north-east India) annually insure against this menace to their crops.

THE COUNTRIES THAT COVER THE EARTH

WE are now free to apply these climatic controls to the earth as it exists to-day, to observe how they operate to make one part attractive to man, while another repels him, and to examine within what limits he is held captive by them and how far his ingenuity has earned for him his independence.

Much of the surface of the earth is taken up by deserts, those of ice bordered by the polar circles, and those of sand which are characteristic of both the northern and the southern tropic. These appear to defeat both man and nature. Between the two tropics lies the region where nature is still on the whole victorious over man, but between the tropics and the ice-bound north and south lie the warm and temperate zones where man has built up his highest civilisations and where his only real enemy is man.

The regions where man has been most successful lie in North America and Eurasia. In the former the land-mass effect, with its formidable extremes of temperature and tendency towards aridity, is counteracted in the east by the modifying influence of the Great Lakes and Hudson's Bay, while in Europe the highly indented coast-line serves the same purpose. Westwards in America and eastwards in Eurasia, however, the climate becomes increasingly powerful, and man is driven from the inhospitable interiors to the milder fringes. In Asia the Himalaya act as a barrier, not only to man but also to climate, leaving the monsoon lands of India, China, and Japan to develop virtually independent of the rest of the continent.

It is in these monsoon lands of Asia that man swarms in his densest millions. In fact, out of an estimated world population of some two thousand millions, one quarter live in China, a fifth in India, and one in thirty-three in Japan.

THE LANDS OF PLENTY : RAIN AND RICE

THE word "monsoon" really means the rainy season, but is generally used to indicate the rain-bearing winds responsible for this. The monsoon reaches India in summer from the south-west, and, as it brings 90 per cent. of the rain to five-sixths of India, the vegetation and prosperity of the country are dependent on it. The monsoon arrives with extraordinary regularity, meeting the Malabar coast about June 3rd, while a second branch of it sweeps up the Ganges valley from the east about the middle of the month, penetrating as far as the Punjab about the end of it.

As the monsoon hurls itself against the Western Ghats, the weather changes with an abruptness which justifies the expression, "the bursting of the monsoon." By the end of October the monsoon has spent itself. Although the rain brings freshness, the air becomes heavy and warm whenever it stops, even for half a day. The high humidity not only saps energy, but mould threatens almost anything not made of metal, and snakes and scorpions take refuge in the houses. However, vegetation grows rapidly, and rice sown in June is ready for cutting in September, while maize is sown and harvested in two months.

By November the wind has established itself in the north-east, and the absence of rain, combined with winter temperatures, make this the best season of the year in India. The north-east monsoon is much less regular than the south-west, but brings two feet of water in autumn to the Coromandel coast, which, being sheltered by the Western Ghats, receives only the dregs of the summer south-west monsoon.

Lying for the most part within the tropics, India feels the effect of the returning sun too soon for spring to be other than brief, and by March the temperatures are again well into the eighties. The earth is parched and cracked, the air is filled with dust, and the torrid heat seems to destroy vegetation to its roots : Europeans, unable to take refuge in the mountains, lose sleep and appetite, and venture out of doors only in the early morning and late afternoon. Thus a dry, hot season succeeds the dry, cool season. In fact, the sensation produced by the climate of Bombay has been described as being akin to being boiled for half the year and baked for the other half.

The wettest regions of India are, therefore, the Malabar coast, between the Western Ghats and the sea and the lower Ganges valley, the rainfall decreasing towards the Punjab. With unlimited sunshine and adequate moisture only one requisite remains for crops to flourish with a minimum of cultivation, namely, fertility of soil. Erosion is rapid on the slopes of the mountains struck by the monsoons, and the plains below them are therefore thickly carpeted with alluvium. In these regions are found some of the greatest population densities in the world, which is all the more remarkable since 80 per cent. of the population is dependent on agriculture.

MAKING THE RAIN-WATER LAST

THE main problem of Indian agriculture is how to arrange for the spreading of the monsoon rainfall over the drier parts of the year and the less favoured parts of the country. In the silt-covered lower Ganges valley water-supplies can be obtained from wells. In the more rocky regions, and particularly in the south-east, water is stored in tens of thousands of " tanks " ; these vary from small, crudely dammed depressions to pools acres in extent and protected by masonry and concrete. In the Punjab the rivers, swollen in summer by the melting snows and glaciers of the Himalaya, supplemented later by the monsoon, vary enormously in level, e.g. in the case of the lower Indus from one inch to thirteen feet : in this area lateral " inundation canals " to distribute this flood-water are common.

The people depend so entirely on agriculture, and the harvest is so irrevocably destroyed by a single monsoon failure, that, wherever a serious deficiency occurs, famine is imminent. Thus a partial failure of the monsoon in 1865 resulted in the death of a million people in Orissa—a third of the total population. The regions suffering most severely are those on the borders of adequate average rainfall, and those people who did not die of hunger were often the victims of epidemics which seized the weakened masses wandering in search of food.

From about 1835, however, the primitive native methods of water-storage began to be supplemented by large scale irrigation schemes executed by the British Government. The Sarda River scheme (150 miles north-west of Lucknow), completed in 1928, has about 4000 miles of distributing canals, commanding an area of over seven million acres, necessitating incidentally the building of over three thousand bridges. The Sukkur scheme in Sind, opened in 1932, is the largest in the world, and includes some 7000 miles of secondary canals ; these irrigate an area which would otherwise be desert, but is now capable of producing £25,000,000's worth of cotton, wheat, rice, millet, and sugar-cane per annum.

Hence it is that to-day, thanks to the part played by irrigation, 20 per cent. of the cultivated land of India escapes the rainfall variations. This, together with the work of the railways in equating areas of want with those of plenty, enables Britain to congratulate itself on there being in India no longer any fear of death from famine.

CHINA : THE LAND OF STRANGE CONTRASTS

IN China things are less clear-cut than in India. When China is mentioned, does it include the outlying areas of Mongolia, Tibet, and Sinkiang as well or not ? Even the boundaries of China proper are no longer precise, for the official (or Nanking) Government controls now only the coastal provinces, while Japanese influence encroaches in the north : the rest is at the mercy of authority which varies from banditry to communism. We are not yet so at home in Peiping as we were in the more familiar Peking. Census figures in England itself are not above suspicion, but in China the limits of error are greatly widened by the unit being, not the individual, but the family. The climate is no exception to the general lack of regularity.

Except for the plain of the lower Hwang-Ho, China is a hilly country, but the ascent to the interior plateaus is relatively gradual, and the approach made easier by the east-west valleys of the principal rivers. The monsoon does not burst in sudden fury, but mounts steadily to its June maximum, and eastward-moving cyclones bring winter rain, except in the north-west, where the winter months are as dry as in India. The temperature variations are much more marked ; there is no Himalayan range to shut out the bitter winter winds from Central Asia, so the average temperature for north China is below freezing for five months in the year : the Peiping winter is made yet more hideous by the dust which these blizzards carry from the loess regions of the north-west.

This loess is a peculiar formation, believed to have originated as the accumulated dust sweepings of Central Asia. It is yellow and extremely fertile, but unfortunately also extremely porous, and, as it occurs mainly where the rainfall drops below twenty inches a year, only limited advantage can be taken of its richness. Apart from the hilly southern half of China, there remain the great alluvial plain of the north and the valley of the Yangtse-Kiang, which includes the Red Basin of Szechwan, famous for its fertility.

The north-west excepted, the difficulty with China is not too little moisture, but too much. While drought has destroyed millions of Indians, floods have drowned even greater numbers of Chinese, and disease has seconded the one as ably as the other. The Hwang-Ho, or Yellow River, derives its name from the loess which it carries down from its upper courses. Arrived at the great plain, its pace slackens, and some of the load of yellow mud is dropped. This accumulates in the bed of the river, whose level consequently rises. To keep it under some control, artificial banks have to be constructed. The river-bed mounts inexorably. Peasants struggle to keep pace with their dykes until in places the river may be fifteen feet above the surrounding plain. In early summer the river rises threat-eningly, and, as the watchmen on the dykes beat their gongs, the farmers come running, day or night, to defend their crops. Desperately they add inch by inch of earth, but sooner or later comes a year when the melting snows of Central Asia are too much for the peasants of the plains. Then the river bursts its banks, submerging land and people on a scale of which statistics convey but a faint idea.

In 1852 the Hwang-Ho changed its outlet to the sea northwards through a distance equivalent to the Thames changing its exit to the Forth. In 1888, "China's Sorrow" engulfed over two million people in one province alone. In August 1933 in another district it flooded five hundred villages and rendered 300,000 people homeless. The Yangtse-Kiang, or Blue River, is more dependable, but the lakes, which act as safety-valves for its floods, are gradually silting up, and in 1932 the river-level at Hankow rose to the record height of fifty-two feet: not only were a million people drowned, but the crops and houses of upwards of fifty million people were irretrievably ruined.

THE RICE GROWERS : UNTIRING NURSES OF THE SOIL

IN length the Yangtse-Kiang is exceeded by the Mississippi-Missouri, the Amazon, and the Nile, and in volume by the Amazon and the Congo. It is, however, the finest inland commercial water-way in the world, for ocean steamers can ascend the 640 miles to Hankow, while smaller ones can penetrate the gorges to the Red Basin, some 800 miles farther inland. In its " basin " (i.e. the total area between its tributaries) live some 200,000,000 people, belonging to what is probably the hardest-working race in the world. Not only is every patch of plain cultivated, but the hills themselves have been terraced into flatness. This is the great rice-growing region of China, while tea, cotton, and silk are also produced in enormous quantities. Once on the river itself, but now on a small south-bank tributary near its mouth, stands Shanghai, which has thrived on the trade of this flourishing valley to such an extent that, in less than a century, it has amassed over one and a half million inhabitants.

Yet for all its fertility and industry, which give crop yields far in excess of those of India and above the average for the world, such is the burden of its population to-day that China is not self-supporting in food-stuffs, but has to import even rice from abroad. It is also characteristic of China that, although possessing some of the largest deposits of coal in the world as well as immense quantities of iron, both of these minerals figure prominently in her imports.

Japan is the third great monsoon area, but it differs from the others in many ways. It is not part of a land-mass, but is made up of four main islands. It also extends farther north. Yet although Hokkaido, the most northerly of the four, lies in the same latitude as the south of France, the severity of its winters recalls those of Finland or western Russia. Even in the south the winters are those of England rather than north Africa, though the summer temperatures are more in keeping with the averages for the latitudes concerned. This apparent departure from the rule that islands experience equable temperatures is explained by the fact that Japan is still within reach of the Asiatic land-mass and by the presence of a cold current which reaches it from the north.

Like India and China, Japan is essentially an agricultural country, but so mountainous are her islands that only 15 per cent. of their surface is available for cultivation. From this limited area over 60 per cent. of the population have to obtain their livelihood. It is not surprising, therefore, that terracing and cultivation are brought to an even higher state of perfection than in China. If the cold current already mentioned has a blighting effect on the climate, it helps the fisheries, while the indented coast provides numerous small harbours, and the forests timber for boat-building ; hence the importance of fish to supplement the limited food resources of the land. The family income is eked out by growing tea or raising silk, both occupations being dependent on labour rather than on land.

AGENTS OF DEATH : EARTHQUAKE AND TIDAL WAVE

WHILE liability to dry weeks necessitates much irrigation, the rivers are small and their valleys deep. Hence neither famine nor floods are serious menaces to Japan. Yet, as in the case of India and China, the high birth-rate of these eastern nations is partially counteracted by natural causes. The agent in this case is the volcano and its associates, the earthquake and the tidal wave. The last two are experienced in the other two countries as well, but are rarer though hardly less formidable in their visitations. The mountain-building forces which created Japan have not yet settled into equilibrium. Hence earth-movements, most of them appreciable only by special recording instruments (seismographs) are so common that in places the annual total is something over six hundred shocks. Mountain-building often results in crustal weakness and this in volcanic activity. An eruption in 1873 cost the lives of 1200 people, while another in 1912 was so violent that buildings ten miles from the crater were damaged by the wind alone.

While volcanic soil is frequently very fertile, newly deposited cinders may devastate large areas and render the fields sterile for a long period. An earthquake in 1891 destroyed 142,000 houses, with a loss of over 7000 lives ; the relatively small loss of life is due largely to the semi-flexible principle on which the houses are constructed to meet this peril. In 1923 occurred the worst earthquake ever experienced in historic times, nearly 100,000 people being killed as the capital was laid in ruins, 128,000 houses being thrown down and 447,000 burnt, while the tidal wave associated with it washed away a further 800. Such is the recuperative energy of the Japanese, however, that in ten years Tokyo had been rebuilt on an improved plan, with the result that Greater Tokyo is to-day the third city in the world, with a population of over five millions.

In spite of having cloistered herself from the outside world for the two and a half centuries preceding 1868, Japan has since then lost no time in proving that, at least as far as she is concerned, the " Unchanging East " is a fallacy. Stimulated by the prestige acquired in the Russo-Japanese War of 1904, she has compressed the western world's slowly accumulated experience into a brief apprenticeship of some sixty years, and has now graduated with honours in the industrial markets of to-day. The frugal standard of living, and therefore of wages, to which her people are accustomed—and with which they are content—enables them to undersell those used to the luxuries of western and American civilisations. The Japanese factories are thoroughly up-to-date, and labour, although well cared for, is not unduly hampered by union restrictions. The depreciation of their currency, and their willingness to supply the wants of customers, instead of trying to determine their wishes for them, are also factors in the remarkable success of Japanese merchants.

QUENCHING THE THIRST OF THE DESERT LANDS : IRRIGATION

IN the monsoon lands, irrigation is in varying degrees supplementary to the rainfall. In Egypt, one of the most ancient of the lands of plenty, irrigation is taken a stage further and used as a substitute for rain. If the Nile were to fail, Cairo's annual inch of rainfall would not save the land from being shrivelled up into desert by the sun. Every year the heavy summer rainfall on the Abyssinian mountains results in the waters of the Nile rising some twenty-five feet. From earliest times the natives have used this water for their crops, flooding one " basin " (*i.e.* embanked field), and then draining it on to the next. Cotton and *bersim* (a kind of clover) each occupy about a fifth of the cultivated land, closely followed by maize and wheat ; minor crops include sugar-cane, onions, dates, and rice. In passing it may be mentioned that " Egyptian tobacco " is grown in Greece and Turkey, but made into cigarettes (and sometimes cured) in Egypt.

In the course of the last hundred years much has been done, first by French and later by British engineers, to regulate the supply of water. This has been effected by the construction of large barrages at Sennar (in the Sudan), Aswan, Asyut, and at the head of the Delta. The Aswan dam has twice been raised in height and its original capacity doubled. Subsidiary to these is a vast network of canals and drains, and the air is filled with the creaking and groaning of the bullock-turned native waterwheels. Much water is wasted in the swamps of the Upper Nile, but plans for avoiding these by canals are now under consideration. This modern irrigation has the advantage of allowing the land to be used throughout the year, making two and sometimes three crops possible instead of one. It is true that the fertilising silt is no longer spread over the fields, and artificial fertilisers have to be used instead, but the net gain both in output and in its certainty is immense. Since almost the entire population is agricultural, and every patch of land depends on irrigation, which in turn is under Government control, it is clear that Egypt enjoys an exceptional unity, provided it is wisely governed.

THE FAVOURED LANDS : WHERE HARD WORK IS REWARDED

WE have seen how essentially agricultural are the crowded peoples of the monsoon lands ; for centuries they have been content to do little more than subsist, until in recent times large-scale irrigation has increased their capacity and enabled them to supply other countries as well. In the temperate lands the change of season is marked by temperature rather than by rainfall. Whereas too seasonal a rainfall can to some extent be provided for by the storage either of water itself or the resulting crops, heat cannot be stored. Man in these regions must therefore be able to protect himself against more or less rigorous winters and possess greater skill in cultivating crops than is necessary in the luxuriant tropics. The temperate regions, lying between the deserts of the tropics and the great subarctic forest belts, include most of Europe and large parts of North America, besides lesser fragments of Africa and the other southern continents.

Within the temperate zones all the continents have small, specially favoured areas which enjoy what has come to be known as a Mediterranean climate. This has three main characteristics ; most of the rain falls in the winter half of the year, and there is more or less complete drought in summer ; the winters are not only rainy, but very mild, and the summer is very hot as well as dry ; the skies in summer are bright and sunny, the cloudlessness accounting for the high temperatures.

The summer climate restricts the natural vegetation to types that are in some degree drought-resisting. Hence evergreens and plants with long roots prevail, and shrubs and thickets take the place of forests. The commoner varieties include the olive, vine, juniper, laurel, lavender, thyme, broom, gorse, and prickly pear. On the higher (better watered and cooler) slopes, forests of chestnuts, oaks, and pines may occur.

WINE AND FRUIT IN MEDITERRANEAN LANDS

THE long summer drought has various repercussions. Thus because good pasture is lacking, cattle are scarce, with the result that olive-oil has tended until recently to take the place of butter in the diet of the inhabitants. Sheep and goats find abundant food in the waste lands in winter, but in summer have to be sent up to the mountain pastures where they wander in charge of communal shepherds—a practice known as "transhumance." The rivers fail just at the season of greatest thirst and when most water is required for irrigation. The grape, on the other hand, ripens at the same time, and this goes far to account for the large wine consumption of the Mediterranean countries, the annual production of Algeria being of the order of a hundred million gallons. In parts of Spain at the height of the season, when every drop of water is needed and commands a good price, it is sometimes cheaper to use wine for mixing mortar, etc., and not infrequently houses are dark red from their plaster having been mixed in this way.

The Mediterranean lands are admirably suited to the

growing of winter wheat, the dry summer ensuring an ideal harvest season, but the limited area available for tillage, owing to the proximity of the mountains to the sea, results in the cultivation being effected by the more personal attention of the spade rather than the wholesale methods of the plough. Hence there is a tendency to leave the growing of grain crops to more spacious lands, and to cultivate instead more profitable crops. Among the most characteristic of these are the citrus fruits (oranges, lemons, grape-fruit), but they require irrigation for the summer months. Other products include wine, tobacco, currants, and scent extracts from flowers.

Good natural harbours are more likely to occur when mountain ranges meet the sea " end on " than when a range runs parallel to the coast. All the Mediterranean regions suffer from the latter arrangement, except in western Asia Minor, so there is a scarcity of good natural ports. Where rivers do penetrate the coastal barrier, they tend to be steep-flowing and subject to torrential spring floods, with the result that they bring down much silt, and their deltas are avoided as ports; e.g. Marseilles is fifteen miles east of the delta of the Rhône, while the exits of the Po and Ebro are also shunned as sites.

The numerous islands with which the Ægean Sea is studded represent the crests of one-time hills, and the same submergence which has helped the seafarers of the Ægean has resulted in the eastern or Dalmatian coast of the Adriatic also being fringed with islands. The submerged coast-line of Dalmatia includes one of the best natural harbours in the world, that of Kotor. Unfortunately it takes more than a good harbour to make a port. Trade cannot flourish unless there is a good " hinterland," i.e. a productive region requiring its services. Thus the magnificent gulf of Kotor is as yet lost to commerce because the mountains shut it off from the interior so effectively that railway-building is impossible, and even the good motor road constructed by the Austrians during the World War zigzags its way so laboriously that it may take two and a half hours to cover what for the proverbial crow would be only an eight-mile trip.

In contrast to this, Marseilles commands the most direct route into western Europe from the Mediterranean, and its trade has increased enormously since the opening of the Suez Canal. Lying between Marseilles and the flourishing Italian port of Genoa is the Riviera, which not only faces the sun, but is shielded by the Maritime Alps from unpleasant reminders of colder conditions farther north. While the Riviera owes part of its popularity to the admirable facilities it offers for spending money with a minimum of effort, its main asset lies in the contrast afforded by its winters to those elsewhere in Europe. For those who like climatic pleasures with a motive, the tangible remains of the ancient glories of the Mediterranean have been commercialised, and cruising liners make history not only live, but pay.

AFRICAN AGRICULTURE AND FASHION'S VAGARIES

CAPE TOWN arose as a revictualling point for ships, rendered all the more necessary by the desert coast to the north. Later the advantages of its climate were appreciated, settlement increased, and it became the base from which most of South Africa was colonised. As in Europe, the cultivable area is strictly limited, and fruit and wine are the chief products. Stock-raising is a feature of the drier margins, but, in addition to sheep, is more specialised in type, including the ostrich and the Angora goat. Although these are domiciled on the plateau fringes of South Africa, the sponsors of this ill-assorted couple live in Paris and Bradford. The former depends for its existence on the vagaries of fashion, and the latter, whose home is in the wilds of Anatolia, sheds its mohair to be manufactured into braid and shawls in Yorkshire.

Whereas in South Africa the Mediterranean area passes eastwards into regions of more plentiful summer rainfall, in West Australia the transition is to semi-desert and finally desert as the rain-bearing " Roaring Forties " exhaust their supply of moisture. There is more space here, and wheat consequently assumes greater importance, while Fremantle, the port of Perth, is the first port of call for vessels reaching Australia from Africa or Asia.

The two Mediterranean regions of the New World differ from those already mentioned in that both California and central Chile have behind a comparatively low coastal range a long, narrow valley of high fertility between it and the much higher main ranges of the Sierra Nevada and the Andes. Both the 500 mile long Great Valley of California and the lesser one of Chile have admirable irrigation from mountain streams, and shelter from both land and sea winds. In sheltered valleys, some 6000 feet above the sea, grow some of the world's largest trees ; many of these Wellingtonias (of which smaller examples may be seen in England) grow to well over 200 feet in height, and a few are so large that it would require nineteen men holding outstretched hands to encircle them ; one of these, when felled, was shown by the rings in its trunk to be 3250 years old, and others are undoubtedly still more ancient.

THE FIRST GOLD RUSH : HOW CALIFORNIA GREW

THE names San Francisco, San Diego, Los Angeles, etc., are a permanent reminder of the part played by the Franciscans, who reached California from Mexico in the eighteenth century. California, however, progressed slowly until 1848, when gold was discovered. But the gold was tantalisingly inaccessible. Without the Panama Canal, New York was 11,000 sea miles from the Golden Gate, which marks the entrance to the Great Valley. By land 800 miles of desert trail stretched menacingly beyond the railhead. Yet the chance of making £500 in a single day blinded thousand after thousand to the hazards and uncertainties of prospecting. By 1850 San Francisco had swelled to 34,000, and Death Valley and Lost Valley had been added to the map.

This, the first of the world's " gold rushes," started California on its way to prosperity, but neither gold nor oil, which was discovered later, are permanent industries, and California's wealth to-day rests on fruit. Los Angeles, which rivals San Francisco with a ferocity unknown in the milder mannered eastern hemisphere, has to supplement its meagre 10 inches of rainfall by drawing from the mountains, 225 miles away. With the water problem solved, it is free to make the most of its climate and scenery, which it does, not only by catering for tourists and others in search of health, but by its Hollywood film industry. Natural scenery ranging from the palm-fringed coast of a Pacific island to a miniature Sahara or a pine-forest background for winter sports are all at hand, and the time-table is safe from intrusions by the weather.

Chile also has its Los Angeles, which, with its capital, Santiago, indicate how the indefatigable Spaniards extended their influence beyond the Andes as well as beyond the Rockies. Central Chile had no gold or oil to lure a foreign community to her distant shores, and even film stars are rare below the Southern Cross. Besides this, what remains of the rapidly tapering continent beyond the Andes is under different rule. She has therefore remained essentially agricultural, and, though her wheat and vines do not enter into her foreign trade, she is self-supporting, and all her many presidents have owned farms and spent some of their time upon them.

WRESTING A LIVING FROM THE LOWLANDS

APART from the limited but favoured Mediterranean regions the " Lands of Hard Work " may be said to include most of the comparatively lowland areas outside the tropics. We will therefore concern ourselves only with the more important regions.

From the Atlantic coast of France to the Yenesei in Siberia stretches a vast plain, almost all below a thousand feet in altitude, the Ural Mountains excepted, and interrupted only by minor features. In this area the climate becomes colder northwards and (from the Black Sea towards the east) drier southwards. The densest settlement naturally occurs along a broad east-west belt between these extremes : the population density also decreases eastwards, partly on account of the increasing severity of the climate, and partly on account of the distance from the main centres of population in western Europe.

While the climate is thus the main control, another important factor is the nature of the soil. Between the great northern plain of Germany and the mountains bounding it on the south lies a narrow belt of specially fertile soil, which, with gaps here and there, has by the Ukraine developed into a two hundred mile wide zone of " black earth." This soil, which derives its characteristic colour from its high humus (decayed vegetation) content, is of exceptionally durable fertility. It continues across Siberia until it meets the mountains beyond the Yenesei, and forms the basis of the chief large-scale farming regions in Eurasia, the most widely-grown crops being wheat and sugar-beet.

To the north of this, much of the land within two hundred miles or so of the shores of the Baltic Sea has suffered severely from the glaciers, which made more than one sortie from the Scandinavian heights. Thus, morainic ridges with frequent lakes and sterile, sandy soils are typical of the area from the Zuider Zee to the Arctic Circle : on them rye and potatoes are the most promising crops. Development of cheap chemical fertilisers and the break-up of the large estates into peasant-owned small holdings, the increasing demand of the cities for dairy and vegetable produce and improved methods of marketing perishable goods are all playing a part in making these once barren regions more productive. There are, of course, scattered patches of better land, but the most important of these is the coastal strip rom Flanders to the Elbe. Here man, not content with erecting dykes to prevent the North Sea from repeating former triumphs, has drained a fertile strip of " polder " land, and on this flourishes some of the most intensive dairy-farming in Europe.

LANDS FROM WHICH THE RAIN IS SHUT OUT

IN Europe the greatest population densities occur wherever coal is mined, though relief and soil also play an important, but smaller, part. In South America, South Africa, and Australia the population with few exceptions is concentrated on the coasts. All three continents have but limited areas available within temperate latitudes, for, as they widen, the climate tends to become too tropical to attract white settlement. It is true that South America stretches a thousand miles farther south than Australia (Tasmania excepted), but even the reduced width of this continent has little to offer besides the Patagonian desert. It is therefore doubly unfortunate that, not only do the rain-bearing winds in these latitudes come from the east, but in two out of the three, Australia and South Africa, their entry is barred by the East Australian Highlands and the Drakensberg Mountains. Thus the regions which are well enough watered to permit of unrestricted agriculture are practically confined to narrow coastal belts. In the more northerly, hotter parts, sugar-cane is the chief crop, but farther south dairy and mixed farming predominate.

The western slopes of both these ranges afford a strong contrast with the seaward side. Here water is scarce, and the remnants of the rivers struggle to the sea with difficulty after sun and irrigation have taken their toll. Except within reach of the rivers, agriculture is out of the question. Stock-raising is, however, a more elastic form of farming, for the number of animals per hundred acres can be varied according to the richness or poverty of the grazing available. This flexibility is also valuable in times of drought, as there is at least a possibility of the animals being moved from the stricken areas to others less affected. Thus vast flocks of sheep are kept in the colder, southern regions, and herds of beef cattle farther north, the dairy cattle being limited to the wetter coast.

The Argentine, on the other hand, is more fortunate, for the level pampas extend inland for some five hundred miles before they meet the foothills of the Andes. Hence, instead of two separated zones, one with too much and the other with too little moisture, the rainfall decreases gradually inland. Farming in this fertile region adjusts itself accordingly, with cattle-raising on the wetter east shading westwards into grain (maize in the north and wheat in the south), and this in turn gives place to sheep, especially in the colder south. The climate continues to become drier westwards, but the mountain streams give rise to oases in the foothills of the Andes, and in these garden settlements sugar-cane flourishes in the north and vines farther south.

The fine soil of this productive region results in a scarcity of road-metal, and the tracks tend to alternate between dust-alleys and mud-trenches which the traffic deepens every year. The flatness, however, simplifies railway building, and the area is well served by a highly efficient network which converges on Buenos Ayres. The largest and wealthiest city in the southern hemisphere stands on the Rio de la Plata estuary. Although difficulty is experienced from sandbanks, ocean steamers can penetrate four hundred miles inland to Rosario, and the Paraguay River provides two thousand miles of navigable water-way northwards, through the Gran Chaco (or great hunting-grounds) and into the Matto Grosso.

WHERE MEN STRUGGLE WITH HEAT AND COLD

An aeroplane photograph of part of the Amazon basin shows an unending expanse of trees, broken only by rivers and their tributaries. These wind here and there, sometimes branching and enclosing odd-shaped islands covered with the same monotonous forest, before they rejoin the main stream. Abundance of water and a wealth of vegetation are the dominant impressions.

If the observer came down to earth he would be aware of other things as well ; of heat and a feeling of oppression. When his senses had become accustomed to the half-light reflected from leaf to leaf down through the interlacing branches overhead, shutting out the sky, his consciousness would awake to the rush of life around him. He would note the decaying vegetation about his feet, the shoots and trees springing out of this ancestral mould and struggling upwards to grasp their share of light ; vines and lianas bound on the same quest, but making use of their sturdier-trunked neighbours in the process ; trees growing unexpected blooms, where orchids have found a root-hold, parasitic on their host.

Insect life is as vigorous as the vegetation ; there abound crickets, sand-flies, wasps, spiders, centipedes, butterflies, ants, bees, innumerable beetles, and, above all, the termites, or " white ants," which are neither white nor entomologically ants. Not only are the eyes oppressed by the exuberance of life which meets them on every side, but the ears are assailed by an unceasing murmur. This rises in crescendo as, with a suddenness unknown in temperate lands, day gives place to night. This stir of sound is all the more disturbing since it issues as a rustling hum, swelled by shriller notes, from such a multitude of unseen sources that it seems to surge upon the listener from every side at once. The ocean limits of these inhospitable regions are bound by mangrove swamps, whose branching roots are uncovered by each receding tide.

" THE WHITE MAN'S GRAVE " : ENEMIES THAT ATTACK BOTH BODY AND MIND

IN tropical surroundings such as these the white man is an alien, not only racially, but physically. His hours of activity are limited at night by darkness, unblended with twilight, and his day by heat, nor can the enforced midday rest be credited towards preparing for the labours of the afternoon, for rest in the recuperative sense is impossible as man stifles in the humid heat. In these regions where a white man most needs all his energies, they are sapped, and his strength undermined by insect-borne malaria or yellow fever or his senses numbed for ever by sleeping-sickness. There is no escape from the moisture which saturates and drips from everything, yet drinking-water must be filtered and boiled until it has lost its savour, and food, which putrifies almost immediately, loses its nourishment in its own monotony.

Nor is the discomfort entirely physical, for such conditions result in nervous strain. Especially is there no relief from insects : ants swarm everywhere, some biting, and some eating almost any wood except teak, leaving nothing but a fragile hollow shell. In such a habitat white men are not numerous, and isolation tends to weaken their resistance along other lines as well. Drink becomes a friend with which a brief escape is possible ; last of all, the white man feels himself unequal to the burden of maintaining in the equatorial forests western standards of civilisation.

The work of the Rockefeller Foundation has banished yellow fever from the West Indies and the Spanish Main, and this disease is also yielding in Brazil, where a staff of 10,000 men is employed to fight it. Sir Ronald Ross traced malaria home to the mosquito, which can be stifled in the larva stage by spraying pools with oil. The activities of the tsetse-fly, responsible for sleeping-sickness, are being increasingly limited by modern research. Hookworm, which undermines the vitality of millions of natives throughout the tropics is, in Africa at least, finding an unexpected enemy in the influx of Japanese rubber-shoes cheap enough for the native to buy. Science, backed by Government control, has taken much of the danger—and some of the unpleasantness—out of life in the equatorial regions, so that, while army officers still draw extra " coast pay " when serving on the Guinea Coast, which has been called " The White Man's Grave," commerce has been able to make important progress.

PROBLEMS OF TRANSPORT IN THE TROPICS

ONCE the health problem has been at least partially solved, that of transport is the next most urgent. The thickness of tropical undergrowth has often been exaggerated, but in some places (e.g. New Guinea) it may take a day's labour to make only a hundred yards of headway when driving even a primitive path through the virgin forest. As the forest is ever trying to recapture what it has lost, it is hardly surprising that the rivers have been used as ways of penetration wherever possible.

Easily first amongst river highways is the Amazon, which has no less than twenty-one tributaries each over 700 miles in length. 7000-ton vessels have ascended to Porto Velho, 1500 miles from its mouth. Here navigation is interrupted by two hundred miles of rapids. A railway to circumvent these was begun in 1871, but finished only in 1912, and it has been said that every sleeper cost a life. To-day the wild rubber trade is at a standstill, and the fortnightly trains carry only Brazil nuts and occasional lean cattle from the plateau.

The Niger is the main river of West Africa, and, although marred by rapids and a swampy delta, it has played an important part in the development of the region ever since it was explored by Mungo Park between 1795 and 1806. Railways from the chief ports have put the interior in touch with foreign markets, the outstanding crops being monkey-nuts in Gambia, palm oil in Nigeria, and cacao (the raw material of cocoa) in the Gold Coast, though minerals are also of importance. In 1891 the total output of cacao from the Gold Coast was 80 lb.: to-day it produces more than half the world's supply.

Here, in contrast to the white-owned plantation system prevalent in East Africa, the African is the main producer, and the Government has provided model plantations where instruction has greatly improved the yield per tree. The Guinea Coast region has its own university, and the African has in many cases become wealthy and highly educated. The " African gentleman " lives in European style ; he produces his own newspapers, and has his own sports clubs and libraries. Perhaps the most striking feature of this rapid development is the absence of a social colour bar to an extent that is probably unknown elsewhere in English-speaking countries.

THE ICY REGIONS UNCONQUERED BY MAN

THE ice of the north polar regions rests on nothing more permanent than sea, and it is therefore left to the polar bears, Arctic foxes, and seals. The South Pole, instead of being at sea-level, is in the heart of a 10,000 foot plateau, so that altitude combines with latitude to produce some of the wildest weather in the world, though penguins manage to survive where the southern continent meets the Antarctic Ocean. This concentration of land in the extreme south is balanced by a vast expanse of ocean to the north of it, and, by the time the southern continents begin, the latitudes are already temperate.

In the north, however, the polar seas are bordered by land ; the low, broken lands which prolong Canada northwards into a useless obstruction of the North-West Passage ; the misnamed Greenland, with its 8000 feet of ice-cap, squeezing glaciers down its valleys to turn into icebergs which sweep southwards towards the trans-Atlantic trade route ; Iceland, with its curious mixture of ice and hot springs ; and,

Found in the
ANTARCTIC

Emperor Penguins

Penguin
(with Young)

Seals

Arctic
Wolf

Arctic Fox

Found in the
ARCTIC

Arctic
Hare

11. HARDY DWELLERS ON THE POLAR ICE.

The quaint penguins and the seals endure the wild Antarctic weather. The more hospitable Arctic supports the seals and bears, and the smaller animals whose coats change to white in winter.

5

lastly, the northern fringe of the great land-mass of Eurasia.

In these regions the soil, where it exists at all, is permanently frozen a foot or two below the surface, which thaws during the long days of summer. Thus, although water is present in abundance for the greater part of the year, it is not available for living things. This, combined with constant winds, prevent the growth of all but the lowliest forms of plant life. On the stony parts lichen or " reindeer moss " is dominant, though elsewhere moss may be found, interspersed with coarse grass. The shelter of the valleys permits the growth of dwarf willows and stunted birches. In these marshy wastes, brightened by oases of flowers for a few weeks in summer, the reindeer—or, as the American variety is termed, caribou—feed, their shovel-like antlers serving to displace the protecting snow in winter.

As lichens grow at the rate of only a fifth of an inch a year, pastures exhausted are not available again for several years, so it is necessary for the herds to be continually on the move. In autumn this migration has a southward trend towards the shelter of the forest borders, and returns coastwards in the spring to escape the mosquito hordes. In early summer the ice of the northward-flowing rivers melts first in their upper courses ; this water has no access to the sea except over the frozen tundra, which becomes an impassable swamp. On the Yukon, in Alaska, the break-up of the ice is not only one of nature's grander spectacles, but one of the few honoured with an annual sweepstake.

Whales and walrus have been almost exterminated from Arctic waters, and the number of seals has been greatly reduced. But even extinction does not save a species from the grasping hand of commerce, for the northern coast of Siberia still carries on a ghoulish trade in ivory from the tusks of ice-preserved mammoths. Not only is the fauna, but also the vegetation of a still earlier age, exploited, for in Spitsbergen, Norway has valuable reserves of coal. Other minerals within the Arctic circle include an annual production of as much as a million tons of iron ore on the mainland of the same enterprising nation, while Sweden has long worked a remarkable iron-ore mountain which stands out over a distance of two miles above her northern plateaus.

There are a few other signs of commercial stirrings, such as the new Soviet port of Igarka on the Yenesei, which already has a population of 13,000, interested mainly in the timber export trade. Sheep have increased in Greenland, and cattle survive in the valleys of northern Russia, but a more promising animal is the Canadian musk-ox, which has future possibilities as a source of food, while the number of reindeer might be greatly increased, especially now that their one enemy—the Arctic wolf—has a price upon his head. The Arctic tundra thus holds out some not very encouraging prospects in the matter of fur-producing and unusual forms of stock-raising, but the main occupants for many years to come are likely to be the geese, duck, snipe, and ptarmigan which flock there in summer.

While these cold deserts of the world need not be visited, save by the curious or venturesome, the hot deserts obtrude themselves inconveniently on man's affairs. These deserts are not always the wastes of shifting sand they are commonly believed to be. Large areas of the Sahara are grey-white with salt, and still vaster ones consist of sand only in its parental form of rock. Other deserts again, such as parts of Arabia, are wildernesses of stones. Vegetation—of a sort—is common in many desert regions. Thus, while in the Gobi a traveller may have to ride 500 miles before a solitary tree breaks the monotony of his horizon, much of the Kalahari, in South Africa, is covered with scattered bushes, and the worst parts of the Australian Desert are effectively barred to man and beast by impenetrable spinifex scrub.

GOLD THAT LURES MEN TO SCORCHING DESOLATION

IN the cold deserts the driest spots, above the all-prevailing marshes, are the most sought after. In the hot deserts the wettest regions are the oases. Apart from these isolated settlements (which may extend for miles), only nomads can extract a living from these ill-favoured regions of the earth. We have seen how mineral wealth can lure men to form unnatural settlements even in the Arctic tundra. The same is true of the tropic wastes, for here and there grains of gold tint the desert sands of West Australia a deeper and richer yellow. Gold was discovered at Kalgoorlie in 1892, and the trek in search of this uncertain wealth followed as inexorably as it had done in the earlier rushes to California, Victoria, and the Transvaal.

Here, without escape from a scorching sun and dust-charged air, civilisation brought water by pipe-line the 350 miles from Perth, and in these unpromising surroundings Kalgoorlie's " Golden Mile " became for a time the richest corner in the world. " The Welcome Stranger " nugget from the Victorian goldfield fetched over £9000, but in that State most of the invaders had turned to the more prosaic, but more certain, trade of agriculture by the time that West Australia was smitten by the fever. So, in its turn, West Australia has yielded pride of place as a gold producer both to South Africa and Canada. The desert offers no alternative of agriculture, but improved mining methods and depreciated currencies have encouraged that most incurable of all optimists, the gold prospector, whose diligence was in 1931 rewarded by " The Golden Eagle," West Australia's record nugget, which enriched its finder by £5400.

The Atacama Desert, in northern Chile, where rain is practically unknown, has preserved an unexpected source of wealth. This takes the form of sodium nitrate, or Chile saltpetre, a mineral which is of great importance, especially as a fertiliser. As this mineral readily dissolves in water, its scarcity elsewhere is understood. The Chilean Government depends for much of its income on export duties on this chemical, and, as shipowners charge cheaper rates rather than have their vessels make the outward trip in ballast, the British coal exporter also benefits. The modern chemist has, however, learnt to make saltpetre out of air and common salt, though not without expense, so another monopoly has passed away, like the indigo which once flourished in the Ganges valley. The valuable iodine, which is associated with the natural product, helps however to keep the Chilean industry alive, while the development of the copper deposits of the Andes provides an additional important resource.

Perhaps the strangest and most ingenious use of all for a desert is the fate designed for the Qattara section of the Libyan Desert, which lies below sea-level. It is intended to bring the Mediterranean by pipe-line into this depression. The water in its descent will provide the motive power for turbines which will supply the whole of lower Egypt with electricity. The sun will then remove the water, leaving behind the salt, which will take more than a thousand years to choke the depression.

Thus deserts can be lived in, if occasion demands, and even turned to profit, nor are they the barriers to transport that once they were. Pipe-lines carry water into the deserts and oil out of them. Even the camel caravans of the Sahara have been mechanised, and a bi-monthly motor service now plies between Algiers and the Niger.

CONQUERING THE VASTNESS OF THE "NEW" LANDS

THE Lands of Difficulty we have considered so far include those parts of the earth where only the hardy can succeed, but where the climate does give a limited amount of quarter. To this category also belong the borders of the already settled areas of the "new" countries. In the former group, man has developed a kind of equilibrium between his powers and nature's limitations, and expresses this in some established mode of life. In the latter, experiment is the dominant note, and the process of adjustment between man and his surroundings is far from complete.

To the south of the tundra stretch the great coniferous forest belts of Canada and Siberia, some 500 miles in width. In the north larch (or tamerack, as it is called in Canada), spruce and birch predominate ; farther south they mingle with fir and pine. If, in the equatorial forest, man feels oppressed by the vigour of life around him, in the *taiga* there is a harshness and desolation in its vastness and something threatening in its silence. In the tropics, growth and decay proceed with haste in a wild struggle for existence. In the north these chillsome forests give the impression that there is time and room for all. The trees stretch slowly upwards with undeviating certainty, and moss clothes the fallen trunks more slowly still.

The first intruders into this forest world came in search of furs, including ermine, mink, sable, muskrat, and squirrel, and their trails ended at the rivers, which form the only natural corridors through the forest. These meeting-places of land and water routes naturally developed into collecting-stations for the pelts. In Siberia this tendency was so universal as to be responsible for a certain poverty of originality in place-names, *e.g.* Tobolsk, the "town on the Tobol"; Tomsk, the "town on the Tom," and a host of others. The names of other trading-posts, such as Fort Nelson and Fort Vermilion in Canada, bear witness to the adventurous nature of the early trading days.

Such vast supplies of timber would seem to imply illimitable wealth, but the gap between the consumer and the sources of supply (except in eastern Canada and Sweden) cannot at present be economically bridged. Timber is best felled in autumn, when the sap has ceased to flow. At that season, too, the snow has levelled and surfaced the forest tracks, so that the logs can be sledged to the rivers and there await the summer thaw. Sometimes thousands of floating logs become interlocked, and it requires a skilful lumberman —or, in the last resort, dynamite—to release the jam. These feats are rarer now with the smaller timber required by the pulp-mills, and light railways are capable of making more independent inroads into the forests than the rivers.

Forest fires, while comparatively rare in the wetter west of Canada and Scandinavia, make terrifying havoc of the timber resources of the north. They appear to be caused mainly by locomotive sparks, lightning, and the carelessness of campers. The Canadian Government maintains an efficient fire-fighting corps equipped with hydroplanes. One of these fires is known to have covered 150 miles in ten hours, and in 1915 a Siberian outbreak was so extensive that its smoke covered an area equal to two-thirds the size of Europe.

In similar regions within reach of the sea, fishing plays an important part in the livelihood of the people. Fish are, however, not uniformly plentiful at all seasons of the year, so the Norwegian tends to be a fisherman in winter and a peasant in the summer, when he may raise a small crop of barley and potatoes. But in Norway only 3 per cent. of the land is under cultivation, for the sterile interior plateaus offer no compensation for the excessive wetness of the coastal mountains, and the long summer days hardly balance the dreariness of the winter nights. Hay, on the other hand, thrives, and is cut on every roadside patch of grass, and then hung on fences, partly to hasten the drying and partly to free the ground at once in the hope of securing a second crop. On the other side of the Atlantic, Labrador is situated in more southerly latitudes than Norway, yet so great is the blighting effect of the polar current with which its inhospitable shores are cursed that agriculture is impossible, and furs and fish offer the only alternative to starvation.

LANDS THAT ARE SPARSE AND ARID HEIGHTS

Two other regions may be included in these settled lands of difficulty, the plateaus of Tibet and those of Bolivia and Peru, ranging from 10,000 to 16,000 feet in altitude. In both regions aridity results in trees being as scarce as they are superabundant in the *taiga*. Maize which takes two months to ripen in the plains of India requires seven in the 10,500-feet valley of Cuzco, which was once the seat of the civilisation of the Incas. Above this, as in Norway, an attenuated agriculture lingers in the form of barley and potatoes, but above 13,000 feet stock-raising alone is possible. Sheep are kept in both regions, but each has in addition an indigenous speciality,

12. THE LLAMA OF THE ANDES

This beast, which is found only in certain parts of South America, should not be confused with the Lamas, the well-known priests and monks of Thibet.

which beyond the limits of its native mountains figures only in city zoos; these are the Tibetan yak and the Andean alpaca, vicuna, and llama—not to be confused with the almost equally numerous lamas of Tibet, who spend their lives amid a vortex of prayer-wheels and superstition.

Even in Canada, emigration has of recent years actually exceeded immigration. While it is some time since Great Britain counted men among her more important exports, since 1930 more people have returned to British shores than have left them. In spite of this growing tendency for countries to be sufficient unto themselves, and despite the still prevailing trend towards the towns—which is the price of the Industrial Revolution—there are unpopulated areas in the world where the pioneer spirit is still active. These, except for eastern Asia, occur in the new continents, mainly beyond the limits of proved adequate annual rainfall.

The deserts of the world are apt to deal harshly with those who intrude even on their fringes. A little rain works so great a transformation that dormant seeds spring into grass and flowers and, perhaps encouraged by such a prospect, the Australian sheep or cattle farmer ventures farther inland than his neighbours. For two years or even more he prospers, and then the desert turns on him. The all-important rain fails. The grass ceases to exist, and only a few trees, a little scrub, and some salt-bush remain. Next year the weakened and diminished flocks are kept alive by hand-feeding, the owner gambling his remaining resources against the prospect that the drought will break. The third year sees still no rain-clouds intervening between the burning sun and the havoc it has wrought, and the eagle-hawks and crows gather for a final orgy. Such conditions occur from time to time where the eastern States extend their limits towards the centre of Australia, but there are still areas capable of supporting denser farming settlement, and others where irrigation and improved transport may encourage new development.

THE CANADIAN'S URGE TO STURDY INDEPENDENCE

Away at the other end of the world, the Peace River flows eastwards from the Rocky Mountains. Here, in the latitude of Scotland, is an old fur-trading post which has given its name to Canada's newest farming enterprise—the Peace River Settlement. In 1927 drought and depression on the prairies dislodged homestead roots which had held since before the War, and the temporary railway termini of this new Far West discharged load after load of migrating settlers. The land is parcelled out by the Dominion authorities in sections one mile square ; if, after three years, the land has been cleared and improved to the satisfaction of the Government it becomes the property of the settler. Despite a tendency towards climatic extremes, the owner can at least be self-supporting. Whether he can make a profit depends on things beyond his control—the weather, transport, and world prices. Whether

he can be happy depends on how far freedom, pride of ownership, low taxation, and small expenses compensate for much
inconvenience, some hardship, and the lack of social, medical,
and educational amenities.

Emigration on a much larger and more rapid scale is
pressing forward the development of Manchukuo. Settlement
is also expanding in South and East Africa, but these regions
cannot be regarded climatically as primarily white men's
lands. Hence, not only are the problems—especially locusts—
different, but far more capital is essential. The mineral
wealth of Southern Rhodesia has greatly stimulated its progress.
This includes coal, which is not plentiful in Africa; chromium,
which previously was obtained mainly from New Caledonia
in the Pacific; gold, copper, asbestos, and many other minerals.
As with plantation farming, however, this can be carried on
only by large companies, and the openings are therefore for
the geologist and engineer rather than for the settler.

SETTING THE WORLD ON PAPER : THE MAP-MAKER'S BUSY TASK

THE nineteenth century saw the pioneering work of exploration virtually completed. Australia, which had consisted
hitherto of a detached rim of settlement, was linked together
through the journey of Burke and Wills across the inhospitable,
waterless desert of the interior. The heart of Africa, which
had been known only through unreliable reports of natives,
was opened up by the magnificent work of Livingstone,
Speke, and Stanley. Expeditions penetrated unknown parts
of America, while feelers were directed into the frozen wastes
of the Arctic and Antarctic continents. By 1900 the bare bones
of the world had been pieced together, the northern and
southern extremities alone holding secrets of their own;
the fog which had loomed over many countries had been
dispersed literally " to the ends of the earth."

Exploration does not cease just because there are no new
lands to discover, but the character of the work changes.
Early journeys into the unknown were fraught with such danger
that men were only too anxious to get from " somewhere "
to " somewhere." They were not concerned with intermediate phases of the journey or with scientific observations
and descriptions; they were simply out to discover broad
facts, and left it to their successors to work in the details.

5 *

The task of the modern explorer is to give form to the skeleton discovered by the early adventurers. This work is called Surveying. As soon as a country is discovered, vague descriptions of mountains, rivers, lakes, etc., must be given concrete form. The surveyor must follow the pioneer, make a scientific study of the region with careful measurements, and from such data produce an accurate map.

However small his field of operation, it can never be considered apart from the whole. His aim must eventually be to map the world with the most accurate method available. As the surface of the world is ever changing, and the developments of science are always producing new and more accurate methods, the surveyor's task is never ending.

The idea of surveying is not new. There are Egyptian pictures of people measuring the ground with what might be described as the forerunner of the chain now used in surveying, which suggest that these people knew something of the art. The Romans are said to have used an instrument not unlike the modern plane table for maintaining the characteristic straightness of their roads.

Early maps were based upon astronomical observations, which were often inaccurate, and not upon linear measurement, which is the basis of all true survey. By the fifteenth century, however, the Arabs, who were conversant with the use of the astrolabe, an instrument for measuring the height of the sun, had also benefited by the introduction of the compass, and were capable of making coastal surveys of surprising accuracy. Their charts form the prototype of modern coastal surveys.

A THOUSAND YEARS' JOB; NOT YET COMPLETE

THE study of a present-day atlas gives a somewhat false idea of the accuracy with which the various regions have been surveyed. For example, the courses of rivers are confidently marked through the frozen tundra of northern Siberia, while in central Brazil the waterways are represented with intricate detail. In point of fact, no accurate survey has been made of either of these regions, and authority for the detail shown is frequently little more than travellers' sketch-maps.

Probably the British have made the greatest headway in surveying. Apart from Great Britain and most of Europe, India is the only large tract of land surveyed with great accuracy, while the Admiralty has a much larger length of coast-line survey to its credit than any other organisation.

Spain and the Balkans are the two parts of Europe most lacking in the accuracy of their surveys. The Russians, on the other hand, have carried the main triangulation of their survey into the heart of Asia, thereby linking up European work with that of India. In Africa, the best surveys are the French and the British, especially in the Gold Coast, Nigeria, Egypt, and Algeria, while the part of South Africa affected by the Boer War has been accurately surveyed by military authorities.

The United States Survey Department has profited by being properly organised from the beginning. The early exploration on an accurate scale was connected with the exploitation of mineral resources, which necessitated both geological and topographical maps. Owing to the size of the country, some areas in the States are still provided only with reconnaissance maps. In South America, only the political boundaries have been surveyed with care. Various other regions have received attention for military reasons, or for the contemplation of irrigation schemes and the exploitation of minerals.

There is much work to be done. For the intrepid explorer, who wants the thrill experienced by the earliest pioneers, there are still the frozen polar wastes, the deep recesses of the Amazonian jungle, and the thirsty desert tracts of south-east Arabia, which appear on maps as little more than names. For the less adventurous, there is original work to be done through Africa, Australia, and South America, while for every one there is the possibility of making a local survey of their own home region.

HOW A SURVEY STARTS

THE fundamental factor underlying all survey work is the determination of latitude and longitude, whereby the position of any point on the earth's surface can be fixed relative to the rest. While surveys of individual areas can be constructed independent of such calculations, latitude and longitude form the only connecting-link between otherwise isolated investigations.

It has long been realised that within the tropics man enjoys a brief escape from his shadow at midday. As the tropics are left behind, the shadow lengthens, and so the length of the midday shadow provides a rough measure of the distance from the equator. Lines joining places at an equal distance from the equator are called lines of latitude, and these approach the poles in decreasing circles parallel with the equator. The angle between either of the poles, the centre of the earth, and the equator is a right angle, hence the latitude of the equator is 0° and that of the poles 90° north or south, as the case may be.

The length of a shadow, however, depends also on the height of the object responsible for it. Therefore, to avoid variability, the unit used is not the length of a shadow, but the other factor responsible for it, namely, the angle of the midday sun above the horizon. A little elementary geometry will show that if this measurable angle be substracted from 90°, the result will be the latitude of the observer.

This observation is most easily carried out at sea, for the horizon is there uninterrupted by intervening mountains and hills. The observer uses an instrument called a sextant, which is not unlike a telescope pivoted to swing vertically, with which to sight the horizon. He then " shoots " or sights the midday sun, and the angle through which the telescope has been swung is read off on a dial. The calculation has then to be adjusted to allow for the time of year, as the position of the sun, being vertically overhead at midday, varies between the Tropic of Cancer in June, and of Capricorn in December.

MEASURING DISTANCE BY THE CLOCK

IN determining longitude, the sun is less helpful. In the course of twenty-four hours, the earth describes one complete revolution under the sun's rays. Consequently, every place along any one line of latitude has successively the same experience of dawn, noon, and nightfall once in the twenty-four hours. Hence the only method of determining longitude is to find how much later or earlier any one of these is experienced than at Greenwich. Noon is the most definite period of the day, so the problem is to determine the moment at which the sun is most nearly overhead (*i.e.* when shadows are shortest) ; this is local noon.

Now, as the earth rotates through 360° every twenty-four hours, it follows that it will rotate through one degree in four minutes. Consequently, for every four minutes that local time differs from that of Greenwich, the observer will be 1° longitude away from the Greenwich meridian. The difficulty, therefore, is to know Greenwich time : before the invention of wireless time signals, the reliability of longitude determinations depended upon the accuracy of the special clock (called a chronometer), which was set to Greenwich time at the beginning of the journey.

HOW THE EXPLORER PLOTS HIS TRAIL

THOUGH accurate positions can be ascertained by these methods, the process involved is far too long and tedious to be of any daily practical value, except in extreme cases. The work of the surveyor is, therefore, to find some more convenient method whereby the features of the earth's surface can be plotted.

The simplest form of survey is that used by the traveller in an unknown land. He is obliged to " travel light," and therefore cannot afford to carry more than the minimum of scientific instruments. His party is probably small, so that no one member can be spared for the single occupation of surveying, and such observations as are made have to be done subsidiary to, and during, the main work of travelling. From this it is obvious that he cannot hope to make anything in the nature of an accurate map of the country through which he passes.

To avoid getting lost, he is obliged to determine his position each day by the methods stated above, but apart from this the best he can hope to do is to keep a rough idea of the direction and distance travelled each day, with comments on the principal features in the immediate neighbourhood of his path. With these data he is able to compile a " route traverse," which consists of a series of straight lines, and which represent his actual path through the country. The " map " is often very inaccurate, and at best is only rough, but is generally sufficient guide to allow of a successor following the same course.

In order to determine the direction (relative to true north) or " bearing " of the various lengths or " legs " of the route traverse, an instrument called the prismatic compass is frequently used. This instrument, being light, easily portable, and simple to use, does not impede rapid travel. It is much the same as an ordinary compass, but is fitted with two sights and a prism so arranged that it is possible to read a graduated dial card simultaneously with sighting an object through the sights.

The instrument is brought out at convenient intervals during the march and the most distant object along the line of march sighted. The direction or bearing with north of this object is read off the dial and noted down. The distance from the point of observation to the distant object is then ascertained either from the rate of march of the party or, more accurately, from an instrument of known circumference somewhat similar to a bicycle-wheel, which is trundled along the ground and the revolutions counted.

It is not necessary to dwell on the possible inaccuracies which may arise in this method of survey as its uses are so limited. Such surveys are never more than individual efforts and cannot aid in the construction of a map. An accurate form of the procedure is, however, useful to support other methods of survey in complicated areas of dense undergrowth, such as tropical forest, where no definite features are visible except the rough path by which they are penetrated. There are many other methods of survey in the field, but, since they all depend on the use of various more or less specialised instruments, a consideration of them belongs perhaps more to the province of the civil engineer than to that of the geographer.

REGIONAL SURVEY : TAKING A PATTERN OF THE WORLD

As the name implies, regional survey consists of the intensive study of a local area. The idea of such a study is that by careful observation of the geology, geography, history, natural history, and present-day conditions it is possible to work out the gradual evolution of the district. The general principles which have governed the development of the local area may then be applied to the world with greater clearness. The small area serves as a living concrete pattern and supplies the life-blood through which the pulses of an otherwise unintelligible world may be understood.

The idea of a local survey is not new. The *Domesday Book*, constructed over eight hundred years ago, was a compilation of detailed information concerning the localities of England. Since Norman times, such surveys have been made for reasons varying from the amassing of information for use by the tax-collector, to the studying of man's environment and his progress therein.

During the last few years there has been an increased interest in this science. The development and growth of

modern geography has led to greater numbers being sent out
yearly from the universities trained to carry out such work.
The leaven which has been at work in the educational system
has affected classroom teaching. No longer are dull facts
rammed in indigestible chunks down young people's throats,
so that ever after they have a distaste for books and class-
rooms. Such methods have given place to open-air lessons,
and geographical teaching has benefited accordingly. The
value of the living model has proved itself, and regional
survey provides an excellent example on which to work.

In 1928 an experiment was carried out in Northamptonshire whereby school children, acting under the instruction
of their teachers, prepared an exhaustive survey of the uses
made of every piece of land in the neighbourhood. Their
efforts were so successful that there arose the idea of extending
such a survey to cover the whole of Great Britain, so that, if
organised properly, it might serve as a permanent record of
the uses to which the land was put. Accordingly, as a result
of the enthusiastic pioneer work carried out by advocates of
regional survey, came the inauguration of the Land Utilisation Survey of Great Britain, which started practical work in
1930.

GREAT BRITAIN SURVEYED BY SCHOOL CHILDREN

To increase the value of this, the idea was to complete
the survey as quickly as possible, since it was appreciated
that land utilisation changed from year to year. The work
was accordingly decentralised throughout the country. The
Northamptonshire experiment had proved that school children
were satisfactory mediums through which to accomplish the
scheme, and wherever possible it was entrusted to school-
teachers. As the labour is voluntary, the progress of the
scheme has naturally been a little uneven, some districts having
completed their tasks before others have more than begun.

As the basic idea of the scheme is to provide a permanent
record, it was essential that from the outset work should be
done as far as possible along similar lines. The 6-inch map
of the Ordnance Survey was, therefore, chosen as a foundation
upon which the work should be carried out ; this series being
especially suitable, since in it every field is clearly marked.
A classification was drawn up whereby all land was divided
into forest, meadow, arable, heaths, gardens, waste, or ponds.
In order to facilitate the marking of maps, the initial letter of

each group was adopted as sufficient explanation to appear on the map. Thus moorland, rough hill pasture, and commons all came under the division of heath-land, and appear in the maps simply as " H." Characteristic colours were also chosen for each group, so that uniformity should be preserved throughout the survey. Original work was encouraged, but in order to preserve unity of scheme it was essential for individual remarks to be confined to the margin spaces.

The completed 6-inch sheets are sent up to headquarters where they are reproduced by a photostat process, and then filed for use as a permanent record. The 6-inch maps are somewhat clumsy in everyday use, and, as the scale is large, many sheets are required to cover an area of size, which necessarily entails considerable cost. Therefore, in order to provide the results of this survey work in popular and convenient form, the data obtained on the 6-inch maps are reduced to the 1-inch scale, and in this form placed on sale to the public.

HOW WE CAN MAKE OUR SURROUNDINGS LIVE

IT is a common thing to hear the residents of places declare that they have never really investigated the local sights. In Dorset it is possible to find a villager of Corfe Castle who has no idea of the history attached to the ruins in whose shadow he has lived and been brought up. How many of the inhabitants of a town like Dorchester, who live surrounded by Roman remains, know more about them than that they attract visitors ? What is the reason ? We become familiar with our countryside and accept it as part of our life, just as we regard a piece of furniture as part of our home. We have never thought to make our surroundings live, or that at our own front door lie features as interesting as the sights we travel miles to see. If we can develop our powers of observation, and turn the study of our home region into an original science, we shall find therein an absorbing hobby.

The idea running through regional survey will be much the same as that of the Land Utilisation Survey, but where the latter had to be kept on broad lines to ensure uniformity for the finished whole, the former permits of a more detailed inquiry and a more original presentation. Local differences and sequences of development can here be given recognition, and local tendencies can be catalogued and preserved before they are swept away on the tide of modern progress. The broad scheme developed by the Land Utilisation Survey cannot do more than make a statement of the uses the land is put to : the local geographer in his regional sketch can seek to answer the inevitable " Why ? "

The 6-inch series of the Ordnance Survey maps again serves as the most practical basis. Map form is, wherever possible, the most concise, and at the same time the most vivid, method of presenting detail. It is possible, by tracing the principal features from a 6-inch sheet, to adapt the map to suit varied requirements. For example, if a map is to represent the geology of a district clearly, it is generally best to eliminate other detail or to reduce it to a minimum, whereas a map of communications necessitates the inclusion of considerable detail. It may sometimes be found an advantage to construct certain maps on transparent paper, so that they can be made to serve a double purpose. For example, it is necessary for the sake of clarity to make a map of the drainage and water-supply of an area as far as possible free from detail. If, however, it is constructed on thin paper and can be placed over a map of similar scale representing the geology, its value is more than doubled.

It is difficult for the amateur to make much progress with such questions as the geology and climate of a district, and most of the data required can be obtained from printed records. The value of such data will, however, be increased and lead to more intelligent deductions in later observations if it is assimilated in the actual field. For example, geological strata, which are clearly defined in the text-books, are often extremely difficult to trace when actually working over the ground. As regards climate, it is possible to attempt local observations, but these are really valueless. Climatic statistics, if they are to be reliable, have to be compiled from observations made over a long period of (preferably 35) years. Moreover, in Great Britain, there are adequate data of this description always available. Although it is essential to include sections of this kind in every regional survey, they will not form the crucial part of the work.

WHERE DOES THE WATER COME FROM ?

THE study of water-supply will provide a thrilling example of how much information can be gained through regional survey. It will be necessary to ascertain from what source consumers in the neighbourhood obtain their water. A map can be constructed denoting regions served by company's mains, by wells, pumps, springs, and streams. Farmers may also obtain water for agricultural purposes from other sources, such as dew-ponds, and these will also be included. The reliability of these sources of water-supply can also be investigated. Have the dew-ponds dried up within living memory ? Do the springs provide even flow throughout the year ? Questions of water pollution may also be studied to discover how far the pollution is due to factories, sheep-dipping, or other reasons.

" Communications " do not merely involve main railway lines and macadam roads, but in order to make a thorough survey of the region, every right of way has to be included. This also involves a description of the development of routes within the district. For example, the bridle-path, familiar in most downland districts, is now comparatively rare, while roads no longer necessarily lead to places, but may aim at avoiding them. The evolution of the by-pass road is a sign of the times and, wherever possible, dates should be included to preserve the sequence of such factors. The lanes of Devon are red ; in Wiltshire they are white. Such features are obvious enough, but the story attached to a pile of road-metal too frequently lies buried beneath it.

Botanical research must also be included. This need not be stereotyped and develop into a catalogue of the vegetation of the neighbourhood. Careful observation may reveal the use of various woods in local building operations ; thatches may vary, reed, straw, or heather being used according to the locality. Plants may be subdivided into food crops, fodder crops, and natural vegetation, while each group presents opportunity for original subdivision.

Man himself, too frequently dismissed by mere inclusion in a population map, provides an interesting study. Examine the crowd collected on the local market-day. Here there is surely no homogeneity of type, yet a broad survey can do little to unravel the intricacies that await investigation.

Much can be learnt from the study of buildings. The materials of which they are made may reveal local wealth in the form of quarries or may be silent witnesses of the development of communication, for building materials are difficult and expensive to transport. Design of houses, barns, and even hay-ricks, all have a purpose underlying them, which only local study can reveal.

THE RACES THAT PEOPLE THE EARTH

THE study of race is so complicated, the field of operations so wide, and the chances of controversy so great that it has merited a science of its own, namely, Anthropology. No attempt can be made here to do more than skim the surface of this science, to endeavour to show the lines on which the anthropologist works, and to give some account of his conclusions.

The term " race " has been inordinately strained from its original meaning, with resulting confusion in modern usage of such terms as " race," " nation," and " people." It is, therefore, necessary to make a clear definition of the word as the anthropologist regards it. " Race " denotes " a group of persons connected by common descent or origin," and therefore should be rigidly restricted to mean " continuity of physical type."

Is this a practical definition ? With this definition in mind, is there such a thing as a pure race ? The more the question is studied, the more complex it proves itself to be. Physical characters, the only key to racial affinity, become mingled when two pure races intermix. As the process of mixture has been going on since time immemorial, it is clear that, in general, a pure race can only be found in a remote region where contact is either improbable or impossible. The Andamanese appear to be an unmixed race, and the unattractiveness of their island home has probably been an important factor in keeping these people free from invasion and possible absorption.

" People " is the term given to the inhabitants of a definite area, and does not denote unity of physical type. Thus the inhabitants of Cuba are a people, yet they are of mixed origin. " Nations " are the products of history, and denote a political rather than a racial distinction.

TRYING TO PROBE THE MYSTERY OF MAN'S BEGINNING

NOBODY knows for certain where and how the human race originated, nor can there be any degree of certainty as to the physical characteristics of the earliest man. The anthropologist seeks, by the scientific study of the limited data in his possession, to bridge the enormous passage of years, and to work out a chronological sequence of events which will help him to solve the mystery of the evolution of man.

The evidence on which he works can be divided into three groups—first, actual remains both skeletal and cultural ; secondly, geological evidence ; and, thirdly, the study of the characteristics and distribution of the races who inhabit the world of to-day. These three sources of information, though considered separately, have definite bearing on each other. Thus a newly-discovered skull may have value for its characteristic shape, but its value is doubled when the geologist can explain the approximate number of years it has lain buried. Similarly, rock-paintings, believed to be the work of early man, can be compared with the art of primitive tribes to-day. In this respect there is a suggestion of affinity between the cave decorations discovered in the south of France and the Bushman art of recent times.

Within the second group of evidence comes the whole question of " land bridges," vital to the anthropologist since it provides him with possible routes for the migrations of primitive peoples. If, however, definite proof can be obtained to confirm conjecture, it would be of no less value to the geographer. For example, there is a theory that during the last ice age a considerable part of what is now the Indian Ocean was then dry land, possibly providing communication by land between Australia, India, and East Africa. It has been suggested that the gradual submergence of this " continent " beneath what is now the Indian Ocean provided the cause for the drifting away of the population from that region to seek homes in safety elsewhere. It is possible that the original Negro race arrived in Africa as a result of such a migration.

The greatest assistance geological evidence can offer is that it can provide some sort of a time-factor with which to gauge the antiquity of man. The discovery of fossil-remains and primitive implements can be correlated with the beds whence they came. The geologist has divided the history of the earth into four great periods of time. Man or his predecessors have been traced back to the beginning of the fourth period, or Quaternary, while there is a strong possibility that he existed at the end of the Tertiary or third period of time.

HOW SHALL WE LABEL THE RACES OF MEN ?

IT is with the third group of evidence that the geographer is chiefly concerned, namely, the study of the human race as it exists in the world of to-day. In order to make a scientific study of the inhabitants of the world, the need for some form or basis of classification immediately arises. The decorations in the Royal Tomb at Thebes show that the early Egyptians had appreciated this fact as early as the eighteenth dynasty. In them they made divisions of mankind according to the colour of their skins ; thus, Egyptians were represented as reddish brown, Semites yellow, Northerners or Westerners as white, and the Negroes of the South black. From the Egyptian point of view, this classification was all-sufficient. Their " world " was limited to the valley of the Nile, only occasional adventurers wandering sufficiently far afield in search of gold and treasures to discover the diversity of types that lay beyond.

As the knowledge of the world grew, and fresh lands and inhabitants were discovered, so it became increasingly difficult to distinguish the races of men. At the close of the Middle Ages, the report of Columbus, on his return from the New World, telling of people of entirely new types, clashed seriously with the Roman Catholic theory then in vogue of the unity of all races. The Pope attempted to meet the difficulty by issuing a decree to the effect that the natives of the newly-discovered continent were true descendents of Adam. In spite of this proclamation, the theory of the plurality of races gained considerable headway.

Probably any one could diagnose a case of measles if the patient were covered with an obvious rash. If, however, a second patient appeared who could boast only a few spots, no such certainty could be expressed. A doctor would have to examine the patient and look for other symptoms to confirm his suspicions. The same thing applies to race. There is no mistaking the fair-haired, blue-eyed Swede as being a member of " the white race," the negro from Central Africa as being " black," or the Chinaman as " yellow." It is the peoples whose skins are of intermediate shades that present the difficulty. For example, among the wandering peoples of north Africa, skins of every shade of *café au lait*, red, brown, copperish yellow, and even black are to be found. We are faced with a difficult problem. Colour provides an insufficient basis, and we have to fall back on other criteria, other "symptoms," before making a decision.

Many attempts have been made to find a suitable basis upon which to classify mankind, but in every case difficulty is experienced. No one criterion is free from limitations. In order to make an exhaustive classification of mankind, it is, therefore, necessary to employ several physical characters. The characters which may be used are of two kinds—those which are readily apparent, and those which require the use of certain instruments for measuring, and a more specialised knowledge.

"WHAT IS HE LIKE?" THE PRINCIPAL FEATURES OF MAN

"WHAT is he like?" is a very common question in everyday life. Our answer is generally something after this manner: "Oh, he is fairly tall, about six feet; he has fair hair, blue eyes, and a rather long, pointed nose." Subconsciously we have catalogued the physical features which are easily discernible, and in so doing have provided a mental picture of considerable accuracy.

In considering stature, the need immediately arises for some sort of standard by which to measure height. If we consider a crowded railway station, the thing that strikes us is the infinite variety in the height of the individuals, although if it were possible to group all the adult men, most of them could probably be described as medium-tall to tall. In considering stature as a racial characteristic, therefore, it is the average height of a people which is of importance. In general, it is true to say that a tall people, such as the negroes of the East Sudan, will not contain really short individuals, and that a pygmy people, such as the inhabitants of the Congo or the Andaman Islands, will not produce men of tall stature. Owing to an absence of a standard of comparison, stature is not of great importance in dividing up the peoples of the world, and is of practical value only when describing extremes.

Herodotus, who lived in the fourth century B.C., classified the racial units of the army of Xerxes by their hair, and this is a means of classification adopted by many authorities to-day. The value of this criterion is greatly increased by the fact that it is so readily distinguished. We are familiar with the woolly hair of the African negro, and can easily contrast it with the lank, straight hair of the Japanese. These, then, form the opposite and extreme groups, the intermediate being represented by the wavy hair typical of most Europeans.

Further importance is attached to hair, for it has been discovered that if the cross section of the human hair is examined beneath a microscope, it appears to have definite shape. This shape may be flat, oval, or round, depending on the nature of the hair, whether it is woolly, wavy, or straight. Classification based on hair, therefore, has the added advantage over some other criteria that conjectures based entirely on observation can to some extent be confirmed by the aid of a simple experiment.

TELLING A MAN'S RACE BY THE SHAPE OF HIS HEAD

OF the second group of characteristics, the only one that need concern us here is the shape of the head. If the heads of the occupants of the stalls and pit are observed from the upper circle of a theatre, they are seen to vary considerably, and if for the usual English audience a mixed audience could be collected from each country in the world, the contrasts would be even more apparent. Some heads appear long in relation to their breadth, and others short, or alternatively these could be described as narrow and broad. For convenience in comparing shapes of heads, a certain formula has been evolved. The ratio of the greatest width of a head to the greatest length is expressed as a percentage, and this is known as the Cephalic Index. When this percentage falls below seventy-five, the head is known as long or narrow; for example, the Eskimo or the Semitic people of North Africa. When it is found to be more than eighty, the head is termed short or broad, as, for example, Mongol peoples; intermediate percentages are described as "medium headed."

Great accuracy can be assured in these measurements by the use of a pair of callipers. The chief value, however, of this method of dividing up the peoples of the world lies in the fact that the operation can be performed on the dead as well as the living. The skull is made of such hard bone that, judging by archæological finds, it survives longer than any other part of the human body after burial. This, coupled with the fact that very little fleshy matter covers the skull of the living being, affords us an accurate method with which to compare peoples of the present time with the remains of early man. The ratio for the skull is sometimes referred to as the

Cranial Index, and is generally between one or two units lower than the Cephalic Index, or ratio of the living head.

There are many more racial characteristics which have been used as a basis of classification, but they are relatively unimportant and not within the scope of this section.

THE GEOGRAPHER'S INTEREST IN THE RACES OF THE EARTH

From this brief account it is possible to appreciate the intricacies of the problem of race. Some attempt has been made to show the anthropologist's method of approach to the subject. It must be remembered, however, that many of the anthropologist's views are based on theory ; the science has made great headway in recent years, but advance has always been checked by the lack of concrete data. Comparatively few human remains of primitive man have been discovered. It must also be appreciated that if a jaw-bone or skull is to supply the key by which an early people are to be recreated in the minds of the anthropologist, there is certainly room for disagreement and even error.

The geographer watches the work of the anthropologist with keen interest, realising that he looks to him for much of his information. He, himself, is not so much concerned with the racial characteristics of the negro race ; whether, for instance, its members have hair which in cross section is flat, or that their nasal index is eighty-eight. These things mean comparatively little to him. His world would not be severely shaken if a discovery of to-morrow proved without a doubt the location of man's earliest home. Neither man's origin nor his subsequent wanderings are of vital importance to him. He is concerned with the distribution of races at the present time, and to some extent with the question of why the different peoples are where they are. But, most of all, his interest lies in their appearance and their way of life.

The geographer seeks to discover whether man obtains the most he can from the region which he occupies, whether he is a slave to his environment as, for example, the Bushman who is hounded about from place to place in search of food by an inclement climate, or whether he has striven to over-come adverse conditions and make the most of a meagre heritage as, for example, the Norwegians and Swedes. For the clue to some of these problems the geographer is dependent on the anthropologist, but in general his approach is from a completely different angle.

FOUR STEPS ON THE ROAD TO CIVILISATION

IF the mode of life of the various peoples of the world is studied, four distinct phases, or stages, in development are apparent. First, we have the peoples who spend their whole life obtaining their means of livelihood either by hunting, fishing, or the collecting of vegetable and other foods. These are in general the most primitive peoples of the world, and may be called the " hunters and gatherers."

The next stage is represented by peoples who, although they spend the greater part of their life wandering about hunting or collecting, yet keep a few domestic animals. These in turn are superseded by the next major group of peoples—the Nomads. As their name implies, they are wanderers, possessing flocks and herds on which they are entirely dependent for their means of livelihood. A further advance is represented by the seasonal Nomads who, although they wander about with their flocks for a greater part of the year, also show some aptitude for a settled life.

The third phase is represented by the settled peoples who are dependent on the cultivation of the soil for their living. A final stage is portrayed in the town-dwellers. These are not in any way directly self-supporting, but are dependent for their food supplies on the labours of others, over whom they exercise but a monetary control.

DOES RACE DEPEND ON CLIMATE ?

ARE the races of man descendants of a common stock, and have their varying characteristics evolved slowly as they migrated to different regions and encountered diverse climates ? Some account has already been given of the physical characteristics of man—skin colour, stature, hair, etc. Can climate have any effect on these ?

It is a commonplace that if we expose our skins to the sun's rays we become sunburnt, the intensity of the colouring depending on the time we are exposed. What is sunburn ? The pigmentation of the skin is due to the presence of various brownish granules in the deeper layers of the skin : this colouring has certain protective value against the fierceness of the sun's rays. Generally the sunburn accumulated during a summer holiday is shortlived, and the skin quickly assumes its normal colour. If, on the other hand, the case of the civil servant or doctor who has spent the greater part of his life in India or the tropics is considered, it will be discovered that in most cases he returns " tanned," and that during the years after his retirement no degree of bleaching becomes apparent. Thus it might be argued that, given time, the colour of the skin permanently adapts itself to its new surroundings. It has, therefore, been argued that a black skin protects against sunlight for, although a dark surface absorbs heat more readily than a light surface, it also radiates heat more rapidly, and under a tropical sun heat dispersion is the potent factor. Since white, on the other hand, is the best colour for retaining bodily heat, a white skin is therefore suitable to cool climates.

From this theory it has been argued that a black skin is the result of a hot climate ; the white skin being more suitable to temperate conditions is found in cooler latitudes ; while the yellow colour of the Eastern races is due to the extreme continental conditions prevailing over the greater part of Asia. Thus it might be expected that the study of the distribution of races would show gradations in skin colour from dark brown or black to white as higher altitudes were reached away from the equator.

COLOUR UNEXPLAINED BY CLIMATE : THE MYSTERY OF MAN'S DIVERSE COMPLEXIONS

So far as the Old World is concerned, this is found to be true, but in the New World and parts of Asia, no such simple distribution prevails. How can we account for the red-skinned peoples, who are found throughout the length of America, with no change in the depths of pigment to correspond with differences of temperature ? With more detailed study, the theory becomes less straightforward. The hot, wet forests of the equatorial regions of the world provide a very similar environment for the dwellers in the Congo, in the Amazon basins, and in the interior of Borneo, yet in these regions people show markedly varying characteristics. The pygmies of the Congo basin have black skins, the tribes who inhabit the Amazon forests have reddish skins, while the Punans of the Borneo jungle have skins which are pale yellow.

If the black skin of the negro is nature's adaptation to the heat of equatorial latitudes, is it possible that the red skin of the Neo-Amerind and the yellow skin of the Punan are but stages in the process ? Is it merely a question of time ? Against this it must be remembered that the aboriginal Australians have practically black skins, and yet inhabit a region of more temperate climate.

If the yellow skin of the Mongolians can be attributed to the dryness of the continental climate prevailing over much of Asia, how can the yellowish skin of the Eskimo be accounted for ? In this case it has been suggested that the cause lies in the long period of cold weather experienced each year—but it is generally accepted that a white skin is more adapted to the conservation of bodily heat, so that some other cause must be found to account for the yellow colour of the Eskimo's skin.

In considering the problem of racial colour, it should be noticed that modern research has proved that man has resided on the earth for thousands, even tens of thousands, of years. In order that true perspective may be observed, it must be remembered that, as historical times are mere fractions of the whole, caution must be used in arguing about prehistoric times from data collected in historic times.

Probably differences in colour arose for some reason independent of climate, and at some very early time. The deeper coloured peoples being better able to sustain tropical heat, and following the law of the survival of the fittest, possibly tended to outlive peoples who were less suitably adapted. Although this theory cannot be proved with present knowledge, it provides more scope to account for the anomalies in colour that occur among the races of to-day.

CAN CLIMATE MAKE PEOPLE TALL OR SHORT ?

THE influence of climate upon the stature of a race is twofold. The direct influence of cold, warmth, and sunlight can easily be appreciated ; food supply, however, which is an all-important factor in man's existence, is itself directly dependent upon climate. Where the climate is rigorous, vegetation is often sparse, or even lacking, consequently in such regions there will be scarcity or absence of vegetable food. In desert regions where rainfall is unreliable, and vegetation can thrive only after rain, the food supply is intermittent. Such things are bound to have an effect on the size and development of the peoples who inhabit these regions.

The short stature of the Eskimos can undoubtedly be attributed to climatic reasons. Besides the bitter climate in which they have to live, they have no vegetable foods on which they can rely. Their means of sustenance, therefore, must depend on the results of hunting expeditions, which, for nine months in the year, have to be undertaken in the worst winter conditions imaginable.

The pygmies, on the other hand, live in a region where food supplies are not such a problem. The thick canopy of vegetation found in the tree-tops, which shuts out nearly all available light from the ground, has probably here played an important part, for the small stature of the pygmy tribes is almost certainly due to deprivation of sunlight.

The natives of the Auvergne region in France, who are smaller than the average Frenchman, the Bushmen of the Kalahari Desert, and the Snake Indians of the inhospitable regions of south-west America, all of whom are typically small peoples, suggest that stature may be dependent on food supplies, the regions inhabited by these peoples having poor and relatively unproductive soils and insufficient rainfalls.

Here, again, it is not safe to assume that climate is the only factor controlling stature. It undoubtedly has some effect, but historical reasons may also play a part. There is the possibility that the short peoples may also be the weak, and they have been driven into unattractive surroundings by their stronger and taller neighbours. Tall stature is connected with the retardation of maturity, which allows of long-continued growth. A temperate climate, where life is neither too hard nor too easy, seems most favourable to the production of a tall race.

DOES HOT, WET WEATHER MAKE THE HAIR CURL ?

WOOLLY-HAIRED peoples, for the most part, inhabit the hot, wet regions of the earth, while those with straight, lank hair are generally to be found in regions that experience cold climate for the greater part of the year. Can there be any connection between climate and the character of the human hair ?

If we examine our own hair in the looking-glass and follow a single hair down to its junction with the skin, we see it grows out of a minute hole. This " hole " is called the hair follicle. If the follicle of a woolly-haired individual were examined under a powerful microscope it would be found to have definite shape, and further examination would prove that in sections it was distinctly curved. The new hair, therefore, as it emerges from the hair follicle, is trained into a curve or spiral. If, on the other hand, the hair follicle of the straight-haired Mongolian is examined, it is found to be straight and in a more vertical position. It has been suggested that these conditions are adaptations of nature, the former to a warm, moist climate, and the latter to the contraction of the skin due to a dry climate. The hair follicle of the wavy-haired peoples is only slightly curved, and therefore might well be an intermediate stage, and adapted to the temperate regions of the world.

The value of hair as a racial criterion has been appreciated only within the last century, so that where cases of adaptation have to be considered, no degree of certainty can be expressed, because the time of research has been so short. For example, the minute downy hairs which cover the adult body are said to be the rudimentary remains of a complete hairy or furry covering typical of the ancestors of mankind. However, the discovery of Egyptian mummies, six thousand years old, show that the human body was at that early date almost hairless. This shows that there has been but little modification during the intervening period. Such examples as this afford a clear picture of the enormous time-factor involved, and make us beware of rash statements and generalisations.

It has been suggested that there is a tendency for the hair of descendants of early English immigrants into America to change in the course of generations from wavy into the lank, black hair so characteristic of the indigenous Indians. This change is supposed to have been due to the change from a damp to a very dry climate. More research, however, is required before such a theory can be accepted.

Migrations, in so far as they are the effect of climatic changes, provide a further indication of the effect of climate upon race. Failure of crops in a given area may result in the depopulation of the area. The inhabitants may be incapable of facing a failing food supply and be forced to migrate to more favoured regions. Intermarriage and race mixture would be a later but more lasting effect of such a movement. The Tartar element in Europe is supposed to have arisen as the result of such a migration.

PYGMIES AND BUSHMEN : THE PEOPLES
OF JUNGLE AND DESERT

As their name implies, pygmies are short, the average
height being about fifty-four inches. Their skin colour
varies ; it is usually reddish yellow, but may be light brown
or even very dark. Their hands are medium in breadth,
their hair is short and woolly, and they often have large,
staring eyes, giving them a characteristic " wild look."
Their bodies may be covered with a yellowish downy hair ;
their abdomens are often protuberant, and their feet are
relatively large and turned slightly upwards. They generally
go without clothes, but the men may wear a loin-cloth of
skin, and the women bunches of green leaves. The pygmies
go about in tribes (Akka, Batwa, Bambute, etc.) or in small
communities, scattered over the equatorial forests of Africa,
more especially in the thickest regions around the Congo.
They are essentially hunters, trappers, and collectors, and
are therefore seldom to be found long in the same place.

These people are daring and agile hunters, using most
skilfully bows and poison arrows, the Batwa successfully
attacking elephants in this manner. They obtain their
poisons from plant-juices and from decaying animal matter
(generally ants), and possess exceptional knowledge both of
poisons and their antidotes. Their dwellings are only
temporary and entirely primitive, being arbours constructed
of bent stems of plantain-leaves. They are usually
circular with a small hole at ground-level, through which
the pygmy crawls on all-fours. Ten or twelve " arbours "
constitute a village.

The pygmies' diet consists mainly of the flesh of birds and
antelope, and such animals as they can shoot with arrows.
They supplement this by eating termites, grubs, larvæ,
honey, and wild beans. They are also fond of bananas,
which they obtain from neighbouring tribes by barter or
by plunder. Vegetables they eat raw, while flesh is broiled
in the ashes of the fire. They therefore require a limited
number of utensils ; a few gourds and pots made of clay
suffice.

The families are usually small, rarely exceeding three in
number. Marriage may take place at the early age of nine
or ten years. The girl has to be purchased from her father,

the price being from ten to fifteen arrows, or, if the girl be extremely attractive, a spear or some tobacco may be added ! A man can have as many wives as he can afford to buy. Birth takes place in the forest, and there is great rejoicing if the child is a boy, while a girl baby may be taken by the father and beaten with plantain-leaves.

It is doubtful if the pygmies have any pure language of their own ; they generally converse in the language of the tribes with whom they come in contact. There is no hereditary chief, but a group may rally round an exceptionally skilful hunter. Life in the equatorial forests is generally short, death commonly taking place before the age of forty. The dead are buried in graves. Belief in life after death is vague, but there is a mythical pygmy devil of the name of " Oudah " who is responsible for calamities, such as sudden death.

Some authorities consider the pygmy peoples to be a retrograde step in the development of mankind, possibly due to the unattractiveness of their habitat, but it is more generally accepted that they are the last survivals of a primitive type who have kept their characteristics from absorption by other tribes and peoples by receding further and further into the gloom of the impenetrable forests.

THE BUSHMEN : BIG BROTHERS OF THE PYGMIES

ANOTHER wandering, hunting group who may be closely allied with the pygmies are the Bushmen. These peoples probably formerly ranged over the whole of South Africa (a fact which is proved by widespread distribution of Bushmen paintings), but with the coming of the Hottentots and Bantus and, later, the white peoples, they have been driven into the dry and unattractive regions of the Kalahari Desert. Here they have to contend with extremes of heat and cold and with arid conditions attendant on a region which can be described only as a sandy waste. The natural fauna of the region are ostriches and antelopes.

The Bushmen are short, the tallest men rarely exceeding five feet in height, while the women are under four feet. Their hair is dark and woolly, and commonly very short, often becoming rolled up into small knots, leaving apparently bare spaces between—a feature which is sometimes given the descriptive name of " peppercorn curls." These people have yellow skins, very small feet, hands, and heads, broad noses, prominent cheek-bones, and bulging foreheads. They possess an interesting eccentricity in the fact that they frequently have no lobes to their ears. The women sometimes have a characteristic accumulation of fat on the buttocks, which gives them a very disproportionate appearance. They frequently wear no clothing, but occasionally don an apron tied behind with a long tail, or a cloak made of skins. They are fond of ornaments, and wear necklaces made of disks of ostrich egg-shell.

As the Bushmen possess no cattle and live entirely by hunting and collecting, they have no settled habitations, but usually occupy caves or holes in the ground. They know, however, how to plait together the hanging branches of suitable bushes to form a rough shelter. They are familiar with the use of the fire drill, and they manufacture rude knives of stone. Of their few implements, by far the most important are their bows and poisoned arrows, on which they depend for game. These are small, and the poison is extremely venomous, being obtained from snakes, trap-door spiders, and certain insects. The Bushmen carry water in ostrich shells fitted with crude stoppers made of grass. They have no pottery. They possess a few primitive drums and flutes made from reeds with which to accompany their songs and dances.

WHERE LAZINESS MEANS AN EMPTY LARDER

THE Bushman is essentially lazy. He has to work hard to find his food and drink, but if he feels well-fed he does not think of laying in store against a time of dearth. He is, first, a " collector," grubbing up the bulbous roots of plants, ants' eggs (sometimes referred to as Bushman's Rice), grubs, caterpillars, and snakes. To these he may add certain fruits, such as melons, which grow if the rainfall permits. These he generally eats raw, though he may roast certain things to provide variety. Only when he is tired of such diet will he attempt to hunt game. He is a born hunter, and knows very well the art of camouflage. In fact, it was because they were generally found hiding in bushes of sympathetic colour that these people came to be called Bushmen.

The patience and endurance of the Bushman are no less wonderful than his skill. Having decided on the quarry, he is content to stalk it for hours, taking advantage of every sand-dune, or, if the country is open, crawling along and holding a small bush before him for protection. When he gets close enough, he fits a poisoned arrow into his bow, takes aim, and shoots. He rarely misses, but even when the arrow has found its mark, the chase is not over ; the Bushman has to wait until the poison takes effect. The time for this varies ; in the case of a buck it may take two hours, but for large game he may have to wait days. He finds this no hardship, because his next meal is secured, and his only effort is to keep the vultures from robbing him of his prize.

The Bushman can go for an incredible time without drinking. Added to this, he has a marvellous instinct for finding water in an apparently waterless waste. He scratches the surface from a likely-looking place, inserts a reed which acts as a filter, and through this he sucks up moisture sufficient to satisfy his meagre requirements.

The Bushman language is very primitive, being a jumble of clicks and guttural sounds, impossible to commit to writing and extremely difficult for a European to understand or imitate.

WIVES WHO ARE SURE OF A FUR COAT

MONOGAMY is the general rule—probably owing to the difficulty of supporting more than one wife. Marriage within a band is not encouraged, and the bridegroom has to present his bride-to-be with a skin cloak. He sometimes has to show his hunting prowess by presenting his father-in-law with a buck. The dead are buried with all their possessions. Stones are placed on the grave to prevent animals disturbing it, and the locality is forsaken for a period of years.

There seems little indication of any form of government. The Bushmen wander about in small detached groups, and the only real organisation is of a cattle raid. From the early settlers' point of view, the Bushmen were expert cattle thieves, with their silent creeping and their poison arrows, and it was probably due to this that they have suffered such heavy losses of numbers at the hands of neighbouring peoples. When found, they were simply shot as vermin, and were threatened with complete extermination.

They seem to be incapable of adapting themselves in any way to modern conditions. The settlement of South Africa

6

has reduced the game, and therefore one of their means of livelihood. They have to resort to a precarious diet, such as they can collect, and they are, as a result, rapidly dwindling.

HUNTERS OF THE ARCTIC : THE ESKIMO

SCATTERED groups of Eskimos are to be found along the indented shores of northern Canada, Alaska, Greenland, and Siberia, an almost continuous stretch of coast-line of five thousand miles. They are seldom found far inland except when they travel thither on a hunting expedition. Antagonism to the Red Indian tribes who roam the desolate wastes of northern Canada has probably played an important part in confining the Eskimo to the coast in this region. They are not a homogeneous people, various groups differing in speech and habits, but they are all bound by the fact that they are hunters, dependent largely for their means of livelihood on the whale, walrus, seal, and fish—products of the sea. It has been said that the seal is to the Eskimo more than the coco-nut palm is to the South Sea Islander. On it he depends for his food, clothing, lighting, and warmth.

The climate is rigorous, as the land of the Eskimos is in the region of the Arctic Circle, and, although for a few weeks in the year temperatures typical of a Scottish summer may be experienced, the winters are bitterly cold (the temperature may fall to more than 20° below freezing), and there is a period when there is no daylight at all. The return of the sun in spring is welcomed with great rejoicing, although it means a busy season of much work after the enforced idleness of the winter months.

The sea is frozen over, except for a few weeks in summer ; the land is bare of vegetation except for sheltered spots where mosses, lichens, and berry-bearing plants, with occasional stunted trees, may grow. Hares, Arctic lemmings, foxes, and polar bears are typical animals of the coast region, while herds of caribou and reindeer, and occasionally musk-ox, wander over the inland plains in search of fresh pasture.

THE ESKIMO'S PASSION FOR HIS JOB

THE harsh conditions of their surroundings have forced the Eskimos into an unending fight for existence. They are a happy people because their means of livelihood, namely, hunting, is also their supreme passion. The culminating joy of life, as expressed by one Eskimo, was " to run across fresh bear tracks and be ahead of all other sledges."

Perhaps the most striking characteristic of the Eskimo is their slightly Mongolian appearance. They are, on the average, shortish in stature; their heads are long and high, with broad, flat faces, prominent cheek-bones, and black eyes, which often appear to be aslant because of the heavy fold of skin above the eyelid. The true colour of their skin is seldom apparent, as washing is by no means a daily habit, and a thick oily deposit tends to darken the brownish or reddish yellow skin that lies beneath. Their hair is straight and lank, and black in colour. Their feet and hands are remarkably small. As a people they are very hardy and capable of great endurance. They begin and end their life travelling, often through unspeakable conditions of blizzard and darkness.

Great attention has been paid by the Eskimo to designing clothing most suitable to their mode of life. Clothes are the women's pride. They are responsible for preparing the sealskins and for sewing the garments. Next to the skin is worn a light shirt made of birds' skins with the feathers turned inwards. Over this is worn a sealskin coat with the hairs turned outwards. The trousers are made of bear-skin. Boots are of sealskin, often without the hairs. The women's costume does not differ greatly from the men's, except that the trousers are often shorter, and there is generally a capacious hood in which the babies are carried. (In summer the sealskin overcoat may be exchanged for a coat of fox fur, which is lighter.) They do not often decorate their skins, but may make narrow lines on their foreheads and chins by drawing a needle, with a sooty sinew for a thread, along beneath the skin.

THE HOUSING PROBLEM IN THE NORTH

IN winter the habitations consist of little houses built with great cunning. They may be occupied for one or more winters, but the Eskimo is essentially a wanderer and soon gets tired of familiar surroundings. The characteristic snow-house or igloo, for which the Eskimo is so famous, is not now used extensively except in the case of emergency. These structures illustrate plainly how the people have taken full advantage of the scanty materials available, for no other building in the Arctic can compete with a well-built snow-house for warmth. Blocks of snow are cut out of drifts with long knives and placed in a circle ; these blocks are then cut in half and placed on the other blocks in a spiral, and the process is continued until a hut, much the same shape as a beehive, results. If the igloo is required for permanent occupation, the women then go inside and thaw the blocks of ice with their lamps. These are then allowed to re-freeze, and thus the whole hut is made compact. An entrance is contrived by a long, low tunnel.

More generally the winter-quarters are built of stone, the chinks between being filled with sods. Ice-huts are made in a hollow in the ground, giving them a subterranean look. The roofs are made of brushwood, if available, but more probably of sods or slabs of stone. A long, low passage again serves as an entrance. In spite of the primitive arrangements and cramped space, the huts appear extremely cosy. The typical manner in which the Eskimo " dresses for indoors " is to retain his boots and trousers and remain naked to the waist. This is because the upper layers of air within the hut get extremely warm, while the temperature of the air on the ground may be as low as freezing-point. In this connection it may be added that the Eskimo will often sleep face downwards in order to breathe the cooler air near the ground. In summer, as extensive wanderings are undertaken in pursuit of caribou, waterfowl, birds' eggs, berries, fish, and seal, tents of sealskin are used.

The word " Eskimo " means " Raw meat-eater," but although there are some communities who eat food (chiefly seal meat) uncooked, there are many who seldom touch it raw. Cooking is not easy with a stone lamp, a wick of moss, and a supply of seal oil. Hunting weapons were formerly only bows and arrows, spears and harpoons, made of wood, and furnished with a sharp point of copper, iron from meteoric or other sources, bone, stone, or ivory at one end, and a rope made of sinews at the other. When the harpoon strikes the body of the animal, the point enters its body, but the precious wood is set free for further use.

In winter, when everything is frozen over, the Eskimos use sledges drawn by husky dogs. These sledges are light and, given a good team of dogs, are capable of covering the ground at high speed. The dogs are harnessed in fan formation and may be released by the unloosening of a single thong if danger threatens. These dogs are ill-fed and cruelly treated, with the result that they are extremely savage, but they are absolutely indispensable to the Eskimo.

PROVIDING FOR THE SIX MONTHS' NIGHT

IN summer, when the ice breaks up in the sea and rivers, boats are used for transport. The kayak, a small canoe-like boat, made of sealskin stretched over a light wooden or whalebone frame, and designed to take a single passenger, is the characteristic craft of the men. In these they hunt with extreme dexterity. The chief weapon of the kayak is the harpoon with its line and bladder, and with this the Eskimo kills walrus, whale, and seal. Bird-hunting and fox-trapping are also part of the summer occupations. By these means the Eskimo seeks to collect sufficient supplies to last him through the darkness of the polar night.

By about the end of September the sea freezes and hunting on the ice begins. In autumn the seals are generally harpooned when they come up to breathe through holes in the ice, and the Eskimos get within range by stalking noise-lessly towards their prey. In spring they are killed while they lie on the ice basking in the sun. Walrus and bear are also killed in the autumn In spring, with the return of the sun, expeditions for hunting the musk-ox or caribou are arranged ; these often last a couple of months, as the Eskimos camp on the killing-grounds in order to dry the skins. No description of the Eskimos would be complete without some allusion to their capacity for subsisting on practically nothing if they are driven to it. They are equally capable, however, of producing the most staggering appetite in times of plenty.

TRIBES OF THE AMAZON : THE POISON SPECIALISTS

THE people who inhabit the Amazon Basin all belong to the same race, the Neo-Amerinds, whose general character-istics are that they have round heads, straight black hair, and cinnamon-coloured faces. Within this race there are many groups, distinguished chiefly by language. The Caribs, Arawaks, Tupi, and Tapuya are typical examples.

These people live in a region of extremely heavy rainfall and intense heat. The seasons of the year are hardly per-ceptible, all the seasons being epitomised in each day. The tropical forest is everywhere dense with luxuriant growth typical of the wet tropical regions of the earth. The typical fauna of the region can be divided into the tree-climbers, such as the sloths, pumas, jaguars, and monkeys, birds, and on the ground, especially near the river banks, alligators, crocodiles, and snakes.

ENEMIES MADE INTO FOOD AND ORNAMENTS

IN this tangled jungle the only highway is the Amazon, which is too wide and too deep to be attempted in the flimsy native craft. The people, therefore, remain in the isolation of the forest, paddling their frail canoes along the intricate network of waterways in one of the least explored regions of the world. The tribes show their superiority over their enemies by eating the conquered and making necklaces of their teeth.

For clothing, the men wear a breech cloth made from the bark of a tree ; the women wear a sort of belt. They are fond of painting themselves, and generally use a purple or orange vegetable stain, which causes the patterns to remain indelible for some considerable time. Tattooing is also commonly practised, and is generally effected with a rake-like instrument which is hammered into the flesh. Girls are tattooed until the age of twelve years, which is the marriageable age ; their chins are then tattooed, which is a sign that they are " finished " and suitably attractive to enter into matrimony. Feather ornaments made from the skins of the forest birds are also worn.

The dwellings consist of thatched huts on poles, each hut being occupied by one family. The hammock is the all-important possession, as the ground is always damp and infested with insects ; also, since they are a wandering people, something light and easily portable is required. Their hammocks are generally made of the fibres of palm leaves, but latterly there has been a tendency for them to be made of cotton, which is grown in Guiana, and traded all over the region.

These people are typical hunters and collectors ; the hot moist climate and luxuriant growth of vegetation does not encourage agriculture in any form. Their staple vegetable diet is manioc, which is a shrub native to the Amazon region. The root is scraped to remove the skin, which is poisonous, and is cut into strips, which are soaked, dried, and powdered into a kind of flour, and then made into a kind of biscuit or bread. Manioc is the only food with any keeping qualities they possess.

There is little new material available with which to make weapons ; their possessions of this nature, therefore, are all the more highly prized. In the south of the region the tribes generally hunt with bows and arrows, while in the north a blow pipe or blow gun, through which a tiny arrow is shot, is more generally used.

They possess considerable knowledge of poisons, some of which are extremely virulent. One poison is called " Wurali," and the secret of its composition is guarded so jealously that, after making it in a hut, they burn it down so as to remove all traces of the method by which it was produced.

The women are responsible for collecting and preparing the manioc, but are otherwise kept in a very secondary position. They are allowed to take no part in dances or ceremonies, for there is a theory that if a woman sees such an event she will not go to heaven. These tribes have a curious idea of heaven. They believe it is divided into two, one being reserved for men, and the other for women.

THE HOTTENTOT : HALF HUNTER, HALF NOMAD

IT is surmised that the Hottentots sprang from a mixture of Bushman and Bantu blood, but unlike the Bushmen, who have never risen above the level of the simple hunter and gatherer, these people have combined with their hunting the keeping of sheep and goats and the raising of long-horned cattle, together with a certain amount of rude agriculture. The Hottentots are intellectually superior to the Bushmen ; for whereas the latter are untamable, the Hottentots are amenable both to civilisation and education.

The Hottentots are better developed physically than the Bushmen. In stature they are a little taller, being on the average about five feet three inches, but they are of the same slight build, with small hands and feet. Their backs show a distinct inward curve, while the buttocks, especially in the case of the women, are often extremely pronounced. The colour of their skin is generally of a sickly yellow or brownish yellow tinge. They have small, fairly long-shaped heads, with high cheek-bones, small elongated eyes, flat noses, and short black hair, which has the characteristic tendency to roll up into tight little knots.   Often they have no lobes to their ears.

These people were probably more widely distributed in the past, but they are now represented by a diminishing group, sometimes referred to as the Naman, who inhabit south-west Africa, north of the Orange River ; other groups have disappeared either by absorption or intermarriage with Bantus. The name Hottentots was given to these people by the early Dutch settlers, and it implies " stammering." It was prob-ably given as the result of the Hottentot language, which, like the Bushmen's, consists of a series of guttural clicks.

Their clothing is now, in many cases, European rather than native, and is generally both unattractive and unsuitable. Formerly, however, the men wore loin cloths of hide with small cloaks of skins across the shoulders. The cloak was of service all the year round ; in winter it was worn with the hairy side in, and in the summer with the fur outside. At night it was used for sleeping in, and when the owner died he was buried in it. The Hottentots carried their knives, pipes, and tobacco in pouches slung round their necks. They wore ivory or copper bracelets, and they occasionally protected their feet by wearing skin sandals. The women also wore skin capes, besides highly ornamented skin aprons and fringed girdles. They were also fond of shell ornaments and ankle bracelets made of raw hide. Both men and women paint their bodies with a substance made from ochre and fat.

The grassland areas, although suitable for cattle, are also favourable to the wild beasts which prey upon the herds, so that animals have to be protected at night. They are, therefore, driven into the centre of the encampment. The huts, which are dome-shaped, are made from twigs and saplings stuck into the ground and bound together. Mats, made from plaited reeds, are placed over the twigs to serve as a roof, and the walls are made stronger by threading twigs in and out through the base of the saplings. A hole in the centre of each hut serves as a fireplace, and round this, on mats made of reeds, the occupants sleep, wrapped in their skin cloaks. The huts are arranged in a rough circle, the size depending on the pastoral wealth of the group. Each family possesses its own hut in which the members eat and sleep, though sometimes the marriageable girls of the group occupy a hut by themselves.

BABIES WHO EACH HAVE A COW OF THEIR OWN

MILK is the principal food of the Hottentots, and this they prefer to drink after it has been kept awhile in wooden pots and allowed to thicken. Each child at birth is allotted a special cow by his parents, and the milk from this animal is reserved for him. Berries and vegetable foods are collected, and such animals as can be killed by hunting and trapping are also eaten. Except at feast times domestic animals are not killed for food, although if an animal dies from natural causes its flesh may be eaten.

The household utensils are simple. Natural objects, such as ostrich-egg shells, which are used as water vessels, are supplemented by rough wooden dishes and a few rude clay vessels, in which the cooking is done. Formerly the Hottentots used to hunt with bows and arrows, but latterly they have been content to use snares to trap their game.

Like most wandering peoples, they live under a patriarchal form of government. They are divided into various groups or " tribes," each tribe having its own chieftain, and each occupying its own territory. Their chief occupation is cattle-breeding, and in this respect they show great skill. They are careful never to exhaust the pasture in any one particular place, but to keep moving sufficiently to be certain of a permanent supply. The women are responsible for milking and for the preparation of food. They are, as a sex, highly respected, and are complete masters of the hut and all its domestic utensils. Marriage is by arrangement between the parents of the man and those of the girl.

NOMADS : THE PEOPLE WHO LIVE BY THEIR FLOCKS

OF all the various groups of peoples who roam the vast steppelands of Central Asia, keeping flocks of sheep and goats and living the care-free existence of the Nomads, perhaps the Kirghiz is the most typical. These people occupy the grassland area to the north of the Sea of Aral, a region which, by reason of its position in the centre of a great land mass, experiences vast extremes of temperature. Probably in this region the all-important horse was domesticated for the first time, and its descendants, the wiry, spirited creatures of to-day, are the Kirghiz' most prized possession ;

6 *

these people might almost be described as having been born in the saddle, they are such wonderful horsemen, and horsemanship remains their greatest joy and pastime—they even give themselves the name of Kazak, which means " horsemen."

The Kirghiz are of Mongol-Tartar stock. They are of medium height and of stocky, almost squat build. They mostly have fair complexions, although some are distinctly brownish. They have small slanting eyes, high cheek bones, broad noses, and little or no beard. These people are nomads, not only by reason of the climate and vegetation of the region they inhabit, but also because they despise any other mode of life. This is evidenced by the fact that they have only one word in their language to serve for both " farmer " and " poor man."

Their whole mode of life and means of subsistence depend on their flocks of sheep, goats, camels, horses, and cattle. Their flocks are enormous, and since they require perpetual food, the nomad has to be constantly moving. This means that he has to erect a temporary shelter at each halting-place or that he has to carry some sort of dwelling with him. Since the vegetation of the steppelands does not provide sufficient building material, the people live in tents which are moderately light and easily transportable.

These tents, or *Kabitkas*, are usually circular, and may be as much as thirty feet in diameter. They have a framework of willow sticks (obtainable from the river banks) which somewhat resembles a domed-shaped bird cage. This lattice-work is then covered over with felt and bound with cords of camel hair, so that it may be strong enough to withstand fierce winds. The *Kabitkas* are made in sections to allow of their being quickly packed on camels. There are no windows ; a hole is left in the roof to permit the ingress of light and the egress of smoke. The interior is furnished with rugs, carpets, cushions, and a few necessary utensils, which are generally made of wood so that they are both light and durable.

THE NOMAD HAS A " HOUSE " FOR THE SEASON

As is usual in the case of nomadic peoples, these tents are generally pitched and taken down by the women. They are used from early spring through summer and autumn until the severe approach of winter forces the nomad to seek suitable winter quarters. These consist of the best site possible which affords pasture for the flocks, a permanent water supply, and some little protection against the extreme bitterness of the winter temperatures. Generally a site in a river-valley is chosen; here the dwelling is erected and, since it is to serve as the only house for the three winter months, it is often built on more durable lines than the summer *Kabitka*. Stabling may also be erected for the horses.

Suitable sites for winter quarters are rare, and, despite the fact that the Kirghiz may cover as much as a thousand miles each way in their wanderings every year, they always return to winter in the same place. Although the chief occupation is still to look after the flocks, winter affords an opportunity for hunting, since at this time of the year the wild animals, like the nomads, are driven south in search of food. Before leaving the winter quarters in spring, it is customary for the nomad to bury such winter necessities as can be dispensed with during the summer months of wandering. These people, as might be expected, use felt and skin for their clothing, although they may have loose coats woven from the wool of goats and sheep, or from cloth made of camel's hair.

Milk and milk products, such as cheese and butter, chiefly derived from mares' milk (though that of the camel, cow, and sheep are also used), are the staple foods. Alcoholic drink is provided in "Koumiss," the Kirghiz' favourite drink, which is made by fermenting mare's milk in a bottle made of a whole goat's skin. Other foodstuffs, such as tea and sugar, are obtained from trading caravans, who exchange them for the rugs and cloths made by the nomads. When food supplies run short, by reason of drought or disease, there is a tendency for deficiencies to be made up by raiding. The most usual time for such expeditions is the autumn, when the horses are at the height of their condition after their summer in good pasture. Their small, wiry horses are particularly suitable, as they are both speedy and enduring and are capable of covering as much as sixty miles in a day on such grazing as they can collect on the way.

The system of government is patriarchal. The unit is the family, but since wealth is gauged by the size of the flocks possessed, families are naturally large. The head of the family is reverenced and respected by all the group. Polygamy is practised, and this can be easily understood, both by the demand for large families, but more especially by the fact that the greater part of the work of encampment, in addition to the strictly household duties which go on all the year round, falls to the women.

FLOCKS THAT SUPPLY THE WHOLE MEANS OF EXISTENCE

THESE nomadic steppe dwellers are completely self-supporting. They make felt for their tents from the wool and hair of their sheep and goats; their clothes and food come also from their flocks. Lack of vegetation forces them to use the dried dung of their animals for fuel; while articles for luxury and trade, such as rugs and carpets, can be made from the wool of their animals during their wanderings.

This fact has had considerable effect on the character of the nomads. As a people, they are extremely proud and haughty, despising alternative methods of obtaining a livelihood. They are also very hospitable, for they realise their own complete dependence on their flocks, and are at once sorry for the solitary stranger. They are generally fatalists; their wealth being entirely counted by the flocks they possess, they appreciate the fact that disaster is constantly at hand in the form of drought and disease. Cleanliness is not their foremost virtue. Of this the traveller is readily aware if he has the misfortune to approach a Kirghiz encampment from the leeward side, for the smell of the hundreds of animals and the stench from the burning dung are peculiarly pungent. Such diseases as smallpox and Siberian plague arise as a result of the overcrowded and insanitary conditions of their winter quarters. If roused, the Kirghiz people are ferocious and warlike; raiding they regard as a necessary sport.

THE KARA-KIRGHIZ SEARCH FOR PASTURE

THE chief difference between the Kara-Kirghiz and the Kirghiz-Kazaks already described lies in their methods of obtaining fresh pasture for their flocks. The Kara-Kirghiz escape the effects of summer drought and winter snows by changing their altitude rather than their latitude.

The Kara-Khirghiz winter on the foothills of the Tien-Shan and Pamir ranges at an altitude of about four thousand feet, in such districts where the streams from the snow-covered mountains can ensure them a reliable water supply before they are swallowed up by the salt desert. In winter they may occupy themselves with a little very primitive agriculture, utilising the fertile alluvial soils which fringe the mountain base. As in the case of the Kirghiz of the plains, however, the care of their flocks remains their chief occupation.

In spring the herds are moved from their winter quarters and tend to follow the rising snow-line, below which the richest grazing is to be found. In summer the high plateaus, often ten or twelve thousand feet above sea level, are covered with a luxuriant growth of grass and flowers, so that the grazing at this time of the year is practically unlimited and capable of supporting enormous herds. The size of the flocks and herds, therefore, is limited only by the problem of the food supply in winter. In autumn the nomads descend once more before the advancing snow to their winter quarters, to eke out the winter as best they can. During the winter their animals shrink to mere skin and bone, while many perish in the snow.

The horse and the camel are not ideally suited for work at these enormous heights, so the Kara-Kirghiz of the mountains of Turkestan depend upon the yak as their chief beast of burden. This animal, which is a variety of ox, has horns, a long shaggy coat of rather woolly texture, and a bushy tail. It is a wonderful beast for strength and sure-footedness, for it will carry a load up to three hundredweight on its back and with it walk over the most precipitous mountain paths. In the hands of the Kirghiz the yak is a docile creature, but it has been known to attack Europeans.

The mode of life of the Kara-Kirghiz is much the same as that of the nomad of the plain. Among his flocks he probably possesses a greater number of cattle, relative to sheep, since cattle are more suited to the shorter distances entailed in search for mountain pasture.

TENT DWELLERS: THE SHEIKH AT HOME

As their name implies " tent dwellers " or " dwellers of the desert," the Bedouin wander over the desert and semi-desert regions of north Arabia and north Africa. Ethnologically they are of Semitic origin, and may have originated in the desert of north Arabia. To-day they are represented by relatively few groups which can be described as pure, the greater number of them having mixed to some extent with Hamites and negroes. These people remain for nine or ten months in the arid desert regions, coming near to settled country only if driven to it at the height of the summer drought.

Most Bedouins are of medium stature. Their complexions have been described as " tawny white," but in general they show considerable range of colour. Their hair is coarse, thick, and jet black. They have well-formed facial features with dark, oval eyes and narrow aquiline noses.

Clothing is generally bought from travelling merchants. The men wear long white shirts reaching to their heels, and wide-sleeved coats, over which are worn shapeless cloaks of coloured cloth. In winter, sheepskin jackets may be worn. Their headgear consists of close-fitting woollen caps, over which are placed squares of cotton or silk cloth folded in triangles so that the points hang down the back and sides, the whole being kept in place by coils of twine. They generally go barefooted, but if the country is rough sandals of camel hide or cloth may be worn. The women's dress is much the same ; the headgear is sometimes longer and the loose over-cloak generally more voluminous and made of dark blue cloth. Bedouin women are rarely veiled, but sometimes draw their cloaks over their faces at the approach of a stranger. They are fond of jewellery and bedeck their wrists and ankles with rings of glass, copper, or iron.

Water supply is generally the most crucial factor deter-mining the site of a Bedouin encampment, while the actual position is chosen by the chief of the band. Surface water is not available, so wells are cleared out, or fresh ones dug, often reaching to a depth of a hundred feet. The water is drawn up in camel's-hide buckets.

The tents may be placed in a rough circle to enable the animals to be herded in safety during the night ; the prouder and more warlike groups, however, despise this method as a sign of weakness. The tents consist of lengths of coarse goat's-hair cloth, dyed black and supported on poles about nine feet high. The size varies considerably, according to the status of the owner. The usual tent cover is about twenty feet long and about twelve feet wide, with a separate strip of material for the back valance. The open face of the tent can easily be reversed by changing over the poles and removing the back strip to the other side ; this feature may have been designed for protection against the sudden sand storms of the desert. In cold weather both ends are often closed.

A sheikh's tent may be as long as thirty or forty feet. It is generally divided into two unequal parts by a partition of goat's-hair cloth. The smaller space is occupied by the chief and his guests, while the womenfolk, children, and slaves live on the other side of the partition, and there prepare the meals.

RICH AND POOR AMONG THE BEDOUIN

THE furnishings reflect the wealth of the owner, but even in the richest men's tents seldom amount to much, since ease of packing and transporting dictate the pattern and material of everything. Carpets, which are used both to sit and to sleep on, cotton quilts, and camel hair pillows are all the luxuries. The food stores are generally kept in bags which are woven by the women from camel or goat hair. The stores, which consist of grain, dates, and coffee, are obtained when the band reaches more settled country during the summer drought. The amount carried varies from one to sixty camel loads, according to the wealth of the owner. Grain, however, is generally regarded as the food of the wealthy, and few Bedouin can afford baked bread, except at festivities. Soured camel's milk and water are usually stored in camel's-skin gourds or bags.

The food of the Bedouin, as of all nomadic peoples, is both simple and monotonous. The chief feature of their diet is that no serious meal is eaten until the evening, when the day's work is accomplished, and the camp settled for the night. The fact that there is no limit to the time they can spend over the meal has not only encouraged them to display the powers of an enormous appetite, but has provided a reason for the tremendous ritual attached to coffee drinking.

Two brief draughts of milk suffice the Bedouin during the day. The evening meal, prepared by the women, generally consists of dates and roasted flour, with sour or fresh camel's milk to drink. Meat is seldom eaten, except at feasts, but on those occasions a communal dish or stew of sheep's carcasses is prepared. This is attacked first of all by the sheikh and his guests, who remove the best and succulent morsels, then by the privileged men, and lastly by the women and children, who finish everything, leaving nothing but bare bones.

THE IMPORTANCE OF FAMILY TIES IN THE DESERT

THEORETICALLY, a camp unit is made up of a collection of *Kins*. Each Kin consists of a group of people who are blood relations, relationship being traced through the male line. A chief or sheikh is chosen from the dominant Kin, and to him all disputes are referred. Descent should control this rank, but there is a tendency for any natural leader to usurp the chieftainship and exalt his Kin to the foremost position in the group. The mode of life and the scarcity of pastures sets a limit to the possible number each camp unit can contain, and it is usual for the more prolific families or Kins to break away and form separate camp units of their own.

Attached to each camp group there may be a certain number of slaves, the property of the richer men, whose duties consist of watering the camels or leading the pack animals on the march. These slaves are generally of negro origin and are forbidden to intermarry with the Bedouin. A sheikh may possess many slaves, and very often he depends on them for protection and advice. Smiths are also attached to the group, and these people, who frequently come from Persia, are responsible for the shoeing of horses and the making and repairing of weapons.

When the group are on the march, the sheikh and fighting men lead the way, riding the best camels, each with saddled mares in readiness, should danger threaten the party. They are followed by the pack camels, led by the slaves, and then come the women and children riding the breeding camels, while behind them all follow the herds. If there is no need for hurry, a day's journey generally consists of about fifteen miles, camp being made before the heat of the afternoon.

The Bedouin lives a life of constant watchfulness from fear of attack. The wealth of a group lies in their herds. Tribal jealousies and blood feuds are common, with the result that raiding is a common practice, both as a means of increasing wealth and of repaying grievances. The characteristic weapon of the Bedouin is the spear or lance, although they have, for several generations, possessed firearms, and with them they show considerable skill. As a people they are hot-headed, and when roused are fearless and shrewd fighters.

The camel is the only indispensable possession of the Bedouin. On it he depends for food. Since neither butter nor cheese can be made from camel's milk, he is often dependent on milk as food for months at a time. A camel in milk gives from a quart to a gallon each day, according to the pasturage. The skin provides the material for weaving and for the packing of bags and bottles. The camel is invaluable as a means of transport, as it is capable of carrying a load of about three hundred pounds and walking a distance of about forty miles if required, while a good riding camel is capable of twice this distance. The camel is able to subsist for long periods without drink, except in the extremely hot season, and is therefore ideally suited to desert life. At the intermittent waterholes it can by drinking anything up to fifteen gallons, lay in store for a journey in the waterless desert. Its greatest value, however, lies in the fact that it is the chief marketable possession of the Bedouin. By exchanging it, he is able to get clothing, firearms and food-stuffs.

THE GREAT AMBITION—TO OWN A CAMEL !

IT is not surprising, therefore, that the camel is highly prized, and even the poorest members of the groups live in the hope that one day they may have a camel of their own. The she-camel is the prized possession, since it gives milk and, if prolific, can increase the herd ; males are consequently kept only for stud purposes.

Horses, on the other hand, may be regarded as an economic loss. They are incapable of travelling long distances in the desert as they go lame and constantly require water. Food and drink have, therefore, to be carried on pack camel for them. In winter they have to be protected from the cold, and in summer sheltered from the heat. Of little value except in warfare or for executing short raiding journeys, yet they are highly prized and, despite the fact that even rich men cannot afford to keep many, a person is considered of no importance whatever if he does not possess one of these animals. Only thoroughbreds are reared, and since feeding and care presents such constant problems, only the mares are kept. White is the prized colour for both camels and mares, and nothing but a white mare is considered a suitable mount for a sheik. In most groups the women and slaves are responsible for the grooming and care of the horses.

WHERE WAR IS A PROFESSION : THE BLOODTHIRSTY MASAI TRIBE

IN the Savannah regions of tropical Africa there are a considerable number of native tribes, most of them of mixed Hamitic and negro origin. These people were for the most part originally stock-owners, but there has been a tendency for the more warlike tribes to seize the cattle of their weaker neighbours, driving them to maintain their existence by tilling the soil. With the arrival of the white settler, the land available for these native pastoralists became greatly reduced. Peaceful settlement was encouraged, with the result that to-day there are found in this region tribes who are at the intermediate stage of being mainly nomadic herdsmen yet showing a definite tendency towards agriculture.

THE MASAI "SUFFERS TO BE BEAUTIFUL"

ONE of the largest of these tribes are the Masai who formerly roamed over the high plateaux around the Great Lakes, but are now located mainly in an extensive reserve north-west of Nairobi. The chief vegetation of the region is tropical grass, but occasional trees grow near the watercourses. Lion, elephant, and buck are indigenous to the region, but have lately decreased in numbers.

The Masai people are tall and slender. Although they have negro blood in their veins, the negroid features are generally considerably modified. Hence thick lips are the exception, and noses, instead of being wide, are often narrow with the bridge well defined. Their skin colour varies from chocolate to dark brown, and they have characteristically small heads, which are, as a rule, long shaped and relatively high.

Few clothes are worn, the women and old men wearing little but capes made of skins or cotton cloth. The young men, or warriors, wind pieces of red calico round their waists, adorn their necks and heads with ostrich feathers, and tie fringes of white fur round their knees. It is customary for all except the young men to shave their heads completely. The youths grow their hair sufficiently long to allow of it being plaited together with strips of leather. The "coiffure" consists of four plaits ; the longest hangs down the back, a smaller one down the centre of the forehead, while the others hang at each side. The plaits are smeared with a mixture of red clay and mutton fat.

As a people they are fond of ornaments and bead necklaces, bracelets and anklets are worn by both sexes. They mutilate their bodies, and it is frequent to find the lobes of their ears pierced and distended with wooden plugs inserted to enlarge the holes. The whims of fashion have even spread to Central Africa, for there are reports of natives who have decided that the lobes of the ear are prettier unpierced, and have therefore

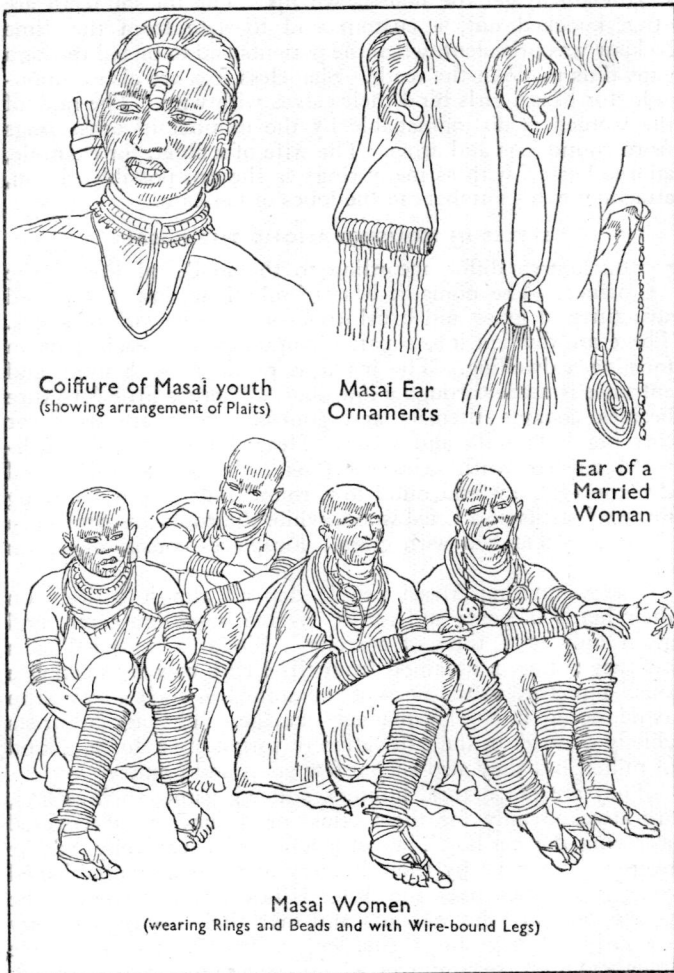

Coiffure of Masai youth
(showing arrangement of Plaits)

Masai Ear
Ornaments

Ear of a
Married
Woman

Masai Women
(wearing Rings and Beads and with Wire-bound Legs)

13. FASHION AND BEAUTY, PAINFULLY ADORNED

*Among the Masai of tropical Africa, only the young men
leave their heads unshaven. A woman's rank is shown by the
number of brass rings she wears on her arms and legs.*

sought aid to get the holes sewn up. The incisor teeth are often knocked out, a custom said to date from the time lockjaw was prevalent, when the patients had to be fed through gaps thus made in the teeth. Shapeless legs are also fashionable, for Masai girls bind their calves with wire. The rank of the women is distinguishable by the number of brass rings worn round legs and arms. The wife of a chief, for example, adorns herself with as many rings as she can possibly get on, attaching extra numbers to the lobes of her ears.

STYLES IN HOUSING AMONG THE MASAI

THE houses differ according to the mode of life of the owner. The nomadic Masai build long, low, flat-roofed structures of grass and brushwood on a framework of sticks. These are divided into separate compartments, each division forming a dwelling. The inside is plastered with mud, and entrance is made through a low door. There is little furniture besides cooking utensils and gourds, which are used for carrying both milk and water. Heaps of grass and brushwood covered with skins serve as beds. The agricultural division of the Masai build low, round huts, the walls being made of sticks and brushwood, while the roofs are conical in shape and thatched with grass. Fireplaces consist of circles of stones.

The wandering Masai people depend almost entirely on their herds of goats and cattle. Game is seldom eaten, and grain only at a time of scarcity. Blood is regarded as a delicacy ; this is obtained from the living cow by making a small puncture in the neck of the animal in such a way as to avoid doing it any permanent damage. The agriculturists chiefly depend on the cultivation of sorghum or durra, a kind of millet, but they also keep a few goats and poultry.

They are not natural hunters, and big game, such as lion, are attacked only for their skins, or if they are discovered worrying the herds. They are, however, a naturally warlike people, who have by their bravery and violence established their superiority over the other tribes of the region. The young men are the warriors and take their occupation very seriously. They are forbidden to marry, and they live together in an encampment where strict training is observed, smoking and excesses of food and drink being forbidden. It is characteristic of the Masai warriors that they never attack at night, or by stealth, but engage their enemies in the open, and there indulge in a hand-to-hand fight to the death. They seldom mass in an army ; generally small bands sally out into the bush and seize their neighbours' cattle, terrorising and killing the owners as a form of sport rather than warfare.

With this incessant demand for fighting men, the care of the herds falls largely to the young boys and old men. The women confine themselves to domestic duties and trading. It seems somewhat ironical that while the young men of the tribe are enjoying these bloodthirsty skirmishes with their neighbours, the women carry on trade with the same neighbours without interruption.

ONE FUNERAL FOR THE RICH AND NONE FOR THE POOR

UNLIKE most African tribes, the Masai do not, as a rule, bury their dead. They simply leave the corpse in a shady place in the bush to the attentions of the hyenas and vultures. Rich men, however, are treated with more ceremony ; their bodies are wrapped up in an ox-hide and put in a shallow trench and covered with stones. If a chief dies, his body is given a form of burial, but after a short lapse of time, the grave is disturbed and the skull removed by the son and heir, who thereafter keeps it ever near him for luck.

In 1890 there was a great outbreak of rinderpest, a cattle disease, which practically exterminated the herds of the Masai people. The loss of both wealth and means of existence caused the Masai themselves to die off in great numbers. Since this plague they have never quite regained their former strength and ferocity.

A RACE OF FARMERS : CHINA'S AGRICULTURAL MILLIONS

CHINA has a population of about four hundred and eighty-five millions. If a map of the distribution of this population is compared with a map showing the ordinary relief of the country, it will be seen that the densest millions swarm in the lowland areas and along the banks of rivers. Apart from a few completely dark spots which would represent a density of over 500,000 per square mile and would obviously be indicative of towns, the population would appear evenly distributed. These factors would seem to indicate a vast population dependent on agriculture for their means of livelihood.

When considering a country which is so vast and which presents such a diversity of conditions, it is impossible here to describe its inhabitants in more than general terms. The Chinese are a race of farmers ; ever since the times of the earliest civilisations they have spent their lives cultivating the land with meticulous care, so that to-day agriculture forms the foundation of the social and economic structure of the country.

It is a land of small holdings in which the family, rather than the individual, forms the unit. Human labour, unaided by anything except a few rude implements and but few beasts of burden, has provided the motive power for this intensive agriculture. Zest for work has been encouraged by the traditional custom for holdings to be passed down from father to son—a system whereby the family effort is reserved for the family's good, and is cumulative with the generations.

WHERE THE EIGHT-HOUR DAY IS DESPISED

THE Chinese farmer is a happy man ; his needs are few, and he asks nothing more from life than that he should be an efficient farmer and teach his children to be good husbandmen after him. He is thrifty to a degree which can hardly be understood in the western world. He wastes nothing, from the odd inches of ground around the edge of his rice-fields to the apparently useless husks and stalks which he burns for fuel. Capable of great physical endurance, the Chinese farmer works in his fields from dawn to dusk, and would despise the idleness enforced by the observance of an eight-hour day.

By religion he is either a Confucionist or a Taoist, but his practical faith consists in a very sincere ancestor worship ; indeed, it is only for the burying of some relative that he will give up a few feet of his precious land. The conical mounds of earth which mark the graves of past generations are a characteristic feature of a Chinese landscape. Where the land is flat and fertile, these often occupy valuable soil.

The families are generally large, the perpetual work of the land requiring many hands, and both children and grandchildren take a share in the work as soon as they are old enough. The wife of the Chinese farmer, besides having the incessant care of small children and performing most of the household duties, also helps her husband in the fields.

As a people, the Chinese are sociable, and therefore prefer living in villages. This tendency has been further encouraged as a means of defence against bandits. For, in times of famine, people from the stricken areas, driven by hunger, attempt to plunder and ravage the stores of their less needy neighbours. Consequently, isolated houses are uncommon, and the people live in tiny villages dotted about the countryside. The buildings, which are very cramped to save precious ground, are made of mud, brick, or woven bamboo. The average Chinese farmhouse consists of three or four rooms arranged around a mud courtyard. The kitchen is the central room, and the sleeping-rooms lead off it. The beds may be warmed by a connecting brick flue—a scheme which makes use of the surplus heat provided by the cooking operations. The threshing floor, manure pits, and vegetable plots are generally in the immediate neighbourhood of the house. Trees, which are characteristically absent from the cultivated fields, are found only in the vicinity of the houses.

PIGS AND POULTRY IN THE PARLOUR

HOUSEHOLD furniture is reduced to bare necessities, simple wooden tables and benches being the only comforts. There are no carpets, since the pigs and poultry consider the living-room as much their property as that of the family. Frequently there is a rough shelf which serves as the kitchen god's shrine, and the walls are sometimes adorned with tablets to the ancestors.

Domestic animals are reduced to the minimum. Pigs, poultry, and an occasional dog live around the family home on such scraps and morsels as they can find. Cows are seldom kept, except by the very rich, since the problem of food is too severe for the average farmer. The larger, and therefore wealthier, farming families can afford a water buffalo or bullock to draw their ploughs, the less fortunate have a pony or donkey. Always there is the consideration that the beast of burden is an added tax on the land ; it has to be fed, and since land cannot be spared for fodder crops the number of draught animals kept on the farms remains very low.

Meat rarely occurs in the diet of the Chinese except at the time of the New Year festival, when one of the farmyard pigs is killed for the feast. Rice is the staple food of the south, and millet of the north, while various pulses, vegetables, and a few eggs provide occasional variety.

The Chinese use primitive methods of agriculture. The implements, evolved from the experience of centuries, are simple and few. Since the Chinese farmer never has much money to spare, his implements must be cheap and easy to repair at home. They are, therefore, generally made of wood, though some hoes have iron blades. Spades, rakes, and wooden hoes are all made with detachable heads, so that it is not uncommon to see a farmer go to his fields with one wooden shank, upon which he can fit each implement as required. The plough, also of wood and iron shod, is a prized possession, and frequently the owner carries it home at night to the safety of his own courtyard. Rollers and millstones are usually made of stone, and therefore form an expensive item for the average farmer.

Only the large farms in the north of China employ hired labour, and though occasionally the villagers may offer each other assistance, it is the general rule for the family to tend the holding unaided. No member of the family remains idle, the aged grandparents and youngest children are left at the homestead to prepare the meal, or posted as guards to raise the alarm should bandits be sighted. The rest of the family help in the fields at whatever job the season of the year demands.

MAKING THE SOIL YIELD ITS UTMOST

IN the southern districts, where rice is the characteristic crop, yields are increased by the process of double cropping. Where climatic conditions are very favourable, three and even four crops have been raised off the same plot of land in a year. This highly intensive culture impoverishes the soil—a fact which the Chinese farmer appreciated decades before the invention of artificial fertilisers. In order to restore fertility, all household refuse, stubble roughage, animal and even human waste is carefully collected and made into " compost " by admixture of earth, then applied in dressings to the fields. Wherever available, mud from the canals and rivers is added.

The rice-fields are generally small and of odd geometric shapes. These fertile plots are unfenced, but are surrounded with low mud partitions which act as dams at the time when the fields are flooded. Little space can be spared for paths and tracks, so the fields are approached by narrow paths which wind along the tops of the dams. Where the country is undulating, the farmer terraces the hillsides, each terrace tending to follow the contour of the hill. The fields are ingeniously arranged so that the water used for flooding can be led along from plot to plot under the action of gravity.

Each farmer sets aside a small field for use as a seed bed; this he keeps highly fertilised and well weeded. Here the rice is planted and the young blades carefully tended so that in the short space of forty days a nursery-field of one acre is capable of producing sufficient plants to stock a holding of ten acres. While the young plants are being thus cultivated, it is possible for an earlier crop to ripen on the other fields.

The fields are prepared for young plants by the aid of a plough which churns up the wet soil and manure until it reaches the consistency of thick liquid mud. Weeds are then removed, and attention is paid to the embankments to make certain they are watertight. The fields are then submerged by artificial means to a depth of several inches and the soil once more carefully prepared with a hoe. The young seedlings are removed from the nursery-bed in bundles. Each bundle has to be delicately treated in order to avoid bruising and damage. Care is taken to shake all traces of soil from the roots before tying the bundles with grass and removing them to further fields. Replanting is a highly-skilled operation; each bundle of seedlings is untied as required, and separated into bunches of four or five, which are then plunged into the wet mud at regular intervals. After this, the crop needs little attention save weeding.

In the north of China, where rainfall does not permit of rice being grown, the farmer confines his attention to the production of millet, kaoliang (a kind of sorghum), and wheat, etc. Here the season is too short for double cropping to be possible, so that there is a tendency for the holdings to be larger, and for a variety of crops to be grown.

MANY-PEOPLED EUROPE : MELTING-POT OF RACES

THE question of Europe is different from that presented by the other continents of the world. Here great waves of culture have spread across the peoples of the continent, uniting by their spell racial stocks which until their coming presented no affinities whatsoever. Thus, by the processes of civilisation, the individuality of the races of Europe has tended to become absorbed.

There is no case of a primitive race being pushed out into the inhospitable fringe lands in Europe, because Europe possesses no fringe lands in the anthropological sense. The only moderately isolated area is the Iberian peninsula, and even here free communication with north Africa, via Gibraltar, has encouraged mixing rather than isolation of peoples.

Europe, therefore, presents a unique problem. Here is a continent, the whole of which is capable, to some degree, of supporting human life, and has throughout the ages, since man appeared on the earth, been called upon to do so.

It may be significant, also, that Europe is, as it were, a " dead end." If a map of the world is studied, it will be seen that this continent forms one vast peninsula projecting from the largest land-mass in the world. It is, therefore, easy to imagine that with immigrations of people surging into Europe, pressed on by some impetus, there was formed within this region a complete melting-pot of races, peoples, and civilisations, from which there was no escape save by retreat or death.

Since the retreat of the ice at the end of the last glaciation, Europe has enjoyed, on the whole, a reasonably attractive climate. Her soil is sufficiently fertile to support a varied vegetation of broad-leaved trees and grassland ; nowhere are there insuperable barriers to the migrations of peoples. And so, ever since man appeared on the earth, Europe has been the scene of mingling races. While there are a few representatives who individually portray characteristics of the original race types, there is no such thing as a pure race in Europe.

In considering the races of Europe, it must be remembered that nationalities have no bearing whatever on race. Spain, France, and Germany are all nations, yet each is composed of more than one race. Another stumbling-block is provided in language. Language is but a branch of culture, and a linguistic link does not necessarily imply racial affinity. Further complication arises with the use of the term Germanic, which is the name given by some anthropologists to the Teutonic or Nordic race in Europe ; it frequently leads to misunderstandings regarding the German people, who are by no means all included in the Germanic race, many of them being of different origin.

THE DARK MEN OF EUROPE'S ICE AGE

THE earliest human remains which have been found in Europe belong to the Palæolithic period. There are scattered traces, chiefly in southern Europe, of a people who, although they share the same fundamental features, show remarkable diversity of type. The various skulls which have been found may show individual responses to the European environment. Little is known of the appearance of these people, but in general they were probably extremely dark and of a primitive type, with long heads.

The conditions prevailing at this time are also significant, owing to the presence of the ice-sheet over a greater part of northern Europe, the climatic belts were possibly shifted southwards. Thus the Sahara Desert region was then well watered, and capable of habitation. As the ice retreated, so the belt of rains receded northwards, and the Sahara region gradually passed back through definite stages into a desert region. With the passing of the ice, the land, relieved of this enormous pressure, rose. At this time, the climate was very favourable to forest growth, and Britain was probably covered with oak and alder forests. Then followed a period of depression, with a warm, moist climate, still favourable to forest growth, fir-trees flourishing on the peat moors of Scotland and Wales at an altitude at least eight hundred feet higher than they do to-day. Gradually the climate became drier, and the vegetation adapted itself to the new conditions ; fir-trees could no longer exist on the upland regions, and many of the peat moors became dry. With the change in flora came also a change in fauna, and the modern types of animals established themselves.

This had a great effect on man in Europe. With the restriction of the open spaces came the inevitable diminishing of his hunting-grounds, except for the coast regions, the chalk and the loess lands. The old hunters had either to withdraw to more favourable regions, such as south Russia, or adapt themselves to new conditions. Life was probably not easy for them, and they became degenerate, seeking for the bare means of existence wherever nature offered them a chance.

THE FIRST MODERN MEN IN EUROPE

As we have suggested, at the time of the maximum extent of the ice-sheet, north Africa probably had a sufficiently moist climate to support a population. The inhabitants were apparently hunters and gatherers. As the drought came, they wandered northwards and entered Europe, probably in considerable numbers, settling at first in the coast regions. These people, who have been called the Mediterranean race, represent the earliest immigration of modern man into Europe. They have certain definite marked characteristics, being cf medium height and slight build, with dark eyes and hair, brownish white faces, and long-shaped heads. These characteristics have remained persistent and are evident amongst the descendents of the race in the present population of Europe.

Some authorities recognise three groups of the Mediterranean race in Europe, each depending upon the route by which immigration occurred. Thus, the most westerly group, or Iberians, entered via Gibraltar, settling for the most part in the Iberian peninsula. Those who entered via Sicily and settled in Italy and southern France have been called the Ligurians, while those who arrived by the most easterly, or island route, to Greece, have been called the Pelasgians.

It seems that these peoples established themselves very thoroughly on the Mediterranean seaboard, and may have produced the earliest beginnings of the " city state." Gradually, however, they spread northwards, the mild oceanic climate of the greater part of Europe being fairly suited to them. Their most northerly extent was probably Britain, traces of them being found in the Clyde valley. Here, as conditions were probably not altogether favourable, the stock would not remain healthy and virile.

A NEW RACE COMES FROM ASIA

Not long after the Mediterranean race began spreading northwards came the second great influx of people. A movement from Asia brought a people who were of thick-set, medium stature, with sallow skin, hazel or dark brown eyes, and hair ranging from chestnut colour to dark brown, and whose heads were very definitely broad.

These people probably entered via Asia Minor and spread along the highland regions of Europe, seizing the grassland pasture areas from the Mediterranean races and everywhere impressing upon them their language and their culture. In the east, the Mediterranean race seems to have been more or less ousted by the new Alpine race, except in the coast region. In other parts of Europe, the Alpine race seems to have succeeded in establishing itself on the upland and therefore more infertile regions. Almost everywhere they have left traces of their occupation, although at the present time the broad-headed element predominates only among the populations of the more easterly countries.

THE BLUE-EYED NORDICS COME DOWN FROM THE NORTH

MEANWHILE the third great race of Europe had evolved; it is not certain when or how it originated. Some authorities suggest Scandinavia, since the type is so well adapted to the wet climate and forest life of the north and north-west. These people are tall, with fair or reddish hair, blue or grey eyes, and fresh pink and white complexions. They have long, oval faces with prominent cheek-bones and remarkably long-shaped heads.

They have spread throughout the whole of north-western Europe, and in this area dominate the population. They have also spread southwards, isolated remnants, such as the tall, fair Lombards, bearing witness to their one-time wider distribution. This distribution of peoples in Europe has been more or less maintained ever since Neolithic times.

Underlying all the turmoil and fierce national spirit of the Europe of to-day lie the three great divisions of Nordic, Alpine, and Mediterranean man. Some attempt has been made to show how these peoples arrived, and where they originated, with an account of their distribution and the regions best suited to each of them. It must be remembered, however, that traces of each of the three races are nearly always apparent in the peoples of any of the countries of Europe, together with remnants of even earlier stocks. Intermarriage and absorption has tended to produce mixed types, but there still persist the three elements within the continent.

The population of Scandinavia, the east of Great Britain, Belgium, Holland, and north Germany and the Baltic lands have remarkably long heads, and tend towards Nordic characteristics. The west of Great Britain, much of France, Iberia and Italy, and a mere fringe round the coast of Greece, possess a population approximating to the darker Mediterranean type, but still with long heads. The broad-headed element persists over most of the east of Europe, through Russia, the Ukraine, the Balkan lands, south Germany, and central France.

GATHERING AND USING THE BOUNTY OF NATURE

IT is a commonplace that this is an age of specialisation. Professors multiply as knowledge grows more and more subdivided ; general practitioners depend increasingly on specialists ; local craftsmanship has been almost superseded by mass production ; local shops give way to branches of powerful organisations, or, even if they do retain the old name above the door, they are becoming increasingly dependent on the large wholesalers who supply them. So to-day the dining-tables of Great Britain display bacon from Denmark, butter from Australia, mutton from New Zealand, beef from the Argentine, apples and cheese from Canada, eggs even from Natal and China, and milk from the Netherlands ; yet all these are things which in a less sophisticated age were produced at home.

The volume of tropical produce, too, has increased enormously, not only actually, but relatively. Thus, in 1610, tea was sold in England for as much as ten guineas a pound, and even by 1780 the annual consumption averaged little over half a pound a head of the population ; by 1932 the consumption had risen to over ten pounds per head. Any one who cares to count the number of new retail fruit shops which have sprung up in the nearest town even in the last ten years will not require further evidence of the prosperity of this comparatively new trade. Rubber, petroleum, and vegetable oils, quite apart from a whole series of minerals, are all things which have entered world trade only in the last half-century. With so much competition only the most efficient producing areas for any commodity can survive, and some attempt will now be made to outline a few of the more important of these.

Maize is the raw material for the bread used mainly by natives in the moister warm regions of the world. Millet feeds the natives of Africa and the Deccan, who live on the drier margins of the tropics. Rye yields black bread from soils too poor to support any better cereal. Wheat is, however, the cereal which commands the best soils throughout the temperate regions.

Parts of the Canadian prairies are carpeted with silt from

one-time glacial lakes. There is light rainfall in early summer and bright sunshine for ripening and harvest. This cheap and fertile land awaited development until the invention of the steamship and the railway provided the all-essential market. Once communications were established, the wheat production rose from twelve million bushels (one bushel = eight gallons) in 1871, to 535,000,000 in 1928, but even with the motor transport of to-day very little wheat is grown more than twenty miles from the railway.

In this large-scale production science has aided the farmer by developing new varieties of wheat, in which the growing period is reduced from 130 to 100 days, enabling the cereal to be grown farther north. Science has also devised new machinery, so that one machine can now both harvest and thresh as much as fifty acres of wheat in an eight-hour day. The average yield per acre is, however, only twelve bushels, compared with over thirty in England.

STARVING PEOPLE AND ROTTING FOOD

IN some years things do not go so well. In 1929 the output was only 300,000,000 bushels, although in 1932 it was 428,000,000, an enormous fluctuation for so important a crop. Damage is caused by hail ; insufficient spring rain leads to drought, and this with high winds results in dust storms, which in extreme cases may bury machinery and hold up road, rail, and even air traffic ; temperatures may rise to 110° F. in the shade ; grasshoppers, weeds, early autumn night frosts, diminishing soil fertility all play their part in wrecking the farmer's hopes. Worse, however, was to come, for by 1933 the world was glutted with wheat, and huge piles of it lay on the prairie lands of Canada and the United States mouldering in the open. The world had 640,000,000 bushels of excess wheat in the same year that its unemployment queues in need of bread also broke new records. The problem was further complicated for the great wheat-growing countries by European tariffs, which resulted in the French and German farmer receiving three times as much money for his wheat as farmers in Canada or the Argentine. As a result of these conditions prices fell, mortgages rose, and banks closed.

This led to restriction, compulsory and voluntary. Restriction method in 1934 under the autocratic government of the United States aimed at a 15 per cent. reduction in the area sown, but only half of this reduction was actually achieved.

14. WHERE THE FRUITS OF THE EARTH ARE FOUND:

Modern sources of natural products tend to become concentrated in a few main centres. Note that Great Britain is largely dependent for her food on countries across the seas.

NATURAL PRODUCTS AND TRADE ROUTES.

As a result of the speeding-up of transport, tropical fruits such as bananas, are now a commonplace in countries such as Great Britain where, fifty years ago, they were unknown.

7

In the Canadian prairies farmers have learnt their lesson of the dangers of too great dependence on one crop, and, where irrigation is available from the Rocky Mountains rivers or where the rainfall is not too low, mixed farming is increasing. The summer of 1934 demonstrated once again with fearful emphasis that prairie-farming must not be judged on one year's yields, but on the average of three or four years, for in 1934 drought again took charge, mocking man's attempts at restriction, and the wheat crop shrivelled to less than half its maximum.

Australia is the only other region in the British Empire able to export wheat in large quantities, and drought-resistant wheats have been evolved to suit the climate. India and South Africa grow large quantities of wheat, but insufficient for export. Among foreign countries with an important surplus for export may be mentioned Argentina, Hungary, Rumania, and, above all, Russia.

A GREAT EXPERIMENT : THE SICKLE AT WORK IN RUSSIA

THE summer climate of southern Russia is similar to that of the Canadian prairies, though the winters, owing to the lower elevation and latitude, are less extreme. The Black Earth belt has in places been cultivated for over eighty years without showing any appreciable decline in fertility. Hence it is not surprising that the pre-War export of wheat reached 165,000,000 bushels, the wheat being grown chiefly on the large estates. The peasant was too poor to buy the surplus, and was compelled to live on cheaper foods. After the Revolution of 1917 the large estates were broken up and the peasant consumed the wheat himself. The low selling price fixed for wheat encouraged him to turn to other crops, although at a later period he was allowed, after having supplied his quota to the State, to sell any surplus in the open market. Production naturally declined, until there was not enough even for the Russian cities.

Then followed a complete reorganisation of the Russian agricultural system. At the root of this was first the establishment of collective State farms on an enormous scale, the largest containing 427,000 acres—the peasant was sent to the Urals if he refused to join—secondly, the introduction of modern machinery and methods, Rostov having now the largest agricultural works in Europe. It was natural that the mechanism of such a sudden and gigantic economic revolution should creak badly at first, that tractors should be manufactured which could not move, that others should be wrecked and left out in all weathers, and that penalties should have to be instituted for mechanics guilty of " wanton cruelty " to agricultural machinery. These defects are of relatively small importance where all the raw materials are produced within the country, and where wages—paid in a managed currency— are under rigid State control.

On the other hand, instead of the difficulty of having to collect the grain from numerous individualist households, the wheat is easily concentrated on each of the collective farms. New chemical factories are turning out large quantities of fertiliser, and power from the Dnieprostroy hydro-electric power plant (the largest in Europe) is being utilised over a wide radius for electric threshing. The yield per acre is already higher on the collective farms than on the small individual holdings.

In Britain wheat is frequently referred to as " corn," though to a Scots farmer corn implies oats. Similarly, millet is known in West Africa as " Guinea Corn," and in South Africa as " Kaffir Corn." Throughout the United States corn is universally understood to mean maize. In Britain, however, maize is called Indian corn ; in France, Spanish corn ; in the Netherlands and Hungary, Turkish wheat ; and in Turkey, Egyptian corn. This widespread cereal, maize, which in the United States exceeds in quantity all the other cereal crops combined, is best suited to regions warmer and rather wetter than are required for wheat. In three months it reaches a height of eight or nine feet—hence the Australian nickname of " cornstalk " for a tall man.

In South Africa, under the name " mealies," it is the principal native food, while in Hungary and Romania it is an important foodstuff, and the Italian *polenta* is also made from ground maize. In more temperate countries, however, it rarely reaches the table except as cornflour, though in Maine (U.S.A.) it is canned green and is popular as a vegetable. Maize is grown extensively in India, but the chief exporter is the Argentine, which sends abroad about six times as much as any other country in the world, though East African competition is increasing.

As an article for export, maize is a crop which suffers from its weight and bulk in relation to its value, *i.e.* it is of " low specific value." Hence its main service, not only in the

United States but in the other countries already cited, is as
a fodder crop. It is sometimes grown as a fodder crop in
countries such as Canada and England, where it would not
ordinarily be hot enough for it to ripen. In the United States
only 1 per cent. of the vast quantity of maize grown in the
corn belt is exported, and, as has been said, " more than one-
third of the crop squeals as it goes to market." In other
words, it is fed to the pigs.

THE HOMES OF OUR MEAT AND FISH SUPPLIES

MODERN methods have made it cheaper to rear cattle on
the grasslands west of the Mississippi, where it is too
dry for arable farming. The cattle are then sent to the corn
belt to be fattened along with enormous numbers of pigs.
The great focus of this activity is Chicago, at the south-west
end of Lake Michigan. In 1833 its population was under a
hundred ; stock used to be shipped alive to the cities of the
east, but first refrigeration (which was introduced in 1874)
and later the highly specialised canning industry changed the
traffic to carcasses and tins. When Chicago celebrated its
centenary in 1933 its population had soared to over three and
a third millions. Its stockyards are capable of receiving
100,000 pigs in a single day, besides proportionately formidable
quantities of cattle and sheep. " Every second that a watch
ticks off a pig is whisked into the machines to emerge in an
attractive assortment of ham, sausage, lard, brushes, chewing-
gum, soap, cosmetics, glue, buttons, combs, knitting needles,
and even sacks of fertiliser to grow more corn and raise more
pigs." So central is Chicago's position and so vast a network
of railways converge on it that its industrial activity results
in a parcel post traffic equal to that of New York and Phila-
delphia combined.

In the meat trade the United States has a formidable
competitor in Argentina. The pampas, or grasslands of
Argentina, resemble the North American prairies, but are more
accessible to the sea and therefore to foreign markets, on
which, owing to the small population, the industry is entirely
dependent. This industry, in fact, owes its existence to
refrigeration, but beef fully frozen loses some of its taste,
though mutton does not suffer to the same extent. Hence an
important step forward was taken when chilling—as opposed

to freezing—was developed (about 1900). Chilled beef is cooled to only just below freezing-point, but it does not keep so long as frozen meat, and requires more ship-storage space : this development allows Argentine beef to be sold in London as cheaply as American beef is sold in New York.

The effect of the introduction of the chilling process is shown by the imports to Great Britain between 1901 and 1910 ; during this period the imports from the United States shrank from 159,000 tons to 24,000, and those from the Argentine and Uruguay rose from 40,000 to 384,000. The industry has benefited greatly by the care taken to maintain an unusually high standard of pedigree stock, and by the increase in the area under alfalfa, a kind of clover which yields about five times as much pasture as ordinary grass, and is, in addition, more drought-resisting owing to its long roots.

THE MANY BY-PRODUCTS OF THE CATTLE INDUSTRY

As in the case of the Chicago pig industry, most of the profit from beef is made through the by-products, which include tongues, ox-tails, sweetbreads, leather, glue, brushes, gelatine, perfume bottle caps, sausage casings, and tennis racquet strings. The demand for bully-beef in the World War encouraged Brazil to enter the tinned meat trade, but both her breed of cattle and the plateau scrublands are much inferior to the cattle and pastures of Argentina and Uruguay.

Sheep tend to be kept mainly for wool purposes in the drier stock-raising regions, and for mutton in the wetter ones. The best breed for wool is the merino, which is the basis of the Australian wool crop ; but in New Zealand, once refrigeration became perfected, the tendency was to develop cross-breeds instead, as they supply better mutton. So efficient are modern transport methods that the freight to England is only a penny a pound, and the export trade of Canterbury lamb (from the Canterbury Plains) has grown to such dimensions that there are now over thirty million sheep on the two islands, or about twenty for every member of the population. Contrary to common belief, however, the value of the wool export is half as much again as that of frozen meat.

Religious scruples prevent vast numbers of Indians from eating fish ; in fact, most of the fishing is relegated to the lowest caste peoples. On the other hand, the Roman Catholic countries form an important market for fish ; and the Buddhists of Siam, whose religion precludes the taking of life, satisfy their consciences and their appetite by arguing that, if a fish removed from the water chooses to die, that is not their responsibility. People such as the Japanese, Scandinavians, and Newfoundlanders, who live in lands which are inhospitable, but have indented coast-lines, are glad to add fish to their slender agricultural resources. In spite of the exigencies of their calling, fisher races venture far afield. Thus the Japanese in Malayan waters bring skill superior even to that of the natives, who themselves are renowned as fishermen, as far afield as South Africa : Breton schooners annually make for the Grand Banks of Newfoundland ; British vessels work from the coast of Greenland to the Arctic wastes beyond the North Cape, while—longest voyage of all—the Norwegians adventure to the pack-ice of the Antarctic in search of whales, which are not fish, but mammals.

Fish thrive mainly in the colder seas. Thus the meeting line — off the coast of Ecuador — of the warm *Niño* (or Christmas) current and the cool *Humboldt* current from the Polar seas is clearly marked by the throng of feeding sea-birds over the latter and by the empty skies over the former. Where, in addition to cool waters, the sea is also shallow, breeding is encouraged and catching made easier. Hence the great fishing grounds of the world are the North Sea, the Newfoundland Banks, and off Japan.

While the river sportsman must be one of the few real craftsmen still surviving, mechanisation has taken control of the sea fisheries, and, with refrigeration and improved transport, has enormously increased the value of the industry. Steam went far to solve one of the many unknown quantities in this uncertain trade, but steamers are now being outnumbered by motor vessels, which have a higher proportion of cargo space and can therefore be made smaller and more economical to run. The 120-ton drifters congregate in hundreds in pursuit of herrings, and, starting on the west of Scotland in the early spring, work round the north and then south to Lowestoft in the autumn.

The trawlers in search of cod, turbot, haddock, etc., are larger vessels of 230-350 tons, and work more independently, some of them remaining out for six weeks at a time, and special carriers take their catches daily to market. Still larger vessels may range as far as 2000 miles from the home port, working under conditions which would require H. M. Tomlinson to describe them ; the severity of winter in

Arctic waters may be such that the crews have to chop their vessels free of ice and frozen snow to prevent them from capsizing. So widely do modern vessels range in search of their prey that one is tempted to wonder whether fish nowadays do not travel greater distances above than in the water.

THE FISH TRADE SPOILT BY TOO MUCH COFFEE

THE Newfoundland Banks have long been the most famous of the fishing-grounds, and a quarter of the population of the smallest British Dominion lives by, for, and on fish. But the industry has been living on its reputation. There is a lack of organisation and co-operative effort ; methods are out-of-date and make little fight against modern British factory ships ; these have motor dories (the small boats which tend the cod lines) and machinery for converting fish refuse into cattle meal or fertiliser and for extracting cod-liver oil ; besides this, their catch can be brine-frozen and released according to the demands of the market. The result of this is that the Iceland fisheries have been growing at the expense of those of Newfoundland, until in 1932 they passed them for the first time.

Apart from these avoidable evils, the economic depression threatened swifter calamity, for Brazil, the world's chief market for salt cod, was visited by a plague of coffee over-production which undermined her power to purchase cod. Disaster in South America had repercussions in the North Sea, for Norway and Iceland had perforce to divert their unwanted cargoes to British ports, where they in turn depressed prices below the British economic limit. Thus, by way of Scandinavia, poverty came to England through plenty in Brazil.

There is, however, a brighter side to the picture, for in 1927 a new process of quick freezing at temperatures as low as $-50°$ F. was developed in Boston (U.S.A.). Fish treated in this way retained on unfreezing their natural juice and flavour unimpaired. As the fish are filleted before the process, more than 50 per cent. of the weight and therefore of transport costs is saved by the elimination of the waste products at the source. A further great advantage is that fresh fish becomes no longer a highly perishable commodity, but one which can be stored and sold as required. This eliminates uncertainty and waste, and the consumer benefits. It also opens up new markets in regions which have hitherto been too distant from the sea to be acquainted with fish which has not arrived either salted or in a tin.

BRINGING THE SUN TO MARKET

IT was not until the War that vitamin-C began to make sorties from the proceedings of scientific societies into breakfast-table menus. It acted as a veritable herald for the " Eat More Fruit " campaign which followed in the 'twenties, and the general public of North America and western Europe, comfortable in the assurance that it was combining duty with pleasure, responded with enthusiasm. Fruit ceased to be confined to the dessert course.

The process had, of course, begun much earlier, for even the value of publicity had long been realised by California with its slogan of " Cultivate, irrigate, exaggerate." Citrus fruits, of which the orange is the hardiest and the lemon the most delicate commercial crop, require plenty of sunshine for ripening, but are also highly sensitive to frost. Hence they thrive best in Mediterranean regions (where the rainfall is in winter), provided irrigation is available to supply enough water during the summer months, though Florida (in which the rain comes mainly in summer) is also an important producer. On clear, still nights cold air tends to sink and stagnate in the valley bottoms, accentuating the frost danger, so that in this industry, too, man has been at pains to eliminate uncertainty as far as is humanly possible. In Florida the trees are frequently protected by mounds of earth piled round them ; but in California, where oil fuel is cheap, orchard-heating is now regarded as essential, and rows of small heaters are lit between the lines of fruit trees whenever the weather reports, or, in some cases, automatic frost alarms, give the necessary warning.

Although citrus fruits were introduced into the gardens of the Spanish missions in California some three centuries ago, Spain for long remained the chief commercial source of supply. In 1869 the first transcontinental railway reached California, and, when the competition of other routes a few years later greatly reduced freights, the orange industry, further stimulated by disease ruining the vineyards, made rapid strides, followed more slowly about 1900 by the lemon. It is estimated that only 8 per cent. of the Californian crop is marketed within a thousand miles of the producing area. This naturally complicates the sale of the fruit ; hence co-operative marketing is a necessity, though the growers are fortunate in having a protected domestic market of high purchasing power.

Poor-grade fruit could not support the cost of the long freights, and this has resulted in the grading being given special attention, thereby ensuring the reputation of the Californian product. This has been ably seconded by efficient advertising, which has made various trade names famous throughout the world. The orange industry is no exception to the growing modern tendency to avoid waste, for the loss on the inferior portion of the crop is much reduced by using it for marmalade, candied peel, and fruit drinks, while the pulp refuse is sold for cattle fodder.

Modern canning methods have prolonged the peach and pear selling season throughout the year, but even the use of an early and a late variety of orange does not cover the whole year, and the winter gap is taken advantage of by countries such as South Africa and Brazil. As these are south of the equator they have their summer at the opposite time of the year from California and Spain ; the coffee slump in Brazil, too, has resulted in an enormous increase in the acreage of orange trees, while Paraguay is another large South American producer, though lacking as yet efficient export organisation.

Orange-growing is also developing rapidly in the Jaffa region of Palestine. Through the enterprise and capital of newly settled Jews the export rose from 830,000 cases in 1921 to 4,220,000 in 1933. The irrigated area of the Rio Grande, which forms a restless boundary between the United States and Mexico, is another area of rapid development of citrus fruit. There are also possibilities in Nigeria, but the oranges there, like those of Brazil, have a greenish tinge, and the foreign demand is not yet sufficient to warrant expenditure on colouring them.

The tissue paper in which oranges are wrapped sometimes provides interesting information. Thus one such wrapper bore the name of a Spanish grower along with the exhortation of a Dutch marketing firm to purchase their article, and the one English word " Selected " for the benefit of the consumer who had failed to respond to either of the others. The grapefruit industry, which has its headquarters in Florida, is of almost post-War growth, the Palestine output being, for example, no less than eighty times larger in 1932 than in 1928.

7*

It is not much more than fifty years since the first bananas were offered for sale in London. Now the industry has an organisation even more remarkable than that for oranges. The banana requires deep soil, heat, and moisture, the chief producing areas, for the European and United States markets, being the West Indies and Central America. It is a more delicate fruit than the orange, and once again refrigeration plays an important part. The tropical regions in which the fruit grows necessitate heavy expenditure on health services, as well as on labour, transport, and marketing costs. Hence considerable capital is required, so the industry is run by a few large companies rather than by a number of individual planters, and these have a virtual monopoly which is not likely to be easily challenged. It is a curious fact that the banana is a close relative of the plant which supplies the raw material for Manila hemp, which makes the finest quality cordage and ropes in the world. It is grown, as its name implies, in the Philippine Islands.

SUGAR'S TROPICAL AND TEMPERATE ORIGINS

SUGAR is an unusual crop in that it is produced in the tropics and in the temperate regions from two different sources, sugar-cane and sugar-beet, while it has even been suggested that wood-pulp has future possibilities. The part played by geographical factors is more difficult to elucidate than in some other cases, owing to the prominence of artificial control in the form of tariffs and subsidies.

Sugar-cane grows in frost-free tropical and semi-tropical countries where the annual rainfall is between forty and a hundred inches, the best crops being obtained from the cooler limits of these regions. Cuba, with its excellent soils and abundance of unused land, is the chief producing area, followed by India, with Java as a close third. Sugar-cane is exacting in labour, all the more so since machine harvesters have not yet been perfected, while the fact that about ten tons of cane are required to produce one ton of sugar means that the problem of sugar-production is closely bound up with that of transport. The same tropical conditions which enable the sugar-cane to grow are, unfortunately, equally stimulating for weeds, and these again require labour to eliminate ; yet, for some four to five months in the year there is a slack season when the labourers are not earning their keep. Hurricanes, too, are a danger to sugar plantations, in spite of the cane being more resistant to their onslaughts than most alternative crops.

Considerable capital is thus required, and is supplied from American sources in the case of Hawaii and Cuba, and from the Netherlands in the case of Java. The Javanese plantations, besides differing from the American sources, both in having a plentiful supply of labour and in freedom from hurricanes, are very intensively cultivated, over 90 per cent. of the area being under irrigation. The yields are consequently exceptionally high, but even this prosperous foundation did not save the sugar companies from being extremely hard hit by the world depression and by over-production, accentuated by an increased tendency to grow the beet-sugar in the mother countries.

The sugar-beet is similar to the ordinary garden-beet, but white in colour and with a larger top growth. Whereas cane-sugar had reached Europe from the East at least as early as the eighth century, beet-sugar was discovered only in 1747. The Napoleonic war cut off the West Indies trade, and under this stimulus the growing of sugar-beet expanded rapidly, until it now extends in a belt across the southern fringe of the great German plain, across Poland, and into the Ukraine of southern Russia. The World War resulted in a marked falling-off in sugar-beet production. Since then the industry has become the darling of protectionists ; in fact, the Netherlands, where careful cultivation produces a high yield, appears to be one of the very few regions where sugar-beet is grown purely on its merits. Thus, while Cuban sugar still owes a great deal of its prosperity to American preference, the United States increased the duty on sugar until it equalled the cost of production. The consequent reduction in the profits made by the Cuban industry resulted in distress in the Island. So acute was this that American investors in Cuban concerns were poorer by an amount which exceeded the total capital of the American sugar-beet industry, for the supposed benefit of which the tariff was imposed. Some countries, not content with discouraging the entry of foreign sugar, add a subsidy to the home-grown article ; the British subsidy worked out at more than the cost of growing an equivalent weight of sugar in the West Indies. This artificial encouragement of beet-sugar has resulted in a world over-production of sugar and a consequent depression of prices.

The sugar-beet yield per acre is only about a third of that

of sugar-cane, and the sugar content, in spite of improved methods, is smaller. It has, however, the advantage that it can be grown a thousand or more miles nearer the consumer. It also is exacting in labour, but the supply of this is relatively good throughout the European sugar belt. Cane-sugar yields rum, yeast, and molasses, while many factories depend largely on the waste cane for fuel to supply the power required to drive the crushing machinery. Sugar-beet is of considerable value as a rotational crop, as it enriches the ground, and the waste pulp is an important source of cattle fodder. Experiments are also being made in Czecho-Slovakia with a view to extracting alcohol to mix with petrol.

CLOTHES FROM EVERY CORNER OF THE WORLD

NEXT to food supplies man's chief concern is with clothing. Furs play an important part in both extremes of civilisation —those on which the Eskimo depends for his existence and those which form the raw material for the Parisian designer. Indirectly the fur traders were largely responsible for beginning the opening up of Canada and Siberia, for " furs " are frequently associated with " firs," and the earliest settlements were fortified trading posts. In this industry the modern firearm has done its work too well, so that the 18,000 sable skins handled by Irkutsk (Siberia) in 1836 had by 1890 dwindled to 80. As a result of the widening gap between supply and demand, attempts to develop fur-farming are increasing, especially in connection with the silver fox. Nor is this all, for the furrier carries on where the breeder leaves off, and produces strange hybrids such as the mink-marmot, which no naturalist will ever recognise, while the coney is no longer " unclean," modern chemicals having given it its entrée into the world of fashion.

Clothing, however, is more usually made from some artificially prepared fabric. The local raw materials for clothing those living in the temperate regions, and consequently in need of aid against the climate, are limited to wool and flax. The simplest fabric to make is felt, which requires a minimum of skill, the natural grease and scaly nature of the wool fibres matting themselves together. Felt has, however, obvious disadvantages for garments, having no pretensions to style or freedom of movement. Flax has been used from very early times, but the cost of preparing the fibre is so high that its cultivation is not so widespread as formerly, the chief areas being Northern Ireland, Belgium, and the countries bordering the south and east of the Baltic Sea.

THE PALM-LEAF EXCHANGED FOR A COTTON GOWN

COTTON began to make serious inroads into the established linen and woollen industries of Great Britain in the course of the eighteenth century, but it was not until 1774 that it became legal for cloth to be made entirely of cotton. With the invention of machine looms and, later, the great improvements in ocean transport, cotton increased rapidly in importance. In tropic regions clothing is not a necessity, at least for the native, and local raw materials tend to extremes; that is, they are either inconveniently temporary of the palm-leaf order or oppressively permanent, such as hair or wool; nor do either of these fabrics lend themselves to the colour and decoration which is so dear to the heart of the native. Thus trade in cotton goods, thin, gaily-coloured, and cheap enough for the Indian, Chinese, and African millions to buy, developed rapidly.

Cotton is another tropical crop, though not quite so rigidly so as sugar-cane, the chief areas of production in order of quality being Egypt, the southern United States, and India. While the rust and smut fungi may attack wheat, and maize fields may be ravaged by pests varying in size from the stalk-boring insect to baboons, the farmer still holds the trump cards. With cotton, however, a win for the grower is far from being a certainty. The opponent in this case is the boll-weevil, a small grey beetle. This pest crossed the Mexican border and invaded the cotton-growing areas of the southern United States, destroying millions of pounds' worth of cotton every year. In fact, it has consolidated its gains to the extent of forcing the growers in this once exclusively cotton area to change to producing a variety of crops, so that a weevil victory in any one year need not necessarily be decisive. The depredations of the beetle received unexpected re-inforcement in over-production, the 1933 carry-over being three times the normal amount. The United States Agricultural Adjustment Administration took drastic action, and no less than ten and a half million acres, more than a quarter of the total United States cotton acreage, were ploughed under, the areas for future years being strictly limited to probable requirements.

Both flax and cotton have a useful by-product in the oil yielded by their seeds. Cotton-seed has to be combed out of the boll fibres, but the flax plant is grown for linen fibre, in the cool temperate climates, or for linseed in warmer regions such as the central Argentine. Cotton-seed is used in a variety of manufactures, such as cattle-cake, fertiliser, soap, oil-cloth, candles, packing sardines, etc.

THE SILK WORM LOSING HIS MARKET : A VEGETABLE RIVAL PRODUCES RAYON

SILK has been accepted for five thousand years as the finest of the fabrics, but an immense amount of labour is necessary for its production. Its supremacy, however, has been threatened, especially since the War, by the rapid development of rayon or artificial silk. In both silk and rayon the raw material, cellulose, is the same, though the resulting product is different, as an animal fibre is produced in the one process and a vegetable one in the other. The forests of Canada and also of Scandinavia are the principal sources of supply of cellulose. So fast has the industry grown that both France and Italy now produce more rayon than silk ; the Netherlands, especially in proportion to its population, is also a major producer.

Great as is the havoc wrought by the drapers in the Canadian forest, the onslaughts of the newspaper proprietors are even more devastating, vast quantities of timber being required annually for paper-pulp. This comparatively new development of using timber in pulp state has the advantage that smaller and less carefully selected timber now has a market value, with a resulting absence of waste. A still more recent modern miracle, which is being developed in the United States, is to reverse the process and make wood out of pulp ; any waste vegetable matter, such as weeds or sugar-cane or maize refuse, is used, and can be synthesised into timber of almost any required degree of hardness and in widths no longer limited by the girth of a tree.

While the great northern forests are being conquered for the pulp mills and then recreated in a civilised symmetry, the equatorial forests still hold their own. It is true that much of the sandal-wood has vanished from the Pacific, and heavy inroads have been made into the ebony and mahogany giants of the Guinea Coast and the West Indies, but in the swamp-protected forest wildernesses of the Congo and Amazon basins man has, if anything, retreated. In England as late as the eighteenth century it took as much as three years to take timber from the heart of the Weald of Kent down to the coast, where it was required for shipbuilding, and, even with modern methods of transport, distance is still an overwhelming factor in the exploitation of these tropical forests.

Rubber, however, is a different matter, for it is obtained by incising certain varieties of trees until a milk-like fluid, called latex, exudes from the cut, the latex flow usually lasting for about half an hour. This latex has sometimes been wrongly regarded as sap, whereas it is more nearly equivalent to the resin of a pine tree. The latex has to be cured soon after gathering, in order to prevent it from decomposing.

SMUGGLING THE RUBBER PLANT OUT OF BRAZIL

IN the early stages of the industry—up to 1900—the world's rubber requirements were met by wild rubber from the Congo and Brazilian forests. Native methods were wasteful, frequently resulting in the destruction of the trees, and their methods of smoke-curing were equally crude ; the supply was therefore not only irregular, but variable in quality. With the development of vulcanisation (treating rubber and sulphur with or without heat) and the growth of the motor industry, the demand for rubber greatly increased. The Brazilians were naturally not at all anxious to lose such a valuable monopoly, and it was only with great difficulty that a supply of the precious seeds was smuggled out of the country and conveyed to Kew. The resulting young plants formed the nucleus of the rubber plantations of Malaya. To-day wild rubber accounts for barely 2 per cent. of the world-production.

The price of rubber after the War soared to over four shillings a pound, and the existing rubber companies made enormous profits. Wholesale planting, especially in Malaya, naturally followed. The fact that the rubber tree does not bear fully until seven years after it has been planted made sensitive reaction between demand and supply impossible, and the inevitable happened. The demand was overestimated and the price of rubber fell headlong. The British growers agreed to restrict their output, and this temporarily checked the fall in price. The Dutch growers, however, were not party to the arrangement and increased their output, with the result that the British planters found that their sacrifices had been worse than in vain. By 1929 the average price of rubber had dropped to 10¼d. a lb., and the weaker and less well-managed estates failed and were bought up by the larger concerns. Three years later the price had slumped to under 2½d., which was less than half the cost of production. This forced 98 per cent. of the rubber-producing areas of the world to unite in another restriction scheme, which became effective in June 1934, and the price of rubber reacted accordingly and reached an economic figure.

The Dutch East Indies and Malaya to-day produce about 85 per cent. of the world's supply of rubber, and of this 45 per cent. is produced in native plantations, and the remainder in estates under European management. The native plantations are inefficiently managed, judged by European standards, but their overhead costs are negligible, and, when conditions are bad, the natives can still exist on their own home-grown supplies of food. The European has improved the yield of his trees from 300 lb. an acre to over 1200, but taxes and overhead charges are high, and, if he fails to make a profit, he is ruined. It remains to be seen which method best survives modern competition.

THE MACHINES TAKE CHARGE

TEXTILE and other industries remained until towards the end of the eighteenth century on a small scale. While this was partly due to the primitive methods of transport, which made the import of raw materials difficult and expensive, and to other factors, the most important cause lay in the limited sources of power available. Even when industries advanced beyond the cottage stage, they were dependent on hill streams for turning the machinery. In other words, power was not transportable, but limited in quantity to what was available at any given spot. The development of coal for power solved both these difficulties and was the foundation for the Industrial Revolution, though coal itself would have been of little use without the invention of the steam engine.

As the demand for coal developed, it began to be appreciated that different types of coal had different uses. Thus at the top of the scale (as regards heating value) comes anthracite, which has the further advantage of being smokeless. The most extensively worked seams are those of South Wales and Pennsylvania (U.S.A.), but there are large deposits in northern China and south Russia. Below anthracite in the heating scale come the steam coals, which are also comparatively smokeless. Next to these are the coking coals, which are important in the iron and steel industry. The iron ores are smelted in blast furnaces, which are sometimes eighty feet high, and the coke (which is mixed with the iron ore) has to be strong enough to resist crushing under this combined weight of coke and ore, since otherwise no air could get through and the furnace would be choked. Then follow the gas coals, which, as their name implies, yield more gas, and are therefore still more smoky. Last of all are the lignites or brown coals.

The economic supremacy of Britain in the nineteenth century was based on having a supply of all these coals (lignite excepted), while some of the fields, notably those of South Wales and Durham, were situated on the coast or within reach of navigable waterways, and formed the basis of an important export trade. Thus, in 1913, a third of the British coal output was exported.

Other countries had, however, been developing their own resources, and in 1899 Great Britain yielded to the United States her position as leading coal producer of the world. Coal-mining Newcastles sprang up in Natal and New South Wales, besides lesser ones in the United States and New Zealand, and the output of the larger European countries advanced rapidly. The British coal exports in 1923 touched the 1913 figure, but by 1931 they had declined by 28 per cent.

This decline, which is absolute as well as relative, is due to a variety of causes. The Dominions, including India, have become self-supporting (except for anthracite), and new mining centres have developed in the Netherlands and Spain, both formerly good customers of Great Britain. Russia, too, has become an exporter rather than an importer. The most easily-worked British seams have become exhausted, and deeper mines are more expensive to work. The plant available is also less efficient than that of the newer mines or those of northern France and Belgium, reconditioned after the War. The use of both water-power and petroleum has increased enormously. Scientific research has made a ton of coal go very much farther than formerly ; thus, since the War, the number of units of electricity which can be generated from a given quantity of coal has practically doubled.

While coal as a commodity is less prosperous than formerly, it still plays a very important part in British industries in providing a high grade, but cheap, form of power essential for the numerous manufactures which form the basis of the British export trade. Thus nearly three tons of coal are still required to produce one ton of finished steel, while the important chemical industry is another large consumer.

We have seen how modern economic pressure has forced all industries to consume their own leavings. The coal industry is an outstanding example of this, for there seems to be no end to the possible by-products. A few of the more outstanding include gas, ammonia, tar, benzol, creosote, solvents for paints, pitch, ink, explosives, and an innumerable array of dyes and drugs.

Apart from by-products, the latest development in the coal industry is the increasing use of lignite. These brown coals have too low a heat value to be worth the cost of transporting for any distance from the mines. The development of electricity generation has, however, made it possible for them to be used at the source of supply, and the power generated can readily be passed to the consumer by cables on the grid system. Great Britain is lacking in this fuel (except for a small patch in south Devon), but Saxony has vast, easily-mined supplies. Whereas, before the War, Berlin actually obtained most of its fuel from England, these lignite fields now form an important fraction of the home-produced fuel which has displaced this foreign supply. Melbourne (Australia) also obtains its electricity from lignite beds to the east, and Bohemia, central Canada, and the United States are also developing their important supplies.

WATER, THE STARTING-PLACE OF MANY INDUSTRIES

WATER-POWER has been used from early times, if only to drive the irrigation wheels in the drier countries of the East. In modern times it has been developed from the simple flour mill into the starting-place for many industries which later rose to their full importance on coal. A map of central England shows how many towns are situated where a Pennine stream leaves the hills, and on the opposite side of the Atlantic the streams of New England are even more important as nuclei, owing to the absence of coal in the vicinity to support them. This is well illustrated by the cotton Manchesters of Lancashire and New Hampshire. Farther south there is an abrupt change of slope before the rivers of the eastern Appalachians finally meet the coastal plain, and this " fall line," as it is called, has also given birth to an important chain of manufacturing towns.

Water-power, to be effective, requires a climate with a heavy and evenly distributed rainfall. Impermeable rock is also an advantage, especially if reservoirs have to be constructed. Rainfall tends to be heaviest in hilly country. Hence water-power usually suffers the disadvantage of being most plentiful where the number of consumers is low, the Niagara Falls, with their magnificent reservoir of the Great Lakes, being a notable exception. Full advantage could not, therefore, be taken of water-power until the development of hydro-electricity, which not only converted it into a more con-venient form of power, but made possible its distribution over a wide area. The most recent development of this is seen in the grid system, in use, for example, in Great Britain, Italy, and the Punjab. This system depends on the use of a number of power stations, some based on water-power and some on coal, inter-linked so as to be mutually sup-porting.

It is a common fallacy to suppose that water-power costs " nothing," but the cost of collecting and conveying it to the turbine stations is generally great, and labour, interest on capital, and depreciation all mount up, while the cost of producing electricity by coal has been more than halved since the War.

Hydro-electricity is of special importance in connection with the production of aluminium from its ores, owing to the high working temperatures (of the order of 1400° F) necessary, nine units of electricity being require for the production of one pound of the metal.

Hydro-electricity is naturally most highly developed in mountainous countries where coal is scarce, such as Japan, Norway, and New Zealand, while Sweden and Switzerland have the additional advantage of natural lakes to regulate their supplies of water. In fact, even flat Denmark now has its electricity supply from Sweden, and the plains of Russia are fed by the largest hydro-electric power station in Europe, that on the lower Dneiper. Tibet, too, has so far forgotten its traditions as to import over the 17,000 ft. passes of the Himalaya electrical equipment for the illuminating of the once Forbidden City of Lhasa.

PETROLEUM TAKES ITS PLACE IN INDUSTRY

THE peasants of Romania had long been accustomed to use mineral oil seepages to grease the axles of their carts, and primitive wells were sunk and oil raised in leather bottles or barrels by very much the same methods that are still in vogue amongst the natives of Burma to-day. By the 'sixties of last century, however, the Pennsylvania industry had started ; under company control much deeper wells were possible, and the commercial career of the third great source of power had begun in earnest.

Petroleum is usually derived, on much the same principle as artesian water, from certain beds of porous rock sandwiched between other impermeable layers. The lattice-work drilling tower or " derrick " is set up over a site recommended by a geologist, and drilling continues until a pocket is struck or until failure is admitted. If all goes well, the pipe is capped with a valve which controls the flow. Sometimes, however, the oil gushes out with such force that the well " blows wild," when it may envelop the entire neighbourhood in an unpleasant and dangerously inflammable spray of oil before it can be got under control. Occasionally, worse may befall and the gusher catches fire ; such fires fed by gas and oil at high pressure may burn for days, weeks, and even months, the record being held by a Romanian well which blazed for twenty-eight months.

While an artesian well, according to the more generally accepted theory, is continually being replenished, there is for an oil well a very definite limit. The scientist is faced with few more anxious questions than " How long will the world's reserves of oil last ? " but early estimates have been so completely discredited by subsequent production figures, that few will venture on the most tentative forecasts. A coal seam can be measured and its probable extent judged with fair accuracy, but an oil pocket may yield oil for days or may continue for years until, without warning, a rush of water through the pipe instead of oil proclaims the end.

California struck oil in 1892 in the most accessible place possible—the coast—and an oil boom followed. Oil discoveries followed apace and derricks sprang up in unexpected corners of the world, from the tropic shores of Mexico to the fog-cursed island of Sakhalin on the eastern border of Asia, in the deserts of Iran and 'Iraq, and among the rain-drenched hills of Burma and Assam. Scanty as are its coal resources, the southern hemisphere seems to have fared even worse in the matter of petroleum, as, apart from the Dutch East Indies, only the Argentine and Peru have a few wells in production. On the other hand, the United States is exceptionally well endowed with productive fields in Pennsylvania in the east and others in the middle west and south. One of the most recent discoveries was that of Oklahoma City, which in December, 1928, was transformed from an attractive market town into an oil metropolis, which sacrificed to the new god its municipal golf course as well as a hospital and a school, anything, in fact, which happened to be above an oil pocket.

Exploitation of oil, especially in the United States, has been very wasteful. Once oil is struck speculation in land becomes rife, and owners of adjacent plots sink wells in an endeavour to tap the same pocket, lest their oil be drained from below their feet. Thus two or more wells are sunk in place of one, and, as the depth may be 6000 feet or more, the waste of money is apparent. Absence of control led to wholesale selling to obtain a quick return while the oil lasted, and the inevitable over-production and depression of prices followed.

HOW MUCH OIL IS THERE IN BRITAIN ?

WITH this lesson before them, it is not surprising that the British Government should make certain that oil within their territory, if and when discovered, should be under State control. So far the total yield of oil to be controlled is some sixty tons per annum from a well in Derbyshire, though there is evidence of small quantities elsewhere. There are, however, important deposits of oil-shale in central Scotland which have been worked since 1851, but the price of petroleum does not make oil-shale an attractive economic source at the present time ; these deposits form a valuable reserve for the future, especially in view of the fact that only 2 per cent. of the world output of petroleum comes from sources within the British Empire, and the British navy is now almost wholly dependent on imported fuel.

When petroleum is heated, the more volatile gases escape first, and can be collected and cooled into liquid form again. The lightest of these include ethers, alcohols, and various solvents ; then, at higher temperatures, follow petrol, illuminating oils, Diesel engine fuel, wax for insulating, and candles, lubricating oils, vaseline, and asphalt.

The pressure which forces the oil to the surface from a depth is due to the presence of gas associated with the petroleum. If water is present in the oil pockets, the oil, being lighter, forms a layer above it, and the gas, if present, collects over this. The gas is prevented from escaping by the impermeable strata over the pocket, and, unlike water or petroleum, is capable of almost indefinite compression. This overlying gas layer is frequently made use of in the United States for power purposes, the price of natural gas being sometimes as low as 2d. a thousand cubic feet, a figure which contrasts strongly with the 4s. or so charged for coal-produced gas.

This natural gas may be due to steady decomposition of the shale bed of the pocket, or may be automatically released from the petroleum layer (when present) by the reduction of the pressure, but, whether this is the case or not, the supply is sufficiently permanent for it to be worth while to connect New Orleans, St. Louis, and other towns with the gas fields by 22-inch pipe lines. Natural gas is ideally suited, both by its cheapness and ease of management, to the manufacture of glass, and is utilised for this purpose both in Pittsburg and in Romanian Transylvania. There is even a small, regularly-used supply at Heathfield in Sussex, but Europe as a whole is as poorly off for petroleum products as it is rich in coal.

TREASURE FROM THE EARTH : THE MINERALS

THESE power resources would, however, be useless, were minerals not available which make it possible to convert the power into useful work. Of these, much the cheapest and most widely used is iron. The extraction of iron from its ores requires carbon and a moderately high temperature. In the Middle Ages the only form of carbon available for smelting was charcoal, a method which is still in use for the highest grades of Swedish steel, which are among the best in Europe. As an acre of forest is required to smelt only three tons of iron, and, as by Elizabethan times iron was already being smelted on a large scale in the Weald and in south Wales, the forests had to be protected by Act of Parliament, and the industry consequently declined.

The substitution of coke for charcoal, about 1750, gave a great impetus to the industry, which was further stimulated by the enormous demands made by the Industrial Revolution in connection with the development of railways and steamships, and Britain rapidly rose to world supremacy in iron. Cast-iron was brittle and wrought-iron expensive to manufacture, so the development of steel (iron containing up to about 2 per cent. of carbon), after the first half of the nineteenth century, marked another important step forward, aided by improved methods of smelting. In 1875 Great Britain was producing half the world's supply of iron. Iron is not only heavy to transport, but is widely distributed throughout the world, so, as with coal, other countries developed their supplies, until to-day Great Britain produces only one quarter of the output of the United States alone.

Just as it would be wasteful of time and energy if every house in a town were to bake its own bread, so in almost all forms of industry, it is cheaper to work on the largest scale that is consistent with the demand for whatever product is concerned. The mining industry is no exception to this rule. As it requires roughly 3 tons of coal to smelt 2 tons of iron ore, the ore usually tends to move towards the coalfields. The richer the ore is in iron, the less unwanted surplus matter there is to transport. Hence the possessors of high-grade ores, such as Sweden and northern Spain, which have, however, inadequate coal resources for treating the ores themselves, find a ready market in the coal-owning countries such as Great Britain and Germany. Both the varieties of steel and their uses have been greatly extended of recent years. Once rare metals such as manganese, nickel, chromium, cobalt, tungsten, etc. are now alloyed with iron to produce steels which are tougher or ligher or stronger than those produced from simpler form las, while the invention of stainless or rustless steel has been, perhaps, the most important advance of all.

WESTERN TRADE ENCIRCLES THE WORLD

PRIMITIVE man was self-supporting in the same way that the less civilised native races are to-day. As soon as his wants exceeded this simple minimum, trade began. Gold, copper, tin, and amber all featured early in the Greek trade of the Mediterranean, as well as purple cloths from Sidon and foreign slaves. Trade currents were naturally strongest between regions with different natural products, but it must be remembered that America was not available for trading purposes until the sixteenth century, and Australia and most of Africa until the end of the eighteenth or the beginning of the nineteenth century. Hence, for long, the two contrasting poles of trade were Mediterranean and later western Europe on the one hand, and India, Turkestan, and China on the other.

The Queen of Sheba came, not very far it is true, but nevertheless from the East to see the marvels of a Mediterranean capital, but such west-bound initiative was exceptional, and most of the effective enterprise from which trade has developed originated in the West. Thus the people of the tropics and the East have felt no urge to exploit their land or minerals. India and central Africa sent no emissaries to trade their wealth for that of temperate lands. The initiative all came from the other quarter, through the Spaniards with their imperious offer of Christianity for gold, through the daring of the Portugese, the trading instincts of the Dutch, and the imperialistic British. In this way the great ocean highways of commerce came to be explored and spurts of trade began to flow along them.

From about A.D. 1000 the commercial supremacy of the Mediterranean had been in Venetian hands and Venice was the gate to central Europe via the Brenner Pass. The discovery of the Cape route to India (in 1486) short circuited the Mediterranean route. In actual distance between London and Ceylon the Cape route is over 3000 miles longer than that via the Mediterranean and Gibraltar. This extra distance was, however, compensated for by being able to dispense with the process of "breaking bulk" (i.e. trans-shipping cargo) which had to be done on the old route and which necessitated part of the journey being over land. In addition to this, land travel is always more expensive than by sea, and the overland routes were rendered even less attractive by the insecurity from pillage which prevailed along them. The eastward extension of this sea route led to the decay of another of the world's great highways, that which bridges the 2000-mile gap between Samarkand and China, across the desert wastes of Turkestan.

Transport progressed by simple addition as trade developed, but the Industrial Revolution upset the evolution time-table. With the invention of railways and steamships transport advanced, if not exactly by leaps and bounds, at least at a rate almost equal. By the forties of last century steamships had made possible regular crossings of the Atlantic. The first railways were naturally chiefly concerned with linking ports with their hinterlands, but when railway building reached continental proportions their importance was correspondingly far-reaching.

DESERT AND MOUNTAIN CONQUERED BY THE RAILWAY

THE first trans-continental railway succeeded, in 1869, in crossing the formidable barriers of the Rocky Mountains and the Great American Desert, and California became part of the United States economically as well as politically. The first Canadian east-west track was not completed until 1885, and its immediate consequence was political rather than economic. It happened that Winnipeg's first railway outlet had been south into the United States, and the Canadian Pacific Railway was constructed only just in time to prevent the allegiance of the western provinces being deflected in the same direction. Once established, the railways were the key to the whole economic life of the prairies. In fact, the greater part of the settlement which followed was due to enterprise, not only on the part of the immigrants, but of the railways, which not only (in the United States) provided cheap outward (and high return) fares, but also acted as land agents and advertised the regions which they tapped.

The next great continental railway (apart from duplication of the American ones) was the Trans-Siberian, completed in 1902. The motives for this feat were again political, but with a bias that was much more strategic than economic. While the Rocky Mountains were the real problem of the Canadian Pacific Railway, with the Trans-Siberian Railway most trouble was given by the mountains bordering the southern shore of Lake Baikal: while this was being overcome, the railway ran in winter over the three-feet thick ice covering of the lake, and in summer was ferried over by steamer. Under the Czars, man power was of little account and technical apparatus scarce, so signalling was carried out by means of " verstmen " (1 verst=two-thirds of a mile), equipped with flags and cabins ; the winter sufferings of this chain of 9000 human mile-posts are not recorded. By 1929 the journey between London and Peiping had been reduced to twelve days, the cost, first class, being something like £100, and by 1934 the immense feat of double-tracking this line had been completed.

After these triumphs of engineering endurance the conquest of the southern continents was merely a matter of time. The next to yield was South America, where the height and steepness of the Andes more than counterbalanced the relative narrowness of the southern part of this continent. This obstacle was finally penetrated by a narrow gauge track which passes through a two-mile tunnel at an altitude of 10,450 feet. The approaches are inclined as steeply as 1–10 and necessitate the aid of the rack and pinion method in vogue on the Swiss mountain railways. It is hardly surprising that the Chilean section cost £40,000 a mile. As with the Rocky Mountain railways, snow is a serious difficulty in winter, and the cost of providing snowsheds is sometimes as high as £10,000 a mile ; in fact it was not until 1919 that the trans-Andean railway was kept open at all seasons. The railway altitude record is, however, held by Peru, where the Andes are crossed at an elevation of no less than 15,665 feet.

A DISAPPEARING RAILWAY BEATEN BY THE DESERT

THE Australian trans-continental railway, completed in 1917, is remarkable chiefly for its monotony, as it includes 350 miles without a curve, across the Great Australian Desert. Just as the Canadian Pacific Railway was built with a view to uniting British Columbia to the rest of Canada, so this Australian railway was made a condition of West Australia's joining the Commonwealth. The projected north-south railway has been completed as far as Stuart in the centre of the continent, where it serves a settlement of some five hundred white people. Its 988 miles from Adelaide have cost something like £6000 a mile, and the undertaking must be regarded as having been sponsored by political argument rather than economics. The country through which the last half passes is such that, when the line is submerged by sand, it is sometimes cheaper to build a new line over the top of the old one rather than disinter it.

Few transport feats have had noisier heralds than the Cape-Cairo Railway, but its protagonists, if they studied any map at all, had been blinded by the red of a political one until they failed to grasp the significance of one portraying population density or even relief. Now that Egypt is no longer under direct British protection, and atlas red in northern Africa has faded to pale pink, even the casual newspaper reader has begun to realise that people want to get into or out of Africa and not through it, except in search of long distance air records. The first African transcontinental railway was less ambitious, but severely practical, and followed the east-west model of the earlier continents. The opening of the Benguela Railway in 1931[1] not only provided a western outlet for the Belgian and

British copper mines of central Africa, but linked Lobito Bay on the west with Beira on the east, both ports being in Portugese territory.

A frequent source of hindrance to railway traffic lies in changes of gauge. Builders of railways in new and undeveloped or hilly countries are usually content with a narrow gauge, frequently of one metre width. This allows of sharper bends and greatly reduces the cost of construction, but also the speed and, to a lesser extent, the carrying capacity. Even the larger gauges are not always uniform : thus waste of time and labour results in Europe from the Russian and Spanish gauges being wider than those elsewhere, and British tunnels, etc, are too small to allow French rolling-stock to travel on any English system. This lack of co-operation is seen at its worst in Australia, where the separate States pay for their originality in choice of gauge (necessitating four changes between Perth and Brisbane) in an enormous annual bill for inter-State trade delays.

Much could be written regarding the development of railways subsidiary to these trunk lines ; of the part railways play in overcoming natural obstacles besides the potent one of distance ; their use to circumvent the forest-screened rapids of the Amazon and Congo ; of the 12-mile tunnel through the Alps ; the still unfinished *Drang nach Osten* to Baghdad and the human tidal wave which the railways daily focus on the great cities of the world.

COMPETITION THE RAILWAYS HAVE TO FACE

To-day railways are being threatened by road competitors with relatively small overhead expenses, and electricity is displacing steam. Railway freights depend on economic circumstances over which the railways have little control. The companies have therefore given their efforts a psychological bias in their endeavour to attract instead greater passenger traffic by means of cheaper fares, greater comfort, and, in the United States and Germany especially, higher speeds, attained sometimes by careful streamlining. In spite of these efforts railway construction seems to be nearing stagnation point, for in 1933 no less than 2400 miles of railway track were abandoned in the United States and only 50 miles of new track laid.

HERCULEAN VICTORIES OVER DISTANCES : THE WORLD'S GREAT CANALS

WE have noticed how the Mediterranean ceased to be the main link between western Europe and the East, but with the completion of the Suez Canal in 1869 it became again a thoroughfare of the first importance. The Panama Canal, completed in 1914, although only half the length of the earlier one, was a still more formidable operation. The intervening land is hilly, necessitating the use of locks and a reservoir to supply them, whereas the Suez is at sea level throughout ; the cause of the failure of the early French attempts was not, however, engineering difficulties, but malaria and yellow fever. The Panama Canal brought the west coast of North America over 6000 miles nearer the east coast.

The dues in both canals are, however, heavy, and depend on the rates of exchange of dollars and francs, for the Suez Canal Company is French, though the British Government holds a controlling share in it. Thus it may cost over £2000 for a 6000-ton ship to make a single passage of the Suez canal and rather less for the Panama transit, although the latter cost two-and-a-half times as much to build. Even in normal times cargo vessels, for which speed is not important, tend to use the older and longer routes, while adverse exchanges accentuate this inclination.

Yet neither of these famous waterways can be cited in answer to the query " Which of the world's canals carries the heaviest traffic ? " Between Lakes Superior and Huron there is a twenty-feet difference in level. Navigation between them is made continuous by the Saulte St. Marie (commonly called the " Soo ") Canal. The enormous traffic in iron ore eastwards and coal westwards, not to mention the lighter freights of wheat and manufactured goods respectively, results in this canal handling five times the annual tonnage of the Suez Canal, despite the fact that it is ice bound for five months in the year. The smallest pair of the Great Lakes, Erie and Ontario, are separated by a drop of 326 feet : the natural waterway solves this by the Niagara Falls, but commerce has to seek other means, and the Welland Canal now allows cargoes from Hamburg or London to be carried untouched a thousand miles into the American continent.

With none of these, nor yet with the Kiel Canal, is associated the world's largest lock. This record belongs to the North

Sea Canal, which enables Amsterdam to turn its back on the Zuider Zee. This canal is larger in section than the Suez Canal, and its lock controlling tidal differences is no less than 1300 feet in length.

WHY THE RAILWAY OUSTED THE CANAL

WHILE these canals play an important part in world maritime trade to-day, the small inland canals from which they have been developed had an even greater commercial influence in their time, for the simple reason that, until the coming of the railways, they had no rivals. Locks were invented in Italy as early as the fourteenth century, but, as late as 1770, the high cost of transport by pack-horse rendered coal an almost prohibitive luxury for the poorer population of Manchester. The growing importance of the coal-fields and their complete dependence on cheap transport led to midland England being riddled with canals, regardless of the hilly nature of much of the country.

These canals played an invaluable part in the industrial expansion of Great Britain, but the different canal companies made no attempt to co-operate with one another, and delays due to this and other causes, such as the numerous locks (*e.g.* 58 in the 16 miles between Worcester and Birmingham), resulted in a crushing victory for the railways. In 1933, however, there was a light revival of interest in English canal transport with the object of modernising the Birmingham-London waterway under unified control.

Another canal which had far-reaching results is the New York State Barge Canal between Lake Erie and New York. Completed in 1825, it not only made it possible for the hitherto undeveloped middle west to be exploited, but, by focusing the resulting trade on New York, established the latter's supremacy over Boston and the other ports of the east coast.

The rivers of the great north European plain, headed by the Rhine, are nearly all navigable for considerable distances, and they have been interlinked by a network of canals, which makes it possible to travel from Paris to the mouth of the Danube entirely by inland waterways. The longest river in Europe—the Volga—is also navigable throughout the greater part of its length, but unfortunately discharges into the Caspian Sea, which has no water outlet, and is little better served by rail. This defect is being remedied by a canal linking the Volga to the Don, which flows into the Sea of

Azov. This link will make it possible to traverse Europe by
water, not only from west to east, but also through an
equivalent distance north to south, from the White Sea to
the Black.

ANCIENT PORTS DESERTED BY THE SEA

WHILE ocean transport has been progressing along with
inland waterways and land routes, the ports, which form
the connecting link between them, have also developed far from
the beaches on which the vessels of the early Mediterranean
sailors used to be drawn up in winter. As we have seen in
an earlier section, one of the commonest sites for a port is on
a river estuary. But rivers are for ever bringing down silt,
whose deposition is hastened by its encounter with salt water.
Thus Eridu, once the port of Babylonia, is now 130 miles
from the sea, and Adria, which gave its name to the Adriatic
Sea, is now an inland hamlet. By 1490 the trade which had
made Bruges famous throughout western Europe had been
choked by the silting of the Zwyn, to be artificially revived in
1907, when the construction of a canal and the outport of
Zeebrugge once again gave Bruges an outlet to the sea. This
process whereby ports seem to move down their estuaries
towards the sea has been hastened in recent years by the
great increase in the size of the ships themselves. A host of
examples might be quoted, such as London and Tilbury,
Bristol and Avonmouth, Buenos Ayres and La Plata, Hamburg and Cuxhaven, Bordeaux with first Pauillac and then
Verdun.

Besides this array of daughter ports, new ones have sprung
up since the War in response to modern needs. Thus the
Gold Coast and Palestine, which formerly had to entrust their
palm oil and oranges to surf boats, have been equipped with
Takoradi and a modernised Haifa, where ships can lie along-
side quays and exchange cargoes with speed and safety.
India's inhospitable coast-line has concentrated her heavy port
expenditure on a few widely-separated centres, but now the
increasing demand for manganese from the Deccan has made
it worth while to divide the thousand-mile gap between
Calcutta and Madras with the fine new harbour of Viza-
gapatam, opened in 1933.

In Europe the Polish port of Gdynia has grown in ten
years from a fishing village to a port of 40,000 people, and
in this period it has amassed an annual trade which it has

taken its neighbour and rival—Danzig—over a thousand years to accumulate. Progress has penetrated to the Arctic coast-line, for the War paid the gigantic price which was necessary to connect Murmansk in northern Russia, which is kept ice-free by the last remnants of the Atlantic Drift, by rail with Leningrad.

The increase in the size of ships has developed another tendency towards concentration on a few large ports as ocean termini or important collecting stations. On these are based smaller vessels which collect and distribute the larger cargoes from and to their several local destinations, just as the post-man is the intermediary between houses and the nearest General Post Office. Such collecting centres are termed entrepôts.

All the large ports are in some degree entrepôts, but some are outstanding in this respect. Thus Singapore, by virtue of its commanding position on the routes between India and the east and south, is a port of call with regular communica-tion with every port of importance in the Eastern hemisphere. This is taken advantage of by innumerable small ports, whose volume of trade, let alone the lack of large harbours, would not be enough to justify ships bound for, say, Antwerp, calling there regularly. London has built up a vast entrepôt trade, largely on account of the world-wide shipping con-nections of its mercantile marine ; even the United States at one time received its supplies of tea through London, of which it used to be said that it was the only place where " any quantity of any goods could be sent at any time with the certainty of being able to find a buyer."

With the growth of modern trade the volume of traffic has increased sufficiently to make it worth while for other ports themselves to deal direct with foreign lands, and in turn they, too, develop as entrepôts for the areas which they serve. Thus, while the trade of the port of London is still increasing, it is no longer unrivalled, for Hamburg, Rotterdam, Antwerp, and Dunkirk, and even the smaller British ports such as Hull, have now grown up and bought their independence.

MOTOR CARS FOLLOW IN THE CAMEL'S FOOTSTEPS

IF waterways deprived land routes of much of their trade, the railway reconquest has been patchy. A railway costs very much more to construct than a road, but railway operating costs are lower. Hence, where there is a large quantity of regular traffic, and particularly if the distances are also large, the railway is the more economical of the two forms of transport. Of recent years, however, the motor-car has come to the front, not only as a competitor of the railways, but as an ally. The dust of the old desert route from Baghdad to Damascus now flies from pneumatic tyres instead of from camels' pads, and motor roads have pierced the forests and linked the lakes of central Africa. Los Angeles and New York, 3300 miles apart, are connected by regular motor services. A through motor road from south to north throughout the length of the New World has been surveyed, and automatic traffic signals already flicker on the forest highway from Bogota to the Amazon.

An aeroplane first flew the Channel in 1909. By 1934 an 11,000-mile Empire Air Mail service was in operation between London and Australia. With progress taking place as rapidly as this, any attempt to give even an outline of the world's major air routes would be out of date before this was printed.

An aeroplane in flight gives a fallacious impression of freedom from the earth. In actual practice the earth obtrudes itself on the organisation of an aircraft service to a greater extent than does the air, or than is ordinarily realised. More power is required to detach an aeroplane from the ground than to maintain it in flight; the design is further restricted by the machine having subsequently to encounter the earth again. Aerodromes have to be established, which is not easy in countries subject to tropical rainfall, which in a few hours can reduce them to the value of a bog. The distance between these aerodromes depends on the amount of fuel the machine can carry, and the fuel itself has to be transported to the landing place. Aeroplanes can cross mountains, but they do so only with a sacrifice of speed and carrying power, besides a certain increase in risk.

Politically there are differences of opinion regarding the ownership of air, though international agreement now recognises the right of one nation to prevent other aircraft from flying over their territory. Iran, having no aircraft of her own, has shown a special taste for maintaining her sovereignty of the air by obstructive use of this principle. Lastly, even when designer and organiser have done their work efficiently, aircraft are still far more at the mercy of the weather than any other form of transport, and an extensive meteorological service is a necessity for their safety.

Air services are limited to freight of high specific value, particularly mails and passengers, though the inaccessibility of the Andean plateaus has made it worth while to use aeroplanes to bring the rarer mineral ores from the interior to the coast. They are, however, not only readily adjustable to a variable demand, but are especially useful in regions where the population is sparse but distances great. Thus a regular air service is in operation up the Mackenzie River of Canada to within the Arctic Circle, while others link the coastal hamlets which fringe the deserts of Australia.

A form of transport peculiar to the petroleum industry is the use of pipe-lines, which are universally employed wherever there is an oil-field with a large enough output to justify the expenditure. These pipe-lines are usually of 8–12 inches diameter, and have relay pumping stations at intervals ranging from 30 to 100 miles, while in cold regions heating arrangements have to be provided to keep the oil sufficiently fluid. Thus oil from beyond the Tigris flows to the Euphrates and then due west via the ruins of Palmyra to the ancient port of Tripoli, once a collecting centre for Tyre and Sidon. A duplicate route from the Euphrates, under British control, makes its way by Transjordan and the Plain of Esdraelon to the port of Haifa.

GEOGRAPHY'S PLACE IN MODERN LIFE

GEOGRAPHY has been condemned as a parasite science, dependent for its life-blood on its unwitting hosts. Its enemies deride the need for such a science, and thereby admit their lack of understanding of the demands made by the modern world. The very fact that the roots of geography tap such varied sources, and that it has so recently become recast into its modern form, make it sufficiently informative and, at the same time, plastic enough to meet modern requirements.

Aeroplanes, express trains, and luxury liners have taken the place of stage-coaches and windjammers. The geographical mile has been shortened. Remoteness, the potent factor in the history of the past, has handed on the keys of destiny to proximity, and allowed the nations of the world to surge in upon a common stage. India is no longer inaccessible from the Mother Country, and the Viceroy flies home for his term of leave. Australia, the uncertain antipodes of two centuries ago, can speak by telephone with London. This new interaccessibility of the countries of the world has permeated even the realm of sport—cricket, tennis, and athletics becoming international concerns.

In the modern world travel is no longer the preserve of the adventurous. It is now possible to winter in tropical sunshine, to return for a few weeks to the busy metropolis before setting off to see the glories of the midnight sun in northern latitudes. World-wide travel is not only the pastime of the wealthy. Commercial travellers are no longer confined to the roads of their own land, but are sent out by business firms to display their wares in every country of the world. This is no extravagance, but a necessity in a new and specialised world of competition. Travel enters more and more into education. It is not uncommon for Negro, Siamese, Japanese, and Chinese students to obtain a Western education, competing with their hosts on equal terms, while American and British education are linked by international scholarships.

These forces, which have gradually interlocked the peoples of the world so that their lives, their education, and their trade have become irrevocably interwoven, have also brought in their wake problems peculiar to themselves. This jostling of nationalities demands that everybody should know something of the characteristics and fundamental differences that exist among the peoples of the world. Geography provides such an education. In it the humanistic side is stressed, and the broad principles underlying the problems associated with colour and race are to some extent explained, without being submerged in a swamp of anthropological detail.

It is impossible to understand the problems of Europe without some geographical background. The World War proved the insecurity of the arbitrary political boundaries of history, and in the Treaty of Versailles an attempt was made to define new boundaries on more geographical lines. The disintegration of the Austro-Hungarian Empire into the new ethnological units provides ample proof of this. The task is by no means simple, for economic and ethnological principles may conflict, and it is this clash which has produced the problem of the Polish Corridor.

The self-supporting unit, essential in the days of slow and uncertain transport, is now replaced by countries which are forced by the strain of economic circumstances to specialise in the products to which they are particularly suited. World trade has developed from the simple exchange of goods into a complex organisation surrounded by artificial barriers and embargoes, in which the politician may become the most significant factor.

The growing interdependence of the modern world must be accepted by everybody. Modern education condemns the acceptance of facts isolated from reasons. Economic geography, in that it provides a knowledge of all the geographical conditions affecting the production, transport, and exchange of commodities, supplies an adequate basis upon which a knowledge of world conditions of trade can be built and understood.

HOW GEOGRAPHY HELPS IN EVERYDAY LIFE

GEOGRAPHICAL knowledge can be of assistance in elucidating many problems of everyday life. Even household shopping demands a knowledge of markets. For example, the housewife needs to know the date to expect Canary potatoes, when these will be superseded by the Jersey variety, and at what time of the year the English product can be considered an economic proposition. A grocer's shop presents concrete examples of world competition in the form of bacon and butter. Although it is not essential to know why a pound of butter can travel all the way from New Zealand and yet be sold cheaper in England than butter from the local farm, it is a widely discussed problem.

Some idea of the time in various parts of the world is of importance in these days of wireless and submarine telephone. It is possible to ascertain such facts, but an elementary knowledge of the geographical principles of longitude and time make such inquiries unnecessary. The cruising habit has seized the British nation, and the question, " What sort of clothes shall I require ? " must be constantly recurring. A knowledge of climate can not only save the purse from unnecessary strain, but may also prove invaluable in the choice of location for a holiday.

In these days good maps are sold at popular prices, and every encouragement is given to people to take holidays by road. With the development of map sense, which can be gained through geographical training, such facilities are enriched, enabling a journey to become not only efficient but interesting.

The railway engineers were in thrall to geographical facts long before the first train left the terminus. These facts have now, however, been pressed into service on the advertisement posters, which proclaim the London and North-Eastern Railway route to be "the Drier side of England," and the Southern Railway to serve the "Sunny South."

Hotel proprietors' appreciation of the magnetic value of a good climate is clearly brought out by the fact that Bournemouth has about ninety times as many hotels per thousand of the resident population as Manchester. A Colorado hotel is so confident of its climatic assets that it offers "Free Board every Day the Sun doesn't Shine." A Swiss hotel, on the other hand, paying a subtle compliment to the geographical intelligence of its prospective clients, advertises its winter-sport facilities as being immune from the effects of the Föhn.

THE NEW WAY OF LEARNING

SOMETHING has been said already regarding the "capes and bays" system of teaching geography, though even the experts of that hardy old tradition may often be brought to heel by meeting them on their own ground with the query, "Which is England's only cape?" Older readers will remember the zealous care with which the different counties were enclosed within an even belt of colour: how the many counties marching with Yorkshire or Buckinghamshire taxed the resources of the paint-box to ensure a contrasting boundary throughout: the time wasted neatly underlining "capital" towns such as Lancaster or Warwick to the neglect of Manchester or Birmingham: and how the height of achievement in map-drawing was to make a faithful copy of the printed article. Above all, apart from the limited artistic licence permitted in map work, the one essential quality required for mastery of the subject was memory. Those blessed with the ability to recollect column after column of catalogued facts were successful, and the geographer was on a par with those who take a fantastic pride in memorising railway time-tables to the exclusion of less transitory knowledge. There was as yet no place for the few who ventured to wonder why cutlery should be so inescapably linked with Sheffield or coal with Newcastle.

Gradually maps began to represent not only the country but the countryside. As if by magic, the political shroud with its man-made boundaries dissolved away to reveal the hills and valleys standing out in bold relief. Towns, which in the older maps had little more significance than bushes in a desert, sprang to life as the mind saw the crowded valley roads on market-day meeting at the inevitable junction town. The art of making sketch-maps was developed, not in futile imitation of the finished product, but as an adjunct to make vivid the interrelation of some particular group of factors. Thus geography began to live and to become a vital link between the classroom and the realities of everyday life.

A decreasing number of public schools are still too closely bound by the classical tradition of the past to find room for so modern a subject as geography, and a certain preparatory school exists where the subject is taught only on wet half-holiday afternoons. On the other hand, in school after school, geography is ceasing to be merely a form subject taught by all and sundry, and has become the province of the specialist. He, in turn, is aided by well-designed geography rooms, where an appeal is made to the eye as well as to the ear by maps supplemented by diagrams, models, pictures, lantern projectors, and even cinema films, not to mention actual specimens of many of the commodities discussed. In the teaching of geography the universities have given a valuable lead, for chairs in this subject have been inaugurated since the War in nearly all of them, including Cambridge and Oxford. It is now possible to obtain a full Honours degree in this once neglected study.

THE PRACTICAL VALUE OF GEOGRAPHY

IN estimating the value of geography in modern education, it is worth expressing Sir Josiah Stamp's opinion that " whatever field of business is being taken up the preliminary training should include . . . a much greater insistence on geography than is usual in these days," and that " as regards geography, taught in the proper way and on modern lines with the necessary physical and ethnological, economic, and historical associations, it is at once the most humanising and practical of studies."

Other prominent business men are beginning increasingly to share this view, and this has its reactions in the part played by geography as a training for careers. A competent knowledge of the subject is of obvious value in all firms whose connections, whether as buyers or exporters, extend beyond their own country, and is of particular importance in a country such as Great Britain, whose prosperity is so closely bound up with foreign trade. Geographical training is also an asset in such matters as journalism, the editing and production of certain classes of books and periodicals, town-planning and colonial administration, and a bias towards surveying may lead to more specialistic work of this nature at home or abroad. While the conservatism of the Navy and Army with unconscious irony excludes geography from their entrance examinations, the more progressive Civil Service regards it otherwise. Thus, in the Foreign Civil Service, geography carries twice the maximum number of marks of any subject except engineering. In addition to these there are, of course, numerous educational appointments connected with the subject in schools, training colleges, and the universities.

The appeal of geography to those interested in education is, however, not so much in the actual knowledge gained, as in the development of the mind, so that, whatever occupation or profession may be adopted, there may be brought to bear upon its technicalities a practical and modern outlook, trained to reason with a world-wide breadth of view.

A PATH THROUGH THE MAZE OF TEXT-BOOKS

IN no subject, other than perhaps theology, is there such a vast and miscellaneous literature, or so much that is worthless if not definitely misleading, as there is in geography. A few suggestions may, however, prove helpful to those wishing to read more about the subject. For those whose interest in the subject is at all deep, two steps are to be strongly recommended. The first is to join the Geographical Association, which has its headquarters c/o Municipal High School of Commerce, Princess Street, Manchester. This has an excellent lending library, besides issuing a quarterly magazine, *Geography*; the annual subscription is 10s., or, without library, 6s. The second step is to obtain (gratis) from Messrs. W. Heffer & Sons Ltd., Petty Cury, Cambridge, their list (No. 422) of geographical books, which provides the most comprehensive account of the literature of the subject so far published. Membership of the American National Geographic Society (16s. p.a. ; address, Washington D.C., U.S.A.) carries with it delivery of its magnificently illustrated monthly magazine, but unfortunately the letterpress is rarely of the same high standard. *The Geographical Magazine*, first issued in May 1935, is a successful attempt to combine photographic excellence with articles which are "popular" and informative. A modern atlas is essential. One of the best is *The Oxford Advanced Atlas* (Bartholomew), or, on a more modest scale, Harrap's *General School Atlas*.

General text-books are legion, ranging from those designed to teach a child of five to read rather than to learn geography up to the unrivalled twenty-two volume *Géographie Universelle*, now in course of publication in Paris. While the choice of a general elementary text-book is largely a matter of personal preference and to particularise is invidious, *The World* (C. Midgeley; Wheaton) can safely be recommended, while a useful outline of the subject is provided by Dr Marion Newbigin's *Modern Geography* (Home University Library, Thornton Butterworth Ltd.). For those interested in the physical side of the subject, *Physical Geography* (P. Lake; Cambridge University Press) is a straightforward, if uninspiring, account of natural transformations on the Earth's surface and their causes. On climate, *The Climates of the Continents* (W. G. Kendrew; Oxford Press) is the standard work, though *Climate and Weather* (H. M. Dickson; Home University Library, Thornton Butterworth Ltd.) gives an adequate summary. *The Weather Map* (Meteorological Office) or *The Drama of Weather* (Sir Napier Shaw; Cambridge University Press) is essential to the understanding of daily weather conditions. *A Junior Plant Geography* (M. E. Hardy; Oxford Press) and *Animal Geography* (M. I. Newbigin; Oxford Press) are satisfactory summaries of these aspects. *A History of Geographical Discovery and Exploration* (J. N. L. Baker; Harrap) is a skilful and detailed summary of a wide subject, whose leading events are brilliantly retailed in *A Book of Discovery* (M. B. Synge; Nelson).

The problems of political geography are admirably discussed in *The New World* (I. Bowman; Harrap), while the same author's *The Pioneer Fringe* is an equally attractive account of modern settlement problems. Of the reactions of man to his environment Ellsworth Huntington has made a special study, and his books (of which the latest is *The Human Habitat*) are all very readable, if expensive. *The World Mapped* (J. J. Curnow; Sifton Praed) is a readable account of the development of maps, while *Maps and Survey* (Arthur R. Hinks; Cambridge University Press) describes how the material for them is collected, and *A Little Book of Map-Projections* (W. Garnett ; Philip) is a simple introduction to this intricate subject. *Land Forms and Life* (C. C. Carter ; Christophers) is an interesting link between maps and man. *Commercial Geography*, by Dr. Marion Newbigin (Home University Library, Thornton Butterworth Ltd.), is an up-to-date discussion of the fascinating problems raised by economic geography.

On regional information text-books are even more numerous than on the world in general, but *Europe* (Thomas Pickles ; Dent), written from the viewpoint of modern geography, is better than some of the more pretentious text-books. *A Picture Geography of the British Isles* (Workman ; Woolworth) is amazing value for money ; *The British Isles* (Laborde) is a well-illustrated and up-to-date summary, but for a full account the reader should consult *The British Isles* (Stamp & Beaver). *North America* (Russell Smith ; Bell) is not only informative, but interesting from the opening " Hell is hot. Did you ever wonder why ? " to the last page. There are scholarly accounts of other continents (particularly in the series published by Methuen), but they can hardly be recommended to the casual reader. For facts *Whitaker's Almanac* is bettered only by *The Statesman's Year-Book*.

DEEP INTO THE PAST : THE EARLY HISTORY OF MAN

by ELSIE M. CLIFFORD, F.S.A.(Scot.)

WHEN a historian embarks on a history of recent times he has to search for the truth from the written evidence at his disposal. By studying this evidence, and the evidence afforded by the art and the literature of his period, he is enabled to form what he believes to be a true picture of the conditions of the time about which he writes. But the further back in time he goes, the more difficult is his task made by the lack of evidence about what may seem to him to be the most important things, and he eventually finds, as he delves deeper and deeper into the past, that he comes to a stage in the history of man's development when there is no written evidence of what man did.

Here history has to cease its work, but there is still a vast period to be studied. It extends from the time of man's first evolution from the lower animals to the time when he began to write and record what he did and thought. It is the business of the archæologist, or " Investigator of Ancient Things," to study this period, and the part of archæology which deals with human remains and products is called " Prehistory." The prehistoric period is vastly longer than the historic period, and in it we cannot hope to work out the affairs of man in such detail as the historian can expect to do, for the relics which prehistoric man has left behind him to tell the tale of his existence are few, because time has destroyed most of them. The only things which have survived the decay of ages to any extent are man's flint tools, and it is chiefly to these that we must look for our knowledge of his abilities. They are nearly all we have in the very early stages to supply what the arts, history, and literature tell us in the later periods of Man's existence.

Nevertheless it is possible, as we shall see, by piecing together the clues which have been left to us, to construct a picture of man's early life. A fascinating picture it is, telling us of man's slow rise above the beasts by means of his superior brain ; of his discoveries of how to use first stone, then bronze and then iron to make life easier for himself ; of the birth of his artistic sense, and of migrations and births and deaths in the dim, remote past. When we realise that our own civilisation, perhaps our very existence, owes not a little of its success to the struggles, trials, and inventions of prehistoric man, we can feel a bond between ourselves and the past which makes archæology one of the most fascinating and absorbing of all studies.

Since tools are the most important remains of early man, it is by means of them that prehistoric times are divided into sections, which are studied separately in this course. The chief divisions are set out in Fig. 15, together with the corresponding geological periods and with approximate dates for the later divisions. (The words " Eolithic," " Palæo-lithic," " Mesolithic," and " Neolithic " are all compounded from the Greek word *Lithos* (a stone) with other Greek words meaning " Dawn," " Ancient," " Middle," and " New," respectively.)

WHERE SHALL WE LOOK FOR EARLY MAN ?

As we have noted in the geological section, the Tertiary period of the geologist is divided up into several stages, the last of which is called the Pliocene. The rocks of this system are best seen on the eastern side of England where these Tertiary beds contain large quantities of shells, of a kind which show that the climate was warmer than it is now. The beds are usually called Crags, and it is with the Red Crag that we are chiefly concerned, because it is at the base of this bed that Reid Moir made the most striking discovery of recent years. He found tools which are now generally accepted as being of human origin. Keith has for long stressed the importance of looking for evidence of man's existence farther and farther back, and it is fitting that Reid Moir, who has probably done most for prehistory, should have his great discovery accepted in his lifetime—so often these things are only realised after the death of the pioneer.

In the great ice age there were four major glaciations or cold periods, called Günz, Mindel, Riss, and Wurm (Günz being the oldest). They were so named by Penck and Brückner, who discovered traces of them in the Alps. The names were taken from tributaries of the Danube. In between these cold periods were inter-glacial or warm periods, the glaciers having retreated northwards, when the fauna (animals) and flora (trees and plants) were replaced

Division.	Corresponding Geological Period.	Characteristics.
(English History begins here)		
The Roman Occupation of Britain		Dates from 43 A.D. to 410 A.D.
Early Iron Age .		Dates from the introduction of iron from about 500 B.C. to 43 A.D.
Bronze Age . .	The recent period in Geology.	From the introduction of metals (about 1900 B.C. to 500 B.C.).
Late Stone Age (Neolithic) . .		The age of polished stone, agriculture, cattle-raising and pottery. About 3000 B.C. to 1900 B.C.
Middle Stone Age (Mesolithic)		Dating from about 10,000 B.C. to 3000 B.C.
Old Stone Age (Palæolithic)	Pleistocene Period.	Remains of man and his flint implements (Palæoliths), first in gravels or other river deposits and later in caves.
" Stones of the Dawn " (Eoliths)	Pliocene Period.	The earliest recognisable man-made flint implements.

15. THE MAIN DIVISIONS OF PREHISTORIC TIME.

If deposits are found containing remains of two definite divisions of prehistoric time, the part containing the older remains is found underneath *the part containing the later remains. For this reason the* oldest *divisions in this table are placed at the bottom, the* newest *at the top. This applies to all the tables in this section.*

by those more suited to warmer conditions. England was joined to the Continent at this time and remained so, at any rate, until Mesolithic times. Thus civilisation, climate, fauna, and flora were very much the same in southern England and in northern France. Again, it must be remembered that forests or absence of forests, taken in conjunction with the type of soil, were factors which affected prehistoric man—heavy clay lands were unsuitable for habitation.

Gravels of the Pleistocene or Quaternary period are now divided into two classes, but it is not claimed that one is older than the other. The first division is glacial, because these gravels often contain boulders too large to be carried by rivers and rocks marked by ice. The marks could only have been produced by ice passing over them or carrying them along. Such rocks are often found on high ground, sometimes as much as a hundred feet above the present river level.

The other kind are fluviatile or terrace gravels, and have been laid down in tiers on the flanks of river valleys, generally at constant heights above the present river level. There are a hundred feet, fifty feet, and twenty feet terraces, and they can be observed (but not continuously) in the Thames and certain other rivers. It is in these terrace-gravels that flint implements are often found.

John Frere, rightly called the father of prehistory, was the first person in England to recognise flint implements, in brick-earth at Hoxne, Suffolk, in 1797. Since Frere's time an enormous number of finds have been made, and from the mass of evidence that has gradually accumulated it has been possible to trace the slow increase of man's skill as a tool-maker, and when a new find is now made it is usually possible to tell whether it belongs to an early or to a late stage. Thus the period when man made his weapons only of stone is divided into three main divisions, the Palæolithic, the Mesolithic, and the Neolithic; in the first, stones were only chipped into the desired shape, while in the third they were often carefully ground and polished. In the same way each of these three periods is further subdivided, each subdivision corresponding to a particular style in tool making. Such collections of tools of similar style are often called "industries." Thus in the Palæolithic period we have "Acheulian" and "Mousterian" industries, and so on.

The divisions of the Palæolithic period are given in Fig. 16.

Time.	Name.	Derivation.	Special Type Stations.
Upper Palæolithic	Magdalenian	From La Madeline, Dordogne, France.	
	Solutrean	From Solutre, Saône-et-Loire, France.	
	Aurignacian	From Aurignac, Haute Garonne, France.	
Middle Palæolithic	Mousterian	From Le Moustier, Dordogne, France.	
Lower Palæolithic	Acheulian	From St. Acheul, near Amiens, France.	Levallois.
	Chellean	From Chelles, on the Marne, east of Paris, France.	Clacton. Cromer.

16. DIVISIONS OF THE OLD STONE AGE

The names of the industries are derived from places where important finds have been made.

HOW DID MAN BEGIN TO BE MAN ?

THERE is little doubt that man's ape-like ancestors were mainly vegetarian in their diet, living upon fruits, nuts, young shoots, and the like. The abandonment of life in the trees and the gradual assumption of the erect posture in walking on the ground, led to man (or his precursor) wandering into new regions where new plants aroused his interest and provided him with food. At the same time he probably began to make use of animal food, but before he became a hunter he was what may be described as a food-gatherer. He got what he could in the way of plant food, and probably added to it such insects, grubs, reptiles, birds, and mammals as he could lay his hands on. It was only when he had invented offensive weapons, traps, and snares, fish hooks and so on, that he could become a true hunter, and fisherman. He used outside agencies to aid him in his struggle for existence. For instance, instead of growing a hairy coat when an ice age came along, he killed an animal and wrapped its skin round him. He discovered fire with which to cook his food, to provide warmth and to frighten wild animals from his camp. He manufactured tools to protect himself and to provide himself with food.

Man is a tool-using animal, and it was probably the force of circumstances that caused him to discover that stones made weapons. This led on to the upright position, the use of fire and of clothing. These discoveries made him more independent of the changes of climate and prepared the way for him to conquer Nature. He gradually acquired a memory for impressions ; he retained his sense of smell and of touch, the latter being by far the most important.

It is largely in consequence of his capacity for making and using artificial tools and weapons that man is now the dominant animal upon the earth. In his bodily structure he is strikingly devoid of natural means of defence and offence. He has no horns, hoofs, claws, or large teeth, nor is he specially powerful or fleet of foot. Fighting has its roots in defensive rather than offensive instincts, whilst warfare proper is the child of civilisation.

The evolution of man as laid down by Darwin in his *Descent of Man* is generally accepted to-day. The human brain is still in the throes of evolutionary change. In numerous cases impressions of the interior of fossil skulls have been taken, and the farther back in time we go, the more imperfect is the human brain, the nearer to that of the anthropoid ape.

SKELETON CLUES TO MAN AND BEAST

MAN takes his place in Keith's " family tree " in Pliocene times, at the point where three branches start :

(1) *Homo sapiens*, or modern man.

(2) *Neanderthal* man, named from a skeleton first found in a cave in the Neanderthal opening into the valley of the Düssel, which is a tributary of the lower Rhine. He had a brain that equalled or exceeded that of modern man in point of size.

(3) *Eoanthropus*, or Dawn man. He is represented by the famous Piltdown skull. The first pieces of this were found

lying on a heap of gravel most probably of Pliocene date, by Charles Dawson at Piltdown in Sussex. The other parts were recovered by him and Sir Arthur Smith Woodward as the result of organised digging. This skull is the oldest of any of the human remains yet found in England and has a brain capacity which equals that of modern Europeans ; it is indeed a national treasure.

Of these three branches, two afterwards died out, namely, Neanderthal man and Eoanthropus. It is, of course, only trained anatomists who can speak with authority about skeletons. All one can do here is to state as simply as one may a few facts that have emerged from their researches. The " Java man " is the oldest skull that can be assigned to the human family.

In the Neanderthal group comes the famous Heidelberg jaw from the Mauer sands, the earliest in this group to be found. There are many others : the Chapelle-aux-Saintes burial—south France ; the Gibraltar skull of 1848—Miss Garrod's find near the Devil's Tower, Gibraltar, in 1925–27 ; the Galilee skull—Palestine ; La Ferrasie—Dordogne, south France ; La Quina—south of France ; Spy—in the province of Namur ; Krapina—in Croatia ; and Le Moustier—south of France. Even these do not exhaust the list. Neanderthal man is always found in association with Mousterian implements ; he probably arose in Europe from the stock to which the Heidelberg jaw belongs.

Mention must be made of the magnificent work of Davidson Black. His finds at Chou-kou-tien, in China, are among the most important ever made, and his untimely death is much regretted. He has diagnosed the human remains found there as representative of a quite distinct and new genus of humanity called *Sinanthropus*, which has also been named Peking Man.

The Rhodesian skull from Broken Hill Mine was found in 1921 in the course of mining. It must be remembered that in South Africa there were no ice ages to dominate the fauna and flora, but there were rainy periods (called pluvial) which may later on be correlated with our ice ages. Thus it is that animals extinct in Europe are living in Africa to-day, but we should not hastily conclude that fossil bones out of this mine are recent because they belong to species of animals that are still alive. Smith Woodward gave this find the name *Homo rhodesiensis*, and Keith agrees it should receive the rank of a separate species. It reveals for the first time the ancestral type of man, and in Keith's opinion represents a Pliocene stage in our evolution.

In late Palæolithic times there are many noted ancient skulls of *Homo sapiens* or modern man to be mentioned. In passing, we remember that in Europe there were two types, which means that they must have been in existence for a sufficient length of time to produce this degree of differences, for a human type changes very slowly. The two types are : (1) Cro-Magnon type, a tall race five feet ten inches to six feet four inches, to which belong the Grimaldi people, who had negroid features, as found in the Grotte des Enfants, Mentone, France ; and (2) the Combe-Capelle type of short people of a height of about five feet three inches. At Predmost, in Moravia, there is a closely related stock. The Chancelade type, from which the Eskimo race is thought by some authorities to have descended, is really a representative of the European stock.

The Chapelle-aux-Saintes burial should be mentioned in particular, as its skeleton was found under an uninhabited rock-shelter, in a carefully excavated trench grave, and was surrounded with beautifully-made tools of Middle Palæolithic or Old Stone Age date, called Mousterian (see Fig. 16). M. C. Burkitt [1] says :

> " It would seem difficult not to see in this a careful or even ceremonial burial, the significance of which is, of course, immense. That man at such a remote period should take such trouble in the disposal of his dead shows, at least, that, unlike the animals, he had ideas about the problem of death. The fact that tools were provided for the dead man suggests that he was still thought to be existing somewhere and possibly needing his tools, or perhaps that he would return to reanimate the corpse and that they would then be required. At any rate, all the circumstances seem to imply a belief in some kind of an existence after death, which in that remote epoch is surely amazing." .

THE " RED LADY OF PAVILAND "

A NUMBER of human remains of Upper Palæolithic date have been found in England. In Paviland, on the south

[1] *The Old Stone Age*, p. 127.

coast of the Gower Peninsula, South Wales, a skeleton was found in 1823, which became famous as the " Red Lady of Paviland " (because the skeleton had been covered with red ochre, which was often done), but Sollas re-excavated this cave in 1912, and proved that the skeleton was that of a tall man. Several skeletons have been found in Mendip, and Keith has said that skulls from Aveline's Hole are the earliest round-headed (brachycephalic) skulls yet found in England. Necklaces of pierced shells were often buried with these people, and at Cro-Magnon (Les Eyzies, France) necklaces of sea-shells were found buried with a skeleton, although the sea was many miles away. A necklace of shells was also found in Aveline's Hole (Burrington Combe, Somerset).

At La Ferrasie, in the Dordogne, the dead were propped up against a wall, stones being placed against them ; but at Krapina, in Croatia, human bones were found in a very fragmentary condition, and they are generally considered to be the remains of cannibal feasts. There is good evidence for such feasts, thousands of years later, in the Bronze Age.

The skull dug up in London in 1925, and known as the " Lady from Lloyds," represents in Keith's opinion " a modification of the human stock first revealed to us at Piltdown, in Sussex."

There were a number of animals alive in the Old Stone Age which are now extinct. The earliest elephant of the Tertiary period is *Elephas meridionalis* ; after this, in a warm period, comes *Elephas antiquus*, or the straight-tusked elephant, and with this we find *Rhinoceros Merckii*, the large hippopotamus, the giant beaver, sabre-toothed tiger, and striped hyæna. When another glaciation came, these died out or went south, and we find instead the Mammoth, or the woolly rhinoceros, the reindeer, the sheep, the cave bear, spotted hyæna, and Irish elk—all animals with thick coats as protection against the extreme cold. The next change sees the last of *Elephas antiquus*, *Rhinoceros Merckii*, and the last " Hippos," while the shells found indicate a warmer climate than nowadays.

When the climate again became cold and dry as in northern Russia to-day (called a steppe period), the reindeer, saiga antelope, ibex, musk sheep, the lemming, marmot, glutton, and the Arctic hare and Arctic fox were found.

DIGGING FOR THE TRUTH IN EARTH AND CAVE

IT is only in the ground and in caves that we can find the
clues which tell us the story of early Man. It is chiefly
through commercial undertakings, such as quarries of all
sorts, gravel-pits, etc., that a large proportion of the existing
early prehistoric material has been recovered in England.
Excavations for docks, large buildings, and sewers have all
added their share.

Wood was probably the first material used for making
tools, a rare and notable example, which measures 15¾ inches
by 1½ inches, if such it be, being recovered from Clacton-on-
Sea. It is a pointed shaft of wood, and was found in association with flint tools. Flint is indestructible, and was the
material commonly, but not exclusively, used. Fine-grained
rocks and obsidian (a natural glass) were employed where
those materials occur. The latter is not found in Britain.

Flint is a material which is something of a mystery. All
one can say is that it is a siliceous substance originally derived
from chalk beds. Early man used flint obtained from these
deposits and from river gravels amongst which it has been
washed from the chalk. There are flint mines in Belgium,
France, Holland, Portugal, Sicily, and Sweden, while in
England the chief mines that are known are at Grimes Graves,
in Norfolk and Cissbury, near Worthing, Sussex.

A great deal of excavation has been carried out at Grimes
Graves, and the reader is advised, if in the neighbourhood of
Brandon, which is only some thirty-five miles from Cambridge, to pay these flint mines a visit. They are under the
care of the Office of Works, and are in charge of an attendant.
They certainly are the most surprising shafts, and could not
have been easy to sink. One measures forty-two feet in
diameter, and is thirty-one feet deep. Tools were made on
the floors between the pits, and a number of discoveries of
great interest have been made there. These include an
engraving on flint-crust and miners' picks of deer's antler, which
are now in the British Museum. Their date has not yet
been satisfactorily settled, although it is generally considered
that they are Neolithic.

Flint, because it is so close-grained, fractures in a peculiar
way, and the great problem is to know whether man or
Nature has made the fracture. Flint is hard and it is also
brittle, so when it is rolled along in the bed of a stream other

stones will knock pieces off it. If flint is left on the surface and frost comes, it will sometimes split, producing a " thermal fracture." Nature can do a great deal of chipping and splitting, but cannot strike a blow in one direction and then turn that flint at right angles and strike another.

If a flint tool is carefully examined along the edge, it will be seen from which direction the blows that took off the pieces were struck. Those readers who really wish to go further into this are strongly advised to get a little book, published by the British Museum, called *Flints, an Illustrated Manual of the Stone Age for Beginners* (price 6d.).

We must consider for a moment the " patination " of flint.[1] The word *patina* (which is accented on the first syllable) is Latin, meaning originally a small bronze dish ; and as ancient bronze often has a smooth and richly-coloured surface due to chemical changes, the word has been applied to such surfaces and used for the surfaces of worked flints. Flint, when pure, is colourless, but it is seldom pure and is often black, sometimes grey, and, in central France, honey-coloured. With the process of time it takes a film of white which makes it look blue or grey, and later still it goes white, while after this it can pick up colouring matter from its surroundings, such as iron oxide in gravel. But patina is not a trustworthy criterion of age. Flint tools of the same age are not always patinated in the same way ; the top half of a tool may have been exposed to the air, while the under surface has been in contact with the soil and will be patinated in a different way, the two faces being of different colours. Sometimes a tool has been re-chipped in a later period, and this will give two distinct patinas.

Flint tools are divided up into families, and there are divisions within each family. There are two forms we must notice now—Core Tools and Flake Tools. A core tool, as its name implies, is made from the core or heart of a flint by chipping pieces from the outside of the lump until the desired shape is obtained. A flake tool, on the other hand, is made from a piece which is " flaked " off the main lump with one blow and then perhaps lightly finished off afterwards.

THE FIRST TOOLS : MAN TRIES AND TRIES AGAIN

THE earliest known tools—the Eoliths or " Dawn Tools "— do not look convincingly as though they were man-made,

[1] *Flints* (British Museum), p. 19.

but when we consider the tools of the earliest part of the Palæolithic period, such as the Chellean hand-axe in Fig. 17, we can see that man must have already had considerable experience in tool-making. It is only reasonable to suppose that the earliest stone tools were merely pebbles of a convenient size picked up on the surface or from the bed of a stream. Then possibly the supply gave out, and it was necessary to chip pieces off—(*a*) to make them more convenient to hold ; (*b*) to make points for splitting, etc. ; (*c*) to make cutting edges. These stages would involve a good deal of trial and error before the fine " artifacts," or artificially-made tools, which are included in the Palæolithic period, were evolved.

Eoliths of the Kent plateau type, which were first discovered by Harrison, are natural slices of crusted flint, generally brown and chipped round the edges. The Darmsden pebble industry probably came next—Reid Moir discovered these at Darmsden, Needham Market, Suffolk.

Rostro-carinates (" keeled beaks "—so called by Ray Lankester), come from the base of the East Anglian crag formations. They are claimed as the predecessors of the hand-axe, from which they are not very different, and they were probably used for the same purpose. They are large, and the leading type resembles an eagle's beak. Both these industries are from *Pliocene* deposits, and those that follow are from *Pleistocene*.

Clacton-on-Sea and Cromer are the " type stations " for the industries, which go under their name, while the others are all in France. The " Cromerian " is a flake industry. The flints are bright orange in colour and very large.

The Chellean and Acheulean industries are characterised by a roughly-flaked hand-axe (or *coup-de-poing*, as it is frequently called), generally with patches of the original crust at or near the butt. The flakes removed are large and irregular, and the side edges are generally zig-zag, becoming even more so in the St. Acheul period, but then sometimes the edges have an S twist, or more frequently are reversed (S). They are usually oval in outline. Chellean and Acheulean tools are essentially core industries (Fig. 17), and are found in North, South, and West Africa, Palestine, India, and western Europe. The *Clactonian* industries are for the most part flake tools, and they are roughly contemporary with Chellean and Acheulean.

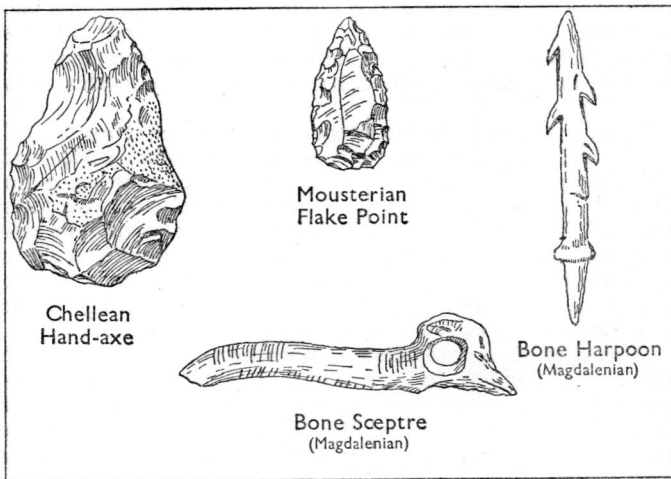

17. SOME OF THE EARLIEST TOOLS MADE BY MAN

The Chellean hand-axe and the Mousterian point are both the work of Neanderthal man, the former being made from a flint core, the latter from a flint flake. The more elaborate bone tools are of a later age and may be the work of true men.

The " Levalloisian " is a flake industry and named after Levallois in France. The flakes were produced in a peculiar way. A lump of flint was flaked all over until it looked like a tortoise (hence it is called a tortoise-core). The under side of the " tortoise " was then struck off, and a well-made tool resulted.

MAN'S FIRST GROPING IN SEARCH OF BEAUTY

WHEN one holds a beautifully-made flint implement in one's hand, such as is shown in Fig. 17, one realises that man as far back as Chellean times had found " form " and was on the way to realising beauty. Salomon Reinach said that the beautiful implements of St. Acheul and Solutré showed an unmistakable taste for symmetry, harmonious lines, and what we may call, in the spirit of Plato, the æsthetics of geometry. The struggle for existence must have been intense when men were surrounded with enemies and had extremely few resources, the most valuable and effective being tools of flint—a poor defence against the mammoth ; yet we find man developing an eye for beauty at this early stage !

Then we come to Mousterian times, when Neanderthal man, with his beetling eyebrows, enormous jaws, and shuffling gait, appeared. He had a definite preference for using flakes, which had been struck off cores, to make tools with. This must have meant an enormous saving in raw material, because it is only when you have obtained a lump of flint and tried to make an implement yourself that you realise the enormous wastage there is ; the making of the tool, however, does not take so long as one imagines.

The climate in Mousterian times became very cold, and reindeer abounded and man lived in rock shelters. Side-scrapers and " points " are the important tools. The former are especially common in the Mousterian period. Their essential characteristic is the possession of a sharp cutting or scraping edge formed along the side of a suitable flake. The " point " is really a double side-scraper, and in outline resembles a subtriangular form of the hand-axe. The Mousterian flake culture seems to have replaced the hand-axe in western Europe and elsewhere, but it is a northern culture. It has been suggested that the flake-tool makers stretched from China to the Rhine, and were a hardy race that could withstand the cold of a glaciation.

THE AGE OF MARVELS IN EARLY MAN

THE culture that comes next in chronological order is Aurignacian, which with Solutrean and Magdalenian are called the Upper Palæolithic. It is not well represented in Britain, while the sudden appearance of the Aurignacian industry in the south of France may be due to a migratory movement or movements. There may have been one such from Asia and another from Africa, or there may have been developments in Europe itself. Some authorities consider this Aurignacian industry is an evolution of the Acheulian and Levalloisian cultures. Next a Solutrean culture comes in to Europe from Asia ; it is characterised by leaf-shaped blades, which are called " laurel leaves," and it was probably from the fusion of this Solutrean with the older Aurignacian that the magnificent art of the Magdalenian age was born, when the flint work deteriorated, but bone was much used for tools.

These three are essentially *blade* industries, utilising long flakes with the longer sides parallel, whereas in Lower Palæolithic times (Chellean and Acheulian, etc.) there was a *core* industry, and in Middle Palæolithic times (Mousterian) a *flake* industry.

The climate had become extremely cold in Mousterian times, but at the beginning of the Aurignacian period it became warmer, and so the period is called an interglacial one. Later on in Magdalenian times another glaciation took place, and it was extremely cold again, driving the inhabitants once more to caves and rock-shelters.

These caves are all of natural formation, and occur only in limestone country. They were made by rivers washing away the rock and forming a valley outside the entrance, or by underground streams finding their way to the river (there are many such in Mendip, Somerset). These streams have produced long winding galleries on different levels, which go in several directions (the caves in Wookey Hole, near Wells, and the Cheddar Gorge may come to the reader's mind). The caverns of this age were very largely filled up with silt, deposited either by drainage from above or by flooding of the valley, on the slopes of which they are often found. It is in such caves that remains of man and beast accumulated through successive ages, and were sealed up. Inhabited caves and rock-shelters are usually on the sunny side of the valley. We know now that man often lived on the shelf, or entrance to the cave, probably feeding and sleeping inside.

In Britain the best known are Gough's Cave, at Cheddar; Wookey Hole Hyæna Den, near Wells, Somerset; Aveline's Hole, Burrington Coombe, and others in Mendip; Creswell Crags, Derbyshire, about four miles from Worksop, Nottinghamshire; Kents Cavern, Torquay; and Paviland Cave, on the south coast of the Gower Peninsula. These and many others were inhabited by man.

THE ARTIST AT WORK ON BONE AND FLINT

ONE English example of palæolithic art comes from Pin Hole Cave, at Creswell Crags, Derbyshire. It is a drawing of a possibly masked human figure engraved on bone

8½ inches long. The drawing is Aurignacian in date, and is considered very like the little human figures at Altamira, North Spain. It is in the British Museum.

Miss D. A. E. Garrod has noted in her *Upper Palæolithic Age in Britain* that there is a development of Aurignacian culture which is called Creswellian (after the caves at Creswell Crags), which went on into Magdalenian times. In these caves we find quantities of tools. There are many more kinds now, and there are also bone and antler ones. Among the flint tools are knife blades, one being a backed blade. It is a piece of flint with a cutting edge, and a blunt back to put your finger on, and is the prototype of our knives to-day. There are points, scrapers of all kinds (side, end, keeled, nose, and round), and gravers [1] or burins of many kinds. (Burin is the French word for graver ; they were largely used for the engravings we are to discuss later.)

The end of the Magdalenian times saw a decline in flint work and an increased use of bone, antler, and other materials ; but the flint blades are often of elegant form. Even those with a minimum of work are long and slender, requiring considerable skill to produce. Notable finds of this Magdalenian period include two sceptres or *bâtons de commandment* (Fig. 17). No one knows what they were used for ; they were probably for ceremonial purposes, but it has been suggested they were arrowshaft straighteners. Both were discovered in Gough's Caves, Cheddar. A harpoon head of deer antler and a necklace of sheels were found in Aveline's Hole, Burrington.

Bracelets were made from rings of mammoth tusks ; beads of ivory and reindeer horn ; lamps from human skulls and from stone ; necklaces from sea-shells, from perforated teeth of reindeer, wolves, and foxes, and from backbones of fish. The horse was much used as food in Aurignacian and Solutrean times, especially at Solutré itself, which proves that the climate cannot then have been too severe ; while lions, bears, hyænas, wolves, foxes, and rhinoceroses were walking about seeking what they might devour.

ANCIENT ART THAT CHALLENGES THE MODERNS

WE must now consider what was perhaps the most marvellous burst of artistic feeling the world has ever seen. Apart from the fact that it is thousands of years old, it appeals

---

[1] For full list, see *Prehistory*, by Burkitt, p. 71.

from its sheer beauty, clearness of outline, and remarkable detail. One doubts if there is any living person who could surpass the artists of that age with only the materials available at the time these paintings, engravings, and sculptures were made. The best examples attain to such a pitch of excellence that it is declared they are superior in some respects to the work of the Greeks.

A Spanish nobleman in 1878 was excavating in a cave at Altamira when his little daughter, who was tired of watching such dull work, walked restlessly about and suddenly cried " *Toros* (bulls)—*Toros*," pointing to the roof of the cave. It was then discovered that this was painted with figures, some nearly life-size, not only of bulls, *i.e.* bison, but of deer, horses, and other animals as well. Drawings of these were published, and people began to search for others, but it was a long time before it was admitted that they were of the same age as the tools found in the caves.

This magnificent art has been divided by M. C. Burkitt into two parts, which he called Home Art and Cave Art.

Home art consists of paintings, engravings, statuettes in bone, ivory, and limestone, reliefs high and low, and sculpture, but paintings rarely survive. Bone tools are often found carved into shapes of animals, or signs or patterns, all of which have reached a very high degree of proficiency. Silhouettes in bone are not found before Magdalenian times— they are very skilfully made from thin pieces of bone cut into shapes of animals. In Aurignacian times true sculptures are frequent and often take the form of female statuettes made from mammoth ivory and limestone, but the well-known horse from the Grotto de la Madeleine at Lourdes is worthy of special attention. These sculptures have a wide distribution, and it is believed that a fertility cult is at the base of the production of female statuettes, but that they gave at the same time artistic pleasure to their creators.

At Sergeac, in the Dordogne, a good painting of a stag of Aurignacian date has survived, and a painted bison of Magdalenian age from Laugerie-Basse, near Les Eyzies, in the Dordogne, southern France, but these are practically all the paintings of Home Art which have survived, besides the ones at Altamira. Burkitt says :

" It was always supposed the Solutreans them-selves were completely inartistic, and that the art which was produced in this period was the work of the Aurignacian people over whom the Solutrean invaders dominated as a ruling caste. The Solutreans, however, were not antagonistic to its production."

One is particularly struck with the genuine beauty of the productions of Magdalenian times—they are really works of art which fill one with amazement. The horse's head from Mas d'Azil is especially fine.

MYSTERY AND BEAUTY OF THE CAVES

CAVE art is even more interesting than the items which are included in the Home art section. Obviously it can only occur where there are suitable limestone caves. There is no doubt as to its authenticity, as it is found in undisturbed deposits associated with a dateable industry and a Pleistocene fauna. Some of the work is covered with stalactite, in other examples the earliest efforts (outline drawings) are covered with paintings, with incised drawings on top of those again. In some cases parts of previously existing paintings were washed or scraped off. This art is found in Aurignacian, Solutrean, and Magdalenian times.

In France and Spain there are many of these limestone caves where the walls are adorned with paintings and engravings—no such decorations have yet been discovered in England. These caves were not inhabited in their depths, and were probably used as cult shrines. Inside the caves the air is very still indeed, and a great feeling of mystery overcomes one on entering.

In cave art ochres were used for colouring, the chocolate to light red being a variety of hæmatite, the orange to yellow being limonite, and oxide of manganese was sometimes used as a blue-black pigment. The paintings then are in shades of red, yellow, and black, and there are no true blue, green, or white. These colours were kept in hollow bones stopped up at one end, examples of which have been found. In one place not only was the red oxide of iron discovered (red ochre), but the pestles of granite and quartzite, which had been used for pounding, and shoulder-bones daubed with red, which had been used as palettes, were also brought to light.

At Niaux a cave is situated in one of the valleys of the Pyrenees, running as a long gallery for almost a mile into the mountain. The sketches there are extremely good. Evidently there were no models, and we suppose that they were drawn entirely from memory. In this cave the scaling of the wall is used to give the outline of the back of a bison ; the black dot is probably a wound. Cartailhac and Breuil suggest that the position of the forelegs indicate that the

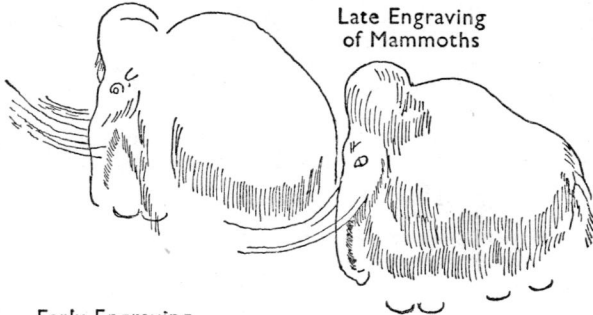

Late Engraving
of Mammoths

Early Engraving
(Rhinoceros Tichorhinus)

Bear of the
Middle Phase

18. PRIMITIVE HUNTER—AND SKILLED ARTIST

The walls of caves in Spain and in the South of France are covered with engravings like these and with paintings in shades of red, yellow, and black. Their beauty is a high tribute to the skill and imagination of early man.

consequences were serious. The objects facing the bison are considered to be boomerangs. There are also engravings of two trout on the floor of this cave.

MAGICIAN'S CHAMBER AND SORCERER'S CAVE

As modelling in the round, the famous bison of the Tuc d'Audoubert (Ariege, northern Spain) would be difficult to equal. The cave is very complicated and difficult of access. The visitor must first take a boat for about eighty yards, then scramble up into a chamber hung with white stalactites. In the corner there is a narrow passage, decorated with

engravings of animals, and at the side there is a tunnel-like
opening, reached by a ladder, leading to another passage
which becomes so narrow that the visitor must wriggle
through like a snake ; then he comes to a much larger gallery
which is perpetually damp and the floor is of clay.   On
the floor there still remain the impressions of naked human
feet, quite small and almost as fresh as when they were made.
This is the " magician's chamber."   In the centre are the
magnificent bison modelled in clay—nearby on the right
there is a semicircular depression forming a sort of small
amphitheatre, and on its clay surface can be seen heel marks,
as if some person had been dancing round the tiny hillock in
the centre, indicating that it may have been a ritualistic
temple.

In the cave of Les Trois Frères, near Toulouse, south
France (named after the sons of Count Bégouen, who discovered it in 1914), is the famous figure of the sorcerer.   This
is in the Salle du Sorcier, which, like the Tuc d'Audoubert, is
very difficult of access.   After going through passages, passing
a little alcove where a lion is engraved and where the graver or
burin that was used to do the work was found, we enter a
small chamber, the walls of which are covered with engravings.   At the end there is a sort of tunnel (also engraved).
Leading out of this is a passage to the right which mounts
rapidly, turns completely round, and opens out as a window
about twelve feet above the ground level of the Salle du
Sorcier.   This window can be compared to a pulpit, and
on the wall just beside the pulpit is the figure of the sorcerer
himself, partly engraved, partly painted.   It is a remarkable
combination of the antler of a stag, face of an owl, a long
beard, the ears of a wolf, the tail of a horse, the paws of a
bear, and the legs and feet of a man.   Burkitt says :

> " The position of the pictured sorcerer dominating
> the little decorated chamber and the audience within
> it, close alongside the natural pulpit where the real
> liv sorcerer would stand, makes it impossible to
> believe that the whole thing is not connected with some
> ritual, and, clearly, all the art manifestations that occur
> here are part and parcel of whatever cult, ceremony or
> ritual it was which must have taken place."

Burkitt is of the opinion that some of these examples were
the work of professionals, and drawn for purposes of ritual.

In favour of this argument it is stated there is a close similarity of technique over wide areas, and the same authority thinks that if the whole of these works were examined by competent artists, from this point of view, it would be possible to divide the work up into " schools " as later work is classified.

It is sad that the human figure is very rarely portrayed by these people, because this would have told us so much that we want to know. Skulls are satisfactory in their way, but it would be so much more interesting if we knew what these people looked like, what colour of hair they had, and so on. Hands were frequently portrayed, sometimes with one or more fingers missing. To this a ritualistic significance may be attached. These are almost all early in date.

WHY DID EARLY MAN WANT TO PAINT?

BURKITT has suggested division of motives underlying this art into three sections :

(1) *Decoration*; (2) *Self-expression*; and (3) *Sympathetic magic*. He sets out his reasons in a masterly fashion in Chapter XII. of *The Old Stone Age*. There is no doubt that decoration was the motive when the painting and engraving of the home sites were done, and probably also when the statuettes, beads of ivory, and reindeer horn, etc., were made. Human beings have always loved to decorate themselves with beads, which were also used as treasure or currency. *Self-expression* is also a possible motive. These were undoubtedly an artistic people and could express their ideas to some effect. Drawing is perhaps as universal as speech. *Sympathetic magic* in these times is quite easy to understand. We have before remarked upon the difficulties of early men, that they were hunters relying upon the chase for food and clothing, and were ever on the offensive against animals. There were also the fearful mysteries of birth and death. We know the food supply was precarious, perhaps monotonous, and variety depended on success in the chase.

LOOKING BACK AT AN AGE OF ACHIEVEMENT

WE can now review the situation so far as the Palæolithic period is concerned. From a study of the early skulls we can work out man's place in nature on the lines laid down

by Darwin, and we can see that we started from an ancestral
stem from which others set out, only to fall by the wayside.

Man's tools, of which we have said so little, are most
important. We realise there must have been predecessors
to the Chelles and St. Acheul tools, and it is only reasonable
to accept eoliths as these predecessors. The sequence of
the remaining periods is an accepted fact, but there is so
much more to know. It is excellent that research is going
on in so many parts of the world. Of primitive art, one can
only again say how wonderful it is, and how little we really
know about its motive. Over the bones of man himself
we ponder and wonder how many generations there have
been since *Homo sapiens* or modern man appeared.

We leave this period with pride, because it is the one
that shows the enormous efforts made by early man, without
which we could not be here. Culturally he had progressed
from eoliths to beautiful Solutrean laurel leaves, he had
passed through a wonderful art phase, had learnt to make
useful and beautiful things in bone, and to utilise natural
things which were beautiful, such as sea-shells, to adorn
both himself and his dead.

We can say the people who followed were the direct heirs
of the Palæolithic folk, and we know that the Palæolithic
foundations are the ones on which the civilisations of the
world have been built. With the passing of the Great
Pleistocene age, and the profound change in the fauna and
flora which succeeded, this period of man's history closes,
and the story of the Mesolithic people begins.

THE LINK BETWEEN HUNTER AND TILLER OF SOIL

THE Mesolithic age has not long been recognised as filling
the gap which was known to exist between the hunting
communities of the Upper Palæolithic and the farming
communities of the Neolithic. Till recently, this period
was treated as a dust-bin. If some one found an industry
that could be classed, neither as Palæolithic nor as Neolithic,
it was placed in the then dimly-known period between the
two, which had no real name, but was called either Transitional or Epi-Palæolithic.

Excavations at Maz d'Azil, a cave in Ariège, south France,
the results of which were published in 1895, gave great

impetus to research, and real advance was then made. It is now known from much recent research that the Mesolithic section has seven main cultures (with local variations), which are connected with the Palæolithic and are clearly separated from the Neolithic. It is an interesting period to study from the point of view of cultural modification and migration with changing climatic conditions and all that this change involves. It began a new era; the Great Pleistocene period was over and the climate was steadily improving. The animals hunted by men were moving off from Europe. Forests were springing up, and life had to be adapted to these changing conditions.

Asturian . .	(Spanish) from the Province in north Spain	
Shell-Mound or Kitchen-Midden	Northern Forest Cultures	
Campignian .	(Named after Le Campigny, 25 miles east of Dieppe)	Roughly speaking, contemporary.
Swiderian .	(Polish)	
Maglemosian .	(The Great Moss)	
Tardenoisean .	(From La Fère-en-Tardenois, 23 miles west of Rheims)	
Azilian . .	(From Maz d'Azil, on the northern slopes of the Pyrenees.)	

19. INDUSTRIES OF THE MESOLITHIC AGE

Certain of these Mesolithic peoples were largely food-gatherers. They were forced to live either on the edge of lakes or on the seacoasts, where they ate principally shellfish. This, with fishing, small game, roots and berries made up the diet of these unfortunate creatures, who were the victims of an altered climate, and all that it entailed. They were clearly making a struggle for existence. The dog was the only domesticated animal; there was no agriculture; the population could not have been big, and it is known that the social groups were very small.

There was a loss of the naturalistic art of the Upper

Culture Periods	Characteristic Trees
Early Iron Age	Formation of Peat
Bronze Age	Pine Yew
Neolithic	Beech Lime
Mesolithic Maglemose Tardenois Mas d'Azil	Alder Oak Elm
Transition (Paleolithic to Mesolithic)	Birch Pine

TABLE OF PREHISTORIC TIMES SHOWING

20. *A table showing the broad periods and predominating characteristics of the vast ages of prehistory. The more recent periods are shown towards the top of the page.*

CULTURES, LAND-MOVEMENTS, TREES AND FAUNA

Characteristic Fauna	Land-Movements and Climate
Two Views of the Mollusc Limnaea ovata	Sub-Atlantic (Moist and Cold)
	Land Continues to Rise until Mediæval Times Sub-Boreal (Warm and Dry)
Periwinkle (Littorina littorea)	Land Sinks, Salt Water Enters the Baltic. Land Rises Again Atlantic (Warm and Moist)
River Limpet (Ancylus fluviatilis)	The Baltic a Fresh-water Lake, due to Land Elevation Boreal (Warm and Dry)
Arctic Sea Mussel (Yoldia hyperborea)	Sub-Arctic (Cold)

20A. *Since the Ice Age, when clear traces of man first appear, the climate of Europe has undergone many broad changes, all of which have influenced the development of man.*

9

Palæolithic age, due possibly to the retreat of the fauna of that time. The art which remained was conventional, such as the painted pebbles of the Azilian, and certain antler-haft carvings of the Maglemose culture. Quite elaborate geometric designs have been found on harpoons and antler shafts of the latter culture. Beads, as in Upper Palæolithic times, were greatly favoured, as were pierced shells and pierced animal teeth.

PEOPLE WHO COLOURED THE BODIES OF THEIR DEAD

RED ochre was used in burials, as in Upper Palæolithic times. Bodies were apparently covered with it, the consequence being that the bones became impregnated with red colour. Among the ceremonial burials the well-known one of Ofnet in Bavaria may be mentioned. There were twenty-seven skulls in two nests, showing signs of decapitation. The skulls belonged to old and young women and young men, some of which were brachycephalic or round-headed, the others being dolichocephalic or long-headed. The old women had many ornaments of perforated shells and stags' teeth, the young women a few, while the man had none. Miss Garrod found in Palestine, in 1931, a skeleton of this period which was contracted (that is, the legs were drawn up to the body), on the skull of which there was a cap with a deep fringe of " dentalia " shells, which were found still in position. The Mesolithic industry in Palestine is called Natufian.

The Mesolithic people are not regarded as an evolutionary stage between the hunting communities of Palæolithic days and the farming communities of Neolithic days, but as survivors of a primitive civilisation in a backward region where the Neolithic culture filtered in relatively late.

The flint industries of this period are found usually on the surface of the ground, frequently in patches of sand, but seldom in any stratified deposit. These industries have a very remarkable distribution ; they extend from Scotland to Australia and from Poland to the Cape. They survived in places beyond the Mesolithic period and have even been found on an Iron Age site.

The *Azilian* culture originated in southern France or in northern Spain, and is characterised by flat bone harpoons, painted pebbles, small round scrapers, burins, and microliths of triangular form. It spread via the Alps to north-west Britain and is probably mixed with Tardenoisean. A harpoon of reindeer antler, with two rows of barbs, was found at Victoria Cave, Settle, in Yorkshire. Several have been found in Scotland. In the British Isles the Azilian culture seems to be confined to north Britain. Seven harpoons of deer horn have been found in Oban, Scotland.

Azilian art is represented by painted pebbles. They are ordinary small river pebbles, often of quartzite, and they are painted with red ochre. It is not known for what purpose

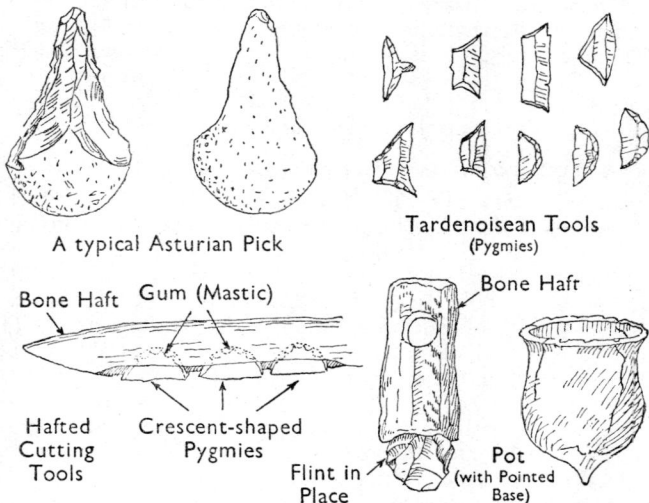

A typical Asturian Pick

Tardenoisean Tools
(Pygmies)

Bone Haft Gum (Mastic) Bone Haft

Hafted Cutting Tools   Crescent-shaped Pygmies   Flint in Place   Pot (with Pointed Base)

21. TOOLS AND POTTERY OF THE MIDDLE STONE AGE

Small tools, called pygmies, and the Asturian pick are typical of this age. The pygmies were sometimes gummed into a groove cut in a bone point, as shown in the drawing.

they were made, but it has been suggested they were money or counting boards, but perhaps they were just playthings.

These people lived for the most part in the mouths of caves or in rock-shelters.

The Tardenoisean culture,[1] called after de Mortillet's station of Fère-en-Tardenois, arrived in two waves, the

---

[1] Tardenoisean tools are frequently called pygmy tools, not because they were made by pygmy or small people, but because they are small tools. It is suggested they should be called microliths—small stones.

first characterised by the "microburin," which is a small tool made on the butt end of a small flake—the type fossil of the Tardenoisean culture—and small tools derived from the Gravette point of the Upper Aurignacian (see Fig. 21). The second wave brought the "trapeze," which is a piece of a flake with two non-parallel sides blunted with chipping —the cutting-edge being the untouched straight side of the flake.   Tools were hafted in a groove along a bone point.

This culture has a wide distribution, and is found with Azilian, with which it is contemporary, in some places in the same levels.   It is found in England, Scotland, Bavaria, north Africa (latest Capsian), Germany, Palestine, Mount Carmel (Natufian), south India, and Australia.   The fauna includes stag, sheep, horse, pig, and dog.

CLUES TO ANCIENT LIFE IN SPAIN AND THE NORTH

THE *Asturian* culture is a comparatively recent discovery in north Spain.   The type fossil is the Asturian pick, which is quite unlike anything else (Fig. 21).   The climate was warmer than in Asturias to-day and perhaps similar to that which obtained during the formation of our Kitchen Middens.

The *Maglemose* culture is found in the Baltic region.   The population lived on rafts on what was then a lake.   Since their occupation, the site has become dry ground as the stools of Scots pine were found above the occupation level.   Here there was very little flint, but extensive use was made of bone and antler, and the type fossil was a small narrow harpoon barbed on one side.   Pierced teeth for ornament occur, and bone tools were decorated.   Amber pendants covered with geometric designs are extraordinary, as are two rough amber sculptures of animals.   Two harpoons from the east Yorkshire coast are of Maglemose type and have been published as such.   There are three other harpoons of this period from the eastern fringe of England, and they are of great interest, one being dredged from the bed of the North Sea which was then dry land, as the flora proves.

Shell Mounds or *Kitchen Middens* consist of masses of shells and other objects thrown out as refuse by man.   These masses have become cemented together.   They were the dust-bins of a people who seem to have lived on shellfish. Pottery, made of poor coarse paste, has been found with either a rounded or pointed base (Fig. 21).   Kitchen Middens in Kiel Harbour are now thirty feet below sea-level.

The *Swiderian* culture is Polish—the type fossil being a tanged flint-point. The *Campignian* culture (the type stations are near Blangy-sur-Bresle in the department of the Seine-Inférieure) resembles that of the Shell Mounds or Kitchen Middens. The Campigny axe, which is a core tool, goes back to Palæolithic days — in fact, the Asturian, Campigny, and Shell Mound or Kitchen Midden cultures can all be said to do so. Charcoal has proved the presence of oak and ash ; and remains of ox, horse, and stag have been detected in Campignian sites.

In Britain the Mesolithic industries have been divided into those of two provinces called A and B.

In Province A the tools show that their makers had no knowledge of how to make the types known as the " tranchet " axe and pick, while Province B contains examples of these implements. Mesolithic remains of Province A have been found in the caves at Creswell Crags, Derbyshire, where one cave—Mother Grundy's Parlour—is considered to have been occupied by the owners for only part of the year. Other Province A remains have been found in the peat near Huddersfield, the Isle of Man, the eastern Counties, south-west Britain, Wales, and Scotland. Remains of the Province B type are found mainly in the east and south of England, a noted site being Kelling Heath near Cromer, where the tranchet-edged axe and many tools have been found. Tatham in Berkshire, Uxbridge and Kimble on the Chilterns have also yielded Province B material.

A LITTLE SPAN OF MOMENTOUS DISCOVERIES

ALTHOUGH the Neolothic age has been curtailed so much, large pieces being swallowed by the Mesolithic age on the one side, and by the Bronze age on the other, we still have about 1200 years remaining to us, from 3000 to 1800 B.C. It has been well said that the Neolithic, or New Stone age, is a very good name for a period we are only just beginning to understand.

Much happened in these comparatively few years. There were four great additions to life, namely :

(1) The practice of agriculture.
(2) The domestication of animals.

(3) The manufacture of pottery.
(4) The grinding and polishing of stone tools.

We used to consider that polished stone axes were the most important things of Neolithic times, but we now know that field monuments and pottery are still more valuable for giving us an insight into conditions of the time. A foreign camp culture was brought into Britain which included pottery known as " Windmill Hill " and another type named after finds at Peterborough. Then came the Atlantic or Megalithic culture which produced monuments of huge stones, and the long burial mounds called barrows. Instead of being merely food-gatherers, the population were now food-producers.

In the first place, men had settled homes, and they soon had more possessions. We know the dog was domesticated in Mesolithic times, and that he would be of great use to shepherds and herdsmen when other animals were domesticated in a world where there were no fences or hedges. Domesticated animals are those that will breed in captivity. This advance is clear at Anau, in Russian Turkestan, where there is evidence that animals were domesticated long before this was done in Europe. The domesticated animals we refer to in particular were sheep, cattle, pigs, and horses.

There is no trace of the ox in Britain until Pleistocene times, when we have a large long-horned wild ox—the original and early ox. Cæsar called it the *Urus*, and it was fairly common in England, but did not reach Ireland apparently. It was an immense animal with very long and strongly-developed horns. In the latter part of the Neolithic period there was another race of cattle whose remains are widely distributed and closely associated with man—the long-faced ox. It is sometimes known as the Celtic shorthorn. It was small, sometimes very small, and slightly built, with horns that varied in length and thickness. Both sexes were horned, and as there is no evidence that it ever existed in Britain in a wild state, it may have been introduced by some of the people who brought the pottery we have already mentioned. From then onwards there were three kinds of cattle—with long horns, with short horns, and with no horns, but the type with long horns, as found at Windmill Hill and Woodhenge, may be said to represent the oldest type of cattle in this country.

Remains of horses are rare in Britain. They are found in the long barrows of the Cotswolds with those of oxen, sheep, goats, and pigs, and from Peterborough with Peterborough pottery, in the Sanctuary and at Woodhenge in Wiltshire. They are also found in north Wales, but it is not clear that the horse had been tamed in Neolithic times.

In the wild state, sheep and goats are extremely alike. There existed in Neolithic days four types of wild sheep from which all our modern varieties seem to be descended. The first of these is the *Mouflon*, with a reddish brown hair coat on top and wool below, only the males having curved horns. It is found in Europe and Asia to-day. The second type is the *Urial*. It is a little lighter in colour than the Mouflon, but both male and female have small horns. The third type is the *Argali*. It is a highland sheep and affords good game-shooting in Central Asia. The fourth type is the American Bighorn. It would seem that the Turbary sheep of Urial stock is the one we find now. It was perhaps brought from Anau, in Asia, where we know it was domesticated, possibly by the people who brought painted pottery to Europe. Goats, pigs, and dogs of more than one variety are found in many Neolithic sites.

We know from remains we have found that the Neolithic men of the Swiss Lake dwellings had barley, wheat, common millet and Italian millet, and many fruits and vegetables, which were probably all wild. They had, however, no oats or rye. It is interesting to note that native Australians use three hundred different wild species of plants, eating the roots, tubers, pith, leaves, fruit kernels, husks, seed, or gum. Agriculture made new implements necessary, and we now find polished axes, or celts, as they are frequently called, and sickles made from wood with flint blades. Slabs of hard stone with stone rolling-pins were used for grinding corn. These people would want shelter for their cattle and storage for their crops. They themselves lived in pit dwellings as described below.

When people live in groups, specialisation begins. It is discovered that one man does a thing better than his neighbour, and so he may be asked to do it for the tribe. Protection of crops against wild animals would have to be arranged for, and in community life a great advance is made because a discovery or an invention can be utilised by, or for, the whole group. This implies also that rules of conduct would have to be introduced to ensure a well-regulated community life.

THE VILLAGE A FULFILMENT OF THE NEEDS OF MAN

IT was perhaps such needs that led to the beginning of our Neolithic village. At Peterborough round huts have been excavated which were sunk into the ground for about 1½ feet, so that a ledge was formed on which to sit. Some rectangular ones are known. Roofs for the round huts were formed by a central pole, and suitable branches reaching from the ground to the top of the pole and lean-to roofs were made for the rectangular ones ; both were covered by branches of trees and skins. At Abingdon, in Berkshire, a trench in which these people had lived, has been excavated.

It is, however, from camps that most of our information has come. Much has been done to show us what Neolithic camps were like, and Windmill Hill, near Avebury, in Wiltshire, has been investigated, and is considered the finest of them all. The distinguishing feature of a Neolithic camp is that it has interrupted ditches—that is, the ditch which runs round the camp as a means of defence has causeways or paths at varying intervals leading into the camp. Windmill Hill is about six hundred feet above sea-level. The earth work consists of three concentric ditches of varying depths. The great importance of Windmill Hill is that the layers permit of accurate dating by the levels at which they occur. It had two occupations, but they did not overlap.

In the lowest level Windmill Hill pottery is found. This is the " type site." Higher up there is Peterborough pottery (named from the type site at Peterborough) ; and higher up still, beaker ware (Abercromby's Type A.). Still higher up and almost on the surface there is early Iron Age and Roman ware, modern china, etc. From the few human bones found we are able to say that these people were dolicho-cephalic or long-headed, and they correspond with the individuals found in the British long barrows. The bones of dog were interesting, and include a complete skeleton. Only one breed (*canis familiaris palustris*) is represented, and this also is found in the Swiss Lake dwellings.

This site has produced an enormous quantity of bones, which prove that these people had very many sheep, goats, pigs, and oxen. Bones of red deer are found, but not of the horse. Pins and awls of bone are common, and there are carved chalk articles of various kinds, pounders and mullers, saddle querns (hand-mills), and rubbing stones (for grinding), which prove they grew corn. The site has for many years been a famous hunting-ground for flint implements, so it is not surprising that this excavation produced great wealth of such articles. The tools include leaf-shaped and lozenge arrow-heads, transverse arrow-heads, chisel-pointed tools, saws, scrapers, knives, and picks. Ground polished axes are found, but always broken and sometimes rechipped. This is surprising in a country where flint could easily be obtained ; the Upper Chalk is in the immediate neighbour-hood, and the flint from it would make excellent tools. That one excavation could produce so much is surprising, and it is fittingly used as the type-station of one group of Neolithic ware.

Whitehawk Camp, near Brighton, and The Trundle at Goodwood, are Neolothic camps which have been excavated. Both of them are on hills, but at Abingdon, in Berkshire, a Neolithic promontory fort on low-lying ground was discovered and excavated.

MAKING THE PATHS THAT LED TO HOME

NEOLITHIC camps are usually on hilltops, above the level of primæval forests, and we may fairly assume that trackways were made at this time, for as culture advanced social life and intercourse began to develop. Before this, trackways were not necessary, as man had no settled home. Prehistoric trackways have been differentiated into four groups : ridgeways, hillside ways, valley routes, and engineered and metalled roads carefully aligned—well represented by Roman roads.

Ridgeways follow the crest-line of the hills. On the chalk downland of south England they appear to be the earliest type of trackway, probably earlier than any of the hill forts. Their characteristic is that of a number of tracks converging and creating deep " holloways " when descent from the highland (in order to cross a river) is necessary.

Hillside ways follow the contours of the hills, on a level alignment just above the spring-line, and may be as old as the ridgeways. The spring-line is the level where rainwater, which has fallen on porous rocks like sandstone or limestone penetrated by joints, is held up by an impervious bed such

9*

as clay. It is then forced to pass along the junction of the two rocks until it comes out at the surface.

Valley routes are usually late in age, but may be early, as when a trackway has to cross a watercourse. Engineered roads are carefully-aligned metal roads.

The " Icknield Way " is an important example of ridgeway. Its course is known from Dorset to near King's Lynn, and it crosses the Thames at Streatley and avoids all other streams. It is not a true ridgeway, but follows the line of the open downs below the summits.

The " Street Way," in Cambridgeshire, is considered pre-Roman and of the hillside way type. It runs from Ashwell to the River Lark. The " Ridgeway " connects the Icknield Way with Avebury, and both probably belong to the Neolithic period. Watling Street, which runs from Dover to Wroxeter, is supposed to be an ancient trackway which the Romans reconstructed, a supposition which is certainly true of many of the smaller trackways in different parts of England.

The " Cloven Way " is an ancient trackway which begins at Totten, near Southampton Water. It runs westward into Wiltshire, and it is thought that the late Bronze Age Urn-fielders, who brought Deverel Rimbury pottery,[1] used this route when they first penetrated England about 700 B.C.

THE EARLIEST ARTS AND CRAFTS

BASKET-MAKING was known in Europe at least as early as the last Stone Age, and relics from the Swiss Lake dwellings show that man was already familiar with the chief technical methods used in the art, but the origin and early development of basketry are unknown. It is possible that matting was the forerunner of basketry, and played a part in its origin. Baskets are made by practically all peoples, savage or civilised, the materials used in their manufacture being the flexible roots, stems, leaves of plants, and splints or strands derived from these sources ; animal products are rarely employed except occasionally in decoration or as straps for suspension.

Woven material was also recovered from the Swiss Lake dwellings. The art of weaving, upon which is based one of the most important industries of civilised communities, is practised by races in a relatively low condition of material culture. Compared with basketry and mat-making, however,

[1] See p. 304.

it is restricted in its distribution, and it is not known to hunting races such as the Andamanese, the Australians, and the Eskimos, nor to many other people in higher stages of culture.

Before pottery was invented such natural objects as gourds, shells, and parts of skulls were used as vessels. The Australian aborigines used skins of kangaroo and other animals for carrying water, cut as little as possible when removed from the body. The old leather bottles and " black jacks " of our civilisation belong to the same series, though they were made of leather instead of imperfectly tanned hide.

LIFE TRANSFORMED BY THE POTTER'S ART

Because Neolithic man had ceased to be a hunter and had become an agriculturist settled in a home, it was now possible for pottery-making to develop. Pottery-making is seldom practised amongst hunting tribes, who make use of utensils of skin, bark, and basketry, which are less liable to breakage during transport. There is little doubt that pottery was a later invention than basketry.

Pottery must have made an enormous difference to life, because it was most useful for cooking and storing food. It did not burn like vessels of wood, bark, and basketry, and it was much cleaner. Because pots eventually became possessions, they were made to look nice, and their makers (usually the women of the community) felt pottery was a great addition. Among people of the lower culture of to-day, to which we may fairly suppose these Neolithic conditions are comparable, all duties are regulated by custom. Women generally make pots and baskets, do the spinning, weaving, and cooking, while men dig the ground, hunt, and fight, and neither must touch the other's work. In Fiji, however, the men do the cooking.

In England on Neolithic sites a number of flint and stone nodules have been found which appear to have been heated and then suddenly cooled, and were possibly used for cooking. These stones were probably made red-hot and then dropped into pots which would not stand the fire, into animal hides lining a pit in the ground, or into wooden bowls. The process of heating stones and dropping them into the vessel would be repeated until the water boiled or the food cooked. This method is known in the Pacific Islands, as well as in

America. Pottery must have made cooking a much easier process.

The manufacture of pottery necessitates a supply of clay. Neolithic man quickly found it was necessary to add sand, ground potsherds, or other tempering material to prevent the vessels from cracking in the fire. Potter's clay may be dried in a hot sun or otherwise, till all the free water is evaporated ; it then loses its plasticity, and becomes hard and brittle. Articles thus produced can be used in a dry climate or for restricted purposes. Thus the Kabyles of North Africa have huge pots of unburnt clay, several feet in height, which are used to hold grain and are kept inside the house.

The surface and colour of a finished piece of pottery depend upon the fineness and the chemical nature of the clay, upon the mechanical treatment of the surface before (or occasionally after) it is fired, upon additions that may be made for decorative or other purposes, and upon the conditions under which it is fired. The ornamentation of hand-made pottery is almost invariably done before firing, whilst the clay is soft, or is only slightly hardened by drying. The colour of it may be red, buff, bronze, or black, and irregularly fired ware may have a mixture of such shades. The inner layers, when exposed by fracture, may often be seen to be of a different colour from the surface, and the interior face of a pot may differ from the exterior. If the clay is baked in a fire which is supplied with an abundance of air, the colour of the earthenware is red. If, on the other hand, the pots are baked in a fire which receives an inadequate supply of air, the pots are black. Pottery can be decorated in very many ways.

Experiments made in plasticene seem strongly to indicate that the intricate articular surfaces (the joints) of the bones of small birds and possibly of mammals were very frequently the tools for producing the familiar " stamped impressions " on Neolithic pottery.

TWO POINTS ON WHICH THE POTTERS THOUGHT ALIKE

WHILE throughout Europe and the Mediterranean region every district seems to have its own peculiarities in regard to Neolithic wares, it is a striking thing that there are two features which are almost, if not quite, universal, namely, the round bottom and the vertically perforated lug (handle). The former is found in the Bacarian pottery of

Egypt, and this is by far the commonest form of base in all Neolithic pottery. The vertically perforated lug was not the only type of handle known to Neolithic pottery, but it is peculiar to that period, and has been found widely distributed from the earliest cities at Troy (Troy iii, 2000 B.C.) right across Europe to Britain. In some favoured cities, as at Troy and in the Swiss lakes, fragments of cord have been found inserted through the perforations, thus revealing that their purpose was to enable the vessel to be suspended. Sinews, thin strips of hide, etc., could be used for this purpose. In Nigeria, where round-bottomed vessels are made to-day, they are placed on the fires and in holes in the ground.

Two main varieties of British Neolithic pottery are now distinguished, namely, "Windmill Hill" or Neolithic A, and "Peterborough" or Neolithic B, Windmill Hill being the earlier. This has now been subdivided at the type station into two parts, the first part being a little earlier and simpler than the second. Windmill Hill is western in its origin, having affinities with a western family from the Rhine and Swiss lakes—in other words, it belongs to Schuchardt's "Leather vessel" family. It is a dark ware characterised by its leathery forms (baggy pots and carinated bowls, the latter shaped with a projecting angle or ridge). It is made of hard paste, is smooth and thin, and has graceful outlines. The decoration, if any, is restrained and limited to neck, rim, or shoulder. It consists of simple lines, shallow grooves, finger-tip fluting, etc. It is frequently found in causewayed (Neolithic) camps, and nearly always on upland sites. It has a wide distribution, being found over the whole length of Britain from Sussex to the Orkneys, and extending eastwards into Bedfordshire and Yorkshire.

Pottery spoons belong to this Windmill Hill family. Examples have been found at Clayton, in Sussex; in Nether Swell Long Barrow, Gloucestershire; and at Niton, in the Isle of Wight.

The other family of Neolithic pottery is named after the site at Fengate on the outskirts of Peterborough. It is highly decorated with cord and comb impressions and pitting. It has northern affinities (Finland and Baltic) and is found in dwelling-places from Jutland and Norway to the Urals and Pontic steppes. The ware is course, soft, soapy, thick, and badly fired. It has thick rims and is decorated with impressions of twisted cord and thread (called maggot pattern), shell edges, and combs. This decoration is in herring-bone and zigzag patterns, which is always in bands right round the body, and the pattern is sometimes taken inside the rim. There are occasional flat bases, but handles are unknown.

Besides occurring in Neolithic sites it is often found in early Bronze Age context (the next period to be discussed), frequently with " beakers " (see Fig. 27). It is never found in the earliest occupation levels in causewayed camps, but almost always in low sites near rivers and coast. This type is the ancestor of the food-vessel and cinerary urns (see Fig. 27). It is found chiefly in the eastern side of England, but extends westwards as far as north Wales and is often found in Wessex. The famous Mortlake bowl in the British Museum, which belongs to this series, is considered to be above the average in quality.

THE CARPENTER'S FIRST CHISEL

At the beginning of the account of the Neolithic period we noted as an innovation the grinding and polishing of stone tools.[1] This was considered an advantage, not because they were pleasanter to look at and to feel, but because they were so much more useful. We know that forests were growing very quickly and that Neolithic man used wood for his buildings. Because of the forests he had to live on the tops of hills, but he found he needed more land. Before he could use it he had to clear the timber, and he then discovered that flint tools which were flaked in the usual manner were sharp enough, but were brittle for this continuous heavy work. He somehow discovered he could grind and polish flint and such rocks as diorite or even close-grained granite. He then obtained an edge that was tough as well as sharp, and could be resharpened. This was the carpenter's first chisel. As long ago as 1879 some Danish prehistorians experimented with Neolithic stone axes, and found it was quite possible for forest fir trees to be felled and worked without the aid of any other tool. Flaking did not go out of fashion by any means, and sometimes a tool will be partly flaked and partly polished.

These stone axes have been discussed by Reginald A. Smith of the British Museum, and he has shown that the axes with a *circular* section at the butt end are the earliest, and that they gradually flatten out until the butt end is *oval* in section.

[1] See p. 262.

The development of these axes has also been worked out in great detail in Scandinavia, where it has been possible to prove the successive forms from excavations of habitation sites, shell-mounds, and megalithic remains, where these axes have been found in stratified deposits. In England they have occasionally been found in hoards, but the majority are surface or isolated finds. Polished stone axes of undoubted

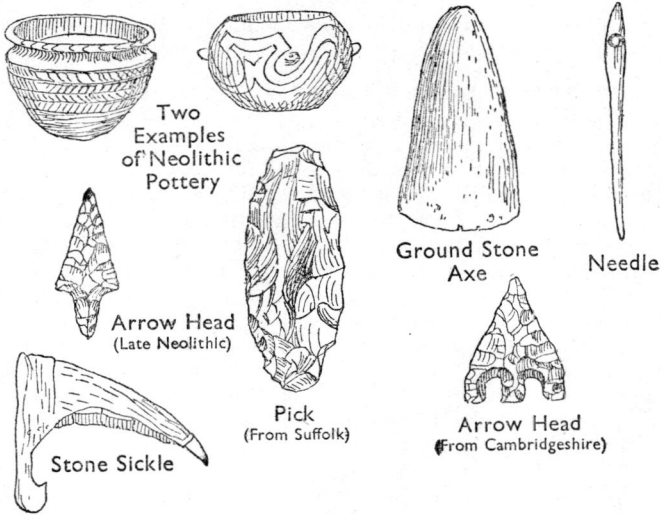

Two
Examples
of Neolithic
Pottery

Arrow Head
(Late Neolithic)

Pick
(From Suffolk)

Ground Stone
Axe

Needle

Arrow Head
(From Cambridgeshire)

Stone Sickle

22. MAN SLOWLY LEARNS TO FASHION NATURE

By 3000 B.C., the period to which the earliest of these tools belong, man had made clear progress. Compare this stone axe (which was held by the narrow end) with the Chellean hand-axe of the old Stone Age shown in Fig. 17.

British origin have been found in Scandinavia. In the Palæolithic hand axes, the bigger end was held in the hand, and the sides and point were used ; but of a ground or polished axe, it was the narrow end which was hafted and the wide end became the " business " end.

Arrow heads furnish evidence of communication with the Continent. The Neolithic types in England have been studied by Reginald A. Smith, who shows that the leaf-shaped arrow head of medium size is characteristic of

chambered long-barrows and Scottish cists, which are
definitely early in the barrow series, and are generally classed
as late Neolithic.

Mace heads, chisels, gouges, picks, fabricators (a small
pick blunt at both ends, like a stone finger), scrapers of all
kinds, daggers, sickles, awls, shoe-last celts from the eastern
area (made of fine-grained rock with flat under surface, the
upper surface being highly convex), are among the many
flint tools in addition to the ones mentioned above which are
known to belong to this period.

WHAT THE LAKE-DWELLER'S DUST-BINS TELL US

LAKE-DWELLING sites are important because so much is
preserved for us in them. They are not confined to
Switzerland, as they are also found in Italy and Hungary,
but they can only be developed in suitable districts. They
also occur in the Bronze Age. In Britain we find them at
Glastonbury in the Early Iron Age. The Crannogs of Ireland
are of this type. Doubtless, safety was the dominant idea,
as on their rafts the people were safe from hostile human
beings as well as from animals.

In 1853 Keller investigated one of the Swiss Lakes after
a particularly dry season when the piles themselves were
uncovered. The piles consist of blocks of wood varying
from three to nine inches in diameter, and from fifteen to
thirty feet long, generally pointed and driven in the marshy
margin or the floor of the lake.

Cross beams to form a platform were placed on the piles ;
as many as fifty thousand piles have been noted on a single
site. Connection with the mainland was kept up by means of
a canoe or a narrow causeway which could easily be destroyed
in time of danger.

Figure 23 will convey to the reader some idea of what these
lake dwellings were like. It is, of course, because the people
of those times threw all their rubbish overboard that these
sites are so interesting, and this rubbish, which includes
pots, implements made from stone and antler, seeds of plants,
pieces of woven material used for clothes, fishing nets, etc.,
are all well preserved. They fell into the soft mud at the
bottom of the lake to be dug up in recent times. Primitive
parallels are to be found at Brunei, in Borneo, and in New
Guinea, where the general life would appear to correspond
to the one under discussion.

23. HOW MEN LIVED IN THE LATE STONE AGE

Lake dwellings of this kind have been found in many parts of the world, but especially in Switzerland. The most important belong to the late Stone Age, 3000–1800 B.C.

MOST ANCIENT SHIP OF ALL : THE CANOE

CANOES were usually made of oak, and were of the "dug-out" type. Pliny noted the use of dug-out canoes by the ancient Germanic tribes, and they doubtless survived in the more backward parts of Europe and the British Isles until comparatively recently. Examples of Neolithic age have been found. They were made from the trunk of a tree with only stone or flint axes and perhaps fire. Among primitive people, fire is often employed in their manufacture to aid in the felling of the tree, the hollowing out of the trunk, the hardening of the wood, and also to enable the sides to be stretched outwards. Hot water may also be employed for the last-named purpose.

There is no form of vessel which is more widely distributed, or has a longer traceable history than the dug-out canoe. Its size ranges from a short, narrow, hollowed-out log holding only two or three people, to well-finished vessels, over a hundred feet in length. One was found in the alluvium of the Clyde in 1708 in which lay an axe made of Greenstone. As this was of the pointed butt type it was not earlier than the end of the Neolithic period, say, 2000 B.C. Another was found at Erith in Kent, from which a polished flint axe and a flint scraper were obtained. In Britain canoes, some sixty-two in number, have been divided into five groups—the first three groups being pre-Roman.

CULTURE ALWAYS A VISITOR TO BRITAIN

WHATEVER Great Britain possesses in the way of culture has had to be brought to it, generally via the Continent, although it may originally have come from the east. Burkitt has divided the streams of culture which reached Central Europe into three : eastern, northern, and western. Common to all was the art of pottery-making, but the decoration on the pottery differed. Burkitt considers Central Asia may have been a cradle of the Neolithic civilisation at the time when its climatic conditions permitted broad pasture lands instead of the present desert wastes, so it is not surprising to find round the basin of the Danube people who were agriculturists, making beautiful pots, grey in colour, very smooth and finely decorated. It is now called Danubian, but elsewhere the pottery differed, and had other names. These people lived in villages in the valleys and not on the uplands. The earliest Swiss lake-dwelling people owe much to this Danubian culture, which spread as far as Belgium.

Central Germany was covered with forest at this time, but later, when this district was forest-free, people came from other areas and all settled down to an agricultural existence, and so there was a great intermixture of stocks in Central Europe. It is difficult to unravel what really did happen, but we can make out a little from the pottery these stocks left behind. In Thuringia there were people now known as Corded-Ware People who had northern blood, and lived on the hills. The *Zoned Beaker* seems to be derived from *Corded Ware*, the *Bell Beaker* from the *Zoned Beaker* and from the latter the *Beaker* sprung. The Beaker people seem to have been cradled in Spain, but their route to Central Europe is not clear.

In Eastern Europe, towards the end of Neolithic times, there appeared some people who made well-burnt beautifully painted pottery. Painted pottery is found at Anau, Russian Turkestan, which we have already mentioned, as well as at Susa and other pre-Sumerian sites in Mesopotamia, where there was an early civilisation, but the pottery from the latter differs from that from the first site and it is not yet known where it came from.

The western stream is closely connected with the northern, the Megalithic building people being important in this connection. A feature of the Northern area is comb-pottery, ornamented with a toothed instrument.

The western stream is exemplified in the Camp de Chassey, on the borders of the department of Saône et Loire and the Côte d'Or, France. This camp would seem to have been a fortified village, some eight hundred yards long, varying in width from 120 to 220 yards in a dominating position of the right bank of the River Dheune and defended with earthworks. It has been particularly rich in finds of every kind and is of late Neolithic date although it was used occasionally in the Early Iron Age. Decorated pottery from here formed one of the elements in the Windmill Hill Neolithic pottery.

Other traces in England of this stream of culture have been noticed at Kit's Coty House, near Maidstone, in Kent, while at Rose Wood, Ightham, which is not far from Maidstone, is the site of a Neolithic village excavated many years ago. Circular basin-like pits were found there, five to ten feet deep and fifteen feet in diameter. At some little distance from Rose Wood is the Coldrum Monument, the remains of a barrow, with a central chamber which measured 12 feet 3 inches in length east to west and 5 feet 8 inches in width north to south. The flat massive stone which formed the southern wall is 7 feet 3 inches high, 11 feet 3 inches long, and 1 foot 9 inches thick. Human bones were found and Keith says that he has no doubt that they were the bones of the people who built this Megalithic tomb.

Twenty-two individuals were represented ; they were of all ages, from newly born children to old men and women. The skulls were not perfect, only five being complete enough to give sure evidence of race. In a great number of them there were peculiarities of formation which could only be accounted for by supposing that the people buried in the tomb were of one family or of nearly related families.

They were people of short stature ; the men were about 5 feet 4½ inches, while the women were about 5 feet 1 inch.

They were thus two or three inches shorter than the modern British average. In size of brain they were not below the standard, indeed three male skulls were higher, as were two female skulls. No importance can be attached to figures founded on five skulls as in every race, ancient and modern, the brain varies widely as regards size. But it does show that Neolithic Man had at least reached the present standard size of brain.

DECAYING TEETH AND HATCHET FACE : PRODUCTS OF CIVILISATION

IN appearance, Neolithic man in Kent was very like his modern successors, the long-headed or dolichocephalic group. The width is seventy-four per cent. of the length and does not materially differ from a modern group of English people of the industrial class, but they are different from a group of people who lived in Hythe in mediæval times. The people of Hythe were on the border line of the brachycephalic (round or short headed) class—seventy-nine per cent. In accounting for the difference in head form between Neolithic and Mediæval people, we must remember that at the end of this (the Neolithic Age) or the beginning of the next (the Bronze Age) Britain was invaded by a round (or brachycephalic) headed people called Beaker people.

Keith says that when we come to analyse the characters which distinguish the people of the Neolithic period from the present population, we see that the changes affect the teeth, jaws, and face. All over Britain at the present day there is a tendency to crowding and irregularities of the teeth ; the palate and jaws do not grow and expand sufficiently in youth to give room for an even eruption of teeth. There is a decided tendency to a narrowing and elongation of the face, producing a " hatchet-shaped " face. The nose is narrow and the palate contracted, with a high vault. The teeth are not worn down as in Neolothic man ; and they are very liable to decay. The front teeth, when the jaws are closed, do not meet edge to edge as in primitive races, but like the blades of scissors, they overlap, the lower passing behind the upper. In the Neoloithic people, all these modern characteristics are absent. Abscesses or gumboils at the roots of the deeply ground teeth were common, but there was not a single decayed tooth to be seen in the Coldrum collection. The teeth are regular and the palates, which were well formed, agree in actual size with those of modern British people.

All the changes which are appearing in the teeth and jaws of modern British people arise, we suppose, from the soft nature of our modern diet. We believe, that were modern men to resume a Neolithic diet, their teeth and palates would again be moulded in the ancient manner. Then there is a difference in the upper shafts of the leg bones—they are compressed from back to front, the shin bones are flattened from side to side and the bones of the ankle and foot show evidences of freer movements. We may perhaps explain these differences as due to the modern conditions in which we live, our clothing, boots, roads, and streets, which have brought about a remoulding of our lower limbs.

When compared with Neolithic Man elsewhere the British examples are found to conform to a type which Huxley called the "river-bed" type. The same type is seen in the Neolithic people of Spain, France, Switzerland, north Germany, and Scandinavia, so that the little group of folk whose remains were buried in the central chamber at Coldrum was not an isolated patch of people, but was a sample of the kind of men who lived in Western Europe in the Neolithic period.

Dental mutilation has been noticed in British Neolithic Man. The practice, which appears to have been confined to one clan or family group, may link these people up with the Pre-dynastic Egyptians, by way of the Iberian Peninsula and Northern Africa.

From the Pant-y-Saer chambered tomb in Anglesey sufficient material was recovered to enable the suggestion to be made, that parturition had occasioned a high degree of infantile, and also possibly, maternal mortality, in that community. The same thing has also been found in other Neolithic sites in England, and during the Copper Age in Minorca; about these finds, Cameron says :

> "These discoveries provided us with a sidelight on one of the tragedies of life, a tragedy that must have been a very real one in those far-off times, with no skilled help at hand to save the lives of the hapless mother and her infant."

Some interesting evidence of the possible connection between the past and the present is afforded by Macdonell's work on the skulls obtained from the seventeenth century " plague-pits " of Whitechapel and Moorfields in London. Measurements of these skulls seem to indicate that a very large proportion of these skulls of two to three hundred years ago were of a type approaching that of the " Long Barrow Men." This may mean that the ancestor of the genuine Cockney is a Long Barrow man, and that perhaps a section of the English population is not Anglo-Saxon nor Scandinavian, nor even Celtic in origin, but may belong to a still earlier race.

The Neolithic period, curtailed as it now is, produced much to further man's onward and upward progress. It is a period of invasion which brought four great additions to life ; the domestication of animals, agriculture, the grinding and polishing of stone tools and the manufacture of pottery. These things made an enormous difference to life. Man learnt how to live at peace with his fellow-men, and to protect his crops from wild animals. If the houses of the living men of the period were poor things, the Long Barrows, which were the houses of their dead, are remarkable. At the end of this period the Beaker people invade our shores and the Bronze Age is almost here.

THE STONE-RAISERS OF BRITAIN

IN discussing megalithic monuments—that is, monuments composed of large stones, no attempt is made to date them ; all we can say is that Long Barrows are Neolithic. The sequence of stone monuments in Britain is generally considered to be (reading from the bottom upwards) :

STONE CISTS	(passage disappears, leaving one chamber only) ;
LONG BARROWS	(passage with chambers) ;
DOLMENS	(2, 3, or 4 stones with a capstone on top).
MENHIRS	(single standing stones) ;

while in Scandinavia it seems to be :

STONE CISTS.
PASSAGE GRAVES.
DOLMENS.
PRE-DOLMENS.

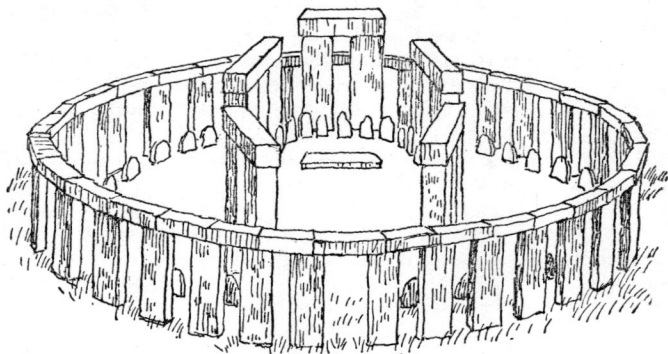

Reconstruction of
Stonehenge

The Tynewydd
Dolmen
(Wales)

The Trethevy Stone
(in Cornwall)

24. AN UNANSWERED RIDDLE FROM THE PAST.
*Monuments consisting of gigantic stones are known in many
parts of Europe, but their purpose and date is still to a large
extent undiscovered. How these stones arrived at the places
where they now stand is a deep mystery.*

The practice of erecting Megaliths, *i.e.* large stones, seems to have come to Britain from southern Spain ; it could have been done stage by stage, and the route is indicated by monuments in Spain, Portugal, Brittany, the western and northern parts of the British Isles, the Orkneys and Scandinavia, and then south to North Germany and Holland.

The cave may have been the ancestor of the megalithic grave. They are alike inasmuch as a cave has (*a*) a shelf outside the entrance, (*b*) an entrance, and (*c*) a dark interior. In a passage grave there are features which agree fairly well with these. It is supposed that the houses of the dead were modelled on those of the living. These megalithic burial chambers were in Britain always covered with earth or in a stony country, with stones.

Long Barrows represent the Atlantic and megalithic aspect of the civilisation of Britain. They are of two types— earthern mounds covering perhaps wooden structures, and megalithic ones incorporating chambered tomb elements. In Minorca they are called navetas ; the Giant's Tomb of Sardinia, and the long rock-cut tombs of the Mediterranean lands are varieties of the same species.

The Long Barrows of the Cotswolds are the best known. They are sometimes placed on the edge of valleys just short of the hilltop. O. G. S. Crawford in his book, " Long Barrows of the Cotswolds," says :

> " There is no doubt that they were intended for the burial of the dead, but the bones deposited in the burial chambers had already been buried or exposed for a time elsewhere, and were subsequently dug up or collected for solemn re-burial in a permanent and more imposing resting-place. There is a good deal of evidence for this theory, and there are many facts which are more satisfactorily explained by it than any other. In the majority of instances where excavation has been carefully conducted and where accurate observations have been made, *complete* skeletons have not been found, but the incomplete remains of several skeletons. In one instance, Pole's Wood South, the size of the burial chamber was not great enough to have contained the total number of bodies found in it, supposing all these to have been placed in it immediately after death."

Nearly thirty skeletons were found in Uley Bury Long

Barrow, near Dursley, Gloucestershire, and thirty-eight in Belas Knap Long Barrow, near Winchcombe, Gloucestershire. It seems very probable that these bones were deliberately broken before being placed in these chambers. It is considered that these long barrows belong to the late Neolithic period, for, as we have already seen, leaf-shaped arrow-heads are typical of the period, and these have been found in Notgrove, West Tump, and Rodmarton Long Barrows, but there is no trace of metal, and no metal object has ever been recovered from any long barrow dating from the period of erection.

A bead made of Kimmeridge shale (a clay deposit of the Upper Jurassic rocks, well exposed in Dorset) was found at Eyford, and is now in the British Museum. Another was found at Notgrove and is in the Cheltenham Museum, together with the leaf-shaped arrow-head mentioned above and some thirty pieces of pottery. Reginald A. Smith has discussed the pottery from Peterborough, and that remaining from these long barrows and in his article the foundations of the study of Neolithic pottery were laid. The most important, because it is the most perfect, is a vessel from Pole's Wood South which belongs to the Peterborough family. It is said that Peterborough pottery is perhaps found in a further long barrow, but that the earlier Windmill Hill pottery is found in twelve long barrows, which include Pole's Wood South, with perhaps one fragment from Gatcombe, and another from Nympsfield tumuli in Gloucestershire.

TWO FAMOUS TOMBS OF NEOLITHIC MAN

PLANS of Belas Knap and of Hetty Pegler's Tump show two types; the former has a false portal at the south end, and three chambers, while the latter has three chambers which are accessible, the two on the north side being walled up, and no false portal.

Hetty Pegler's Tump is one of the finest long barrows in England and is well worth a visit. It is in the parish of Uley, and is two miles from Dursley, Gloucestershire. From the escarpment north of the barrow, one of the finest views in the country can be obtained. Thurnam, who dug into it in 1854, says it is 120 feet long, 85 feet in greatest breadth, and 10 feet high. Some of the skulls were placed in the museum of Guy's Hospital, and Thurnam's account speaks of two stone axe-heads (one of flint, and one of hard greenstone) being found in the neighbourhood of the barrow, but not in the barrow. The greenstone axe has disappeared, but the flint one is at Guy's Hospital with the skulls.

Belas Knap is in the parish of Charlton Abbots, about two miles from Winchcombe, Gloucestershire. It was in a most ruinous condition before H.M. Office of Works repaired it. An investigation of the barrow was undertaken on behalf of the Bristol and Gloucester Archæological Society, which elucidated its plan and gave a number of structural details.

Roman coins have been found in several long barrows in the Cotswolds which shows that they were opened in Roman times, while in Anglo-Saxon times three were reopened in order to bury people in them.

It has been noted that there is a very large quantity of arrow-heads to be seen in collections which have been made in this Cotswold area, and it is said there are probably more arrow-heads in the Royce Collection at Stow-on-the-Wold, Gloucestershire, than there are in the whole of Wiltshire. Another thing noted was the apparent scarcity of polished axes, but several have been found within the last few years, nearly always broken and rechipped.

West Kennet, Wiltshire, was excavated by Thurnam in 1860. It was then 336 feet long, 40 feet wide at the west end, and 75 feet wide at the east, which was also the higher end. It had one chamber approached by a passage, which contained four skeletons, nearly 300 flint flakes, a quantity of Neolithic (Peterborough) pottery, and some beaker sherds.

Wayland's Smithy Long Barrow, in Berkshire, is of great interest. It is 185 feet long and 43 feet wide at the south end, and it has one chamber at the south end which is not in the middle of the barrow. Two currency bars of the Early Iron Age were found outside the entrance at the foot of one of the stones, and remains of about eight skeletons were recovered from the floor of the chamber. This chamber is the origin of the cave legend which has been kept alive above all by Sir Walter Scott, who gave a garbled version of it in " Kenilworth." Wayland the Smith figures in northern mythology, and the monument was illustrated about A.D. 700 on the Franks Casket, a Northumbrian carving in whale's bone, and first mentioned by name in A.D. 955 in a Charter, both of which are in the British Museum. Commenting on these currency bars, the report goes on to say :

" The discovery of currency on such a site inevitably leads to speculation. According to legend, a traveller whose horse had cast a shoe on the adjacent ridgeway had only to leave a groat on the capstone, and return to find his horse shod and the money no longer there. But the invisible smith may have been in possession centuries before the Saxon recognised him as Wayland, and the ancient Britons of Cæsar's time may have been in the habit of offering money here either in return for farrier's work or merely as a votive offering to the local god or deity. In Sicily, a similar tradition can perhaps be traced back to classical times."

MODERN SURGERY PERFORMED BY THE ANCIENTS

WILTSHIRE is the classic region of earthen long barrows and they are also found on the chalk uplands of Wessex, Sussex, Yorkshire, and Lincolnshire. The burials usually occur at the east end, and in number range from one to eighteen skeletons with skulls that were in some cases deliberately broken before death occurred. Cremations have been found in three barrows, of which Wor Barrow, in Dorset, is the best example.

Grave goods are scanty, but include a leaf-shaped arrowhead and Windmill Hill pottery, which in one barrow is represented by an almost complete bowl. Beaker pottery [1] was found in two barrows which had been opened in Beaker times in order to bury a skeleton. Another was opened in later Neolithic times, because Peterborough ware (the later of the two Neolithic wares) was found with the later burial.

In Yorkshire the barrows are smaller and contain cremated interments as a rule. Even on the limestone in that county no stone chambers exist. Leaf-shaped arrow-heads and typical Windmill Hill pottery have been found.

Trepanning was practised in Neolithic times, *i.e.* removing portions of the skull from the living subject by sawing or scraping, and also trephining, which is an improved form of trepanning with guiding centre-pin. This practice is widely distributed in space and time, and has been a custom among some of the Neolithic inhabitants of Europe. Cases are rare in Britain, but a trephined skull was found in Bisley Barrow, near Stroud, Gloucestershire; it is now in the British Museum. It is a curious object, well worth inspection.

[1] See p. 290.

STONEHENGE : THE GREATEST ARCHAEOLOGICAL MYSTERY

CAMDEN, writing the story of Britain in the sixteenth century, saw no reason to ascribe a date before the Roman Conquest to any notable monument, with the sole exception of Stonehenge—a great tribute, but not too great. Stonehenge is most impressive, and is undoubtedly one of the most remarkable monuments in the world.

The date of Stonehenge has been discussed on many occasions, and, despite scientific post-war excavation of half of the monument undertaken by the Society of Antiquaries, it is still our greatest archæological problem. The stones used are of two kinds—Sarsen and others, foreign to the Stonehenge district. Sarsens (sometimes called grey wethers) are blocks of sandstone, sometimes silicified into quartzite, which represent the harder parts of a Tertiary deposit (Bagshot sand) that once spread over a large part of the chalk country in south and south-east England, the rest of which has been weathered away.

It is believed that the foreign or blue stones came from the Prescelly Mountains in Pembrokeshire. There are thirty-four foreign stones, twenty-nine of them are dolerites, four rhyolites, and one a sandstone (altar-stone), and it is considered that they were transported by land. It is estimated that they weigh from two to two and a half tons each, and the distance from Prescelly to Stonehenge overland, allowing for the detour necessitated by the river Severn (it is assumed that the Severn could be forded between Gloucester and Worcester), is about 170 or 180 miles. It is argued that even if carried part of the way by sea, these ancient people could, and did, transport large masses of stone overland. Therefore, if it is possible to convey a large block of stone across bad country for ten miles, it is equally possible to convey it a hundred, given the requisite labour, time, and motive. The altar stone is of micaceous sandstone, and almost certainly came from South Wales, perhaps partly by sea.

Such a collection of foreign stones is not found in any other monument. Isolated cases are known where single stones have been transported, but it is difficult to understand why so many were used at Stonehenge. The eastern portion of the Prescelly Mountains has been described as a " pre-historic Westminster." It contains one of the richest collections of megalithic remains in Britain, and in Thomas's opinion there was a removal of a venerated stone circle from the eastern end of the Prescelly Mountains to Salisbury Plain, and that Stonehenge, as we know it, was rebuilt, the stones being dressed and reduced in size, in conformity with a more advanced type of megalithic work.

There are four circles, called the " Blue Stone Horseshoe," the " Trilithon Horseshoe " (the largest stone is 29 feet, 8 inches long, and of this eight feet is buried), the " Blue Stone Circle," and the " Sarsen Circle."   The last excavation revealed two hitherto unknown circles.   The diameter of the outer circle is that of the dome of St. Paul's.   Pottery of the Early Iron Age and Romano-British periods, cremated bones, antler picks, flint implements, and Beaker pottery high up in the silt of the ditch of the earthworks were found.

A MARVEL OF THE PAST REVEALED BY A WONDER OF THE PRESENT

AIR photography is a post-war science which has been of remarkable use to archæologists.   Woodhenge, about two miles north-east of Stonehenge (so called by Mrs. Cunnington, who subsequently excavated it) was discovered in this way from an air photograph taken in 1925.   It is a remarkable monument, and it was established conclusively that all the holes there had held timber posts.   It was the first of its kind to be excavated in England.   It has six rings of post-holes, which have been lettered A to F, " A " having sixty post-holes.   In the central ring, " F," the crouched skeleton of a child, with its skull cleft, was buried.   It is assumed to have been a sacrifical or dedicatory burial, for which there are parallels among primitive people.

The Sanctuary, on Overton Hill, near Avebury, Wiltshire, was rediscovered and excavated in 1930.   It was found that, in addition to the stone circles which were on Stukeley's map, there were other rings which are lettered A to G, some of them were of timber.   The outer ring consisted of forty-two stones, and was 130 feet in diameter.   The pottery is very unusual and is assigned to the Middle Bronze Age.   A few beaker sherds were also found.   A skeleton was found in ring " C " which may have been, as at Woodhenge, in the nature of sacrifical or dedicatory burial.   It is thought to date from Beaker times.

A circle similar to Woodhenge has been observed and excavated near Norwich, while at Bleasdale, Lancashire, in an area not associated with prehistoric remains, is a wood circle, which has been investigated. It appears to belong to the Middle Bronze Age.

A GREAT MONUMENT BECOMES THE VICTIM OF UTILITY

THE next Megalithic monument to be described is Avebury, in Wiltshire. When Aubrey wrote of Avebury in the seventeenth century the monument seems to have been more or less complete, but by the early eighteenth century a great deal of it had been destroyed. In order to clear the land for grazing, great pits were dug and the stones buried. Another method used to destroy them was to dig a pit by the side of the stone so that it fell, then loads of straw were burnt under it. When it was heated, water was poured on, and a sledge-hammer was brought into play, which reduced the stone to pieces. Destruction has been going on almost to our own day, for now only five per cent. of the Sarsen Monoliths (single blocks of stone) remain.

A ditch called the Great Fosse encloses an area of twenty-eight and a half acres. A vallum or rampart of great height, having a circumference of 4442 feet compared with one of 1107 feet round Stonehenge, runs around the outside of the ditch. The diameter of Avebury would correspond to the circle of Aldwych if the curve were completed to meet the Thames Embankment.

It is possible that at Avebury we may have an amphitheatre. The ramparts would serve to seat the congregation and separate them from the priests on the flat central space, where there were two circles of stone. If the vallum or rampart was for defence, it would be on the inner edge of the fosse.

Excavations have been undertaken here on behalf of the British Association. They were confined chiefly to the fosse on the southern side of the monument, but one cutting was made into the vallum. During these excavations there were found forty-four antler picks, three bone shovels made from shoulder-blades, flint implements and pottery, some of which is of Peterborough type. Beaker pottery was discovered on much the same level. No metal of any sort was found in the lower part of the silting of the ditch, but the general conclusion is that the Avebury monument must be referred to the Early Bronze Age.

The West Kennet Avenue, which led from the stone circles on Overton Hill to the Avebury monument, was over a mile in length, and was destroyed in 1724. The avenue originally consisted of 200 stones set in pairs, and some details of the excavation which has been commenced there have already been published. Many buried stones have been recovered, and evidence has been found to corroborate the statements we made earlier as to how similar stones were destroyed ; the chalk shows much evidence of fire in some of the holes where the monoliths have disappeared. The buried stones are being re-erected. Beaker burials have been found in association with two stones, and one at least is considered contemporary with the erection of the stone with which it was found. Incised ornament has been noted on some of the buried stones, and attention is drawn to the careful dressing of the Avebury stones before either erection or transportation, in contradistinction to the practice at Stonehenge. A kind of pecking or bruising on some of these stones was observed, which recalled the greenstone celt of the early Neolithic period in Scandinavia.

THE STORY OF THE WHISPERING KNIGHTS

THE Rollright Stones, or the Whispering Knights, are situated in the parish of Little Rollright, not far from Chipping Norton, in Oxfordshire ; while the King Stone, on the other side of the road, is in the parish of Long Compton.

The Whispering Knights consist of five stones, and the King Stone is a great Monolith which Stukely said was eight feet high and seven feet broad ; he considered it part of a long barrow. It has a semicircular notch towards the top. Similar notches in the pairs of uprights, which formed a sort of port-hole, are recorded at Rodmarton, Belas Knap, Avening, and elsewhere.

The folk-legend of these stones is that a nameless king set forth to conquer all England. He met a witch, sometimes called Mother Shipton, to whom the ground on which Rollright stands belonged. The king was close to the top of the hill from which the village of Long Compton would be visible in the valley below, when she stopped him and said :—

> " If Long Compton thou canst see
> King of England thou shalt be."

The king, who thought his success assured, cried out exultingly :

> " Stick, stock, stone,
> As King of England I shall be known."

So he took seven strides forward to the top of the hill, but
instead of looking down on Long Compton there rose before
him the long mound of earth which still stands before the
King Stone, and the witch said :

> " As Long Compton thou canst not see
>   King of England thou shalt not be.
>   Rise up, Stick and stand still, Stone,
>   For King of England thou shalt be none ;
>   Thou and thy men hoar stones shalt be
>   And I myself, an eldern tree."

Thereupon the king and his men were turned into stones
where they stood, the king on the side of the mound and
his army in a circle behind him, while the witch herself became
an elder tree.   But some day, they say, the spell will be broken.
The stones will turn into flesh and blood once more, and the
king will start as an armed warrior at the head of his army to
overcome his enemies and rule over all the land.   The proof
that the " eldern tree " is a witch is that it bleeds when it is cut.

The fairies dance round the King Stone at night.   Will
Hughes, a man of Long Compton, now dead, declared he had
actually seen them dancing round—" They were little folk-
like girls to look at."   Chips were taken from the King Stone
for luck, and it is recorded in 1859 that a visitor was informed
that the stones were daily diminishing " because people from
Wales kept chipping bits off to keep the Devil off."

Other stone circles in Britain are " Long Meg and her
daughters," near Penrith, Cumberland, and Arbor Low, in
Derbyshire.   Seventeen stone circles still exist in Cornwall,
the best known being the nine maidens at Boxawen-un, in
Bunyan's parish, between Penzance and Land's End.

The Long Stone at Minchinhampton, Gloucestershire, is
seven and a half feet high, and is made of Dagham Stone from
the Great Oolite, which is known locally as " holey stone."
A legend says that if a child with ricketts was passed through
one of the holes in this stone (the larger hole is twelve inches by
five inches) by its mother, it would be cured.   A second stone
is built into a nearby wall, and they are probably the remains
of a long barrow.

Very many large stones, whether included in megalithic
structures or left standing alone, have pits and " cup-and-
ring " markings on them, which are mysterious but almost
universal in the prehistoric world.

SCENES OF ELABORATE FUNERAL RITES

Bryn Celli Dhu, in Anglesey, is a chambered cairn (a cairn is a mound of stones) containing a single many-sided chamber, about eight feet across, roofed by two cover stones, and approached by a passage 26 feet long, of which the inner 20 feet were roofed. It is 160 feet in circumference. There were two rings of stones which were linked up with the passage and the chamber. One of the uprights of the chamber was found to have an incised pattern on it. The evidence of elaborate funeral rites is stressed by Hemp, who believes it was the scene of human sacrifice. Its date is thought to be 1500 B.C. Skeletons were found in the chamber when it was first opened many years ago. In the post-War excavation and repair by H.M. Office of Works fragments of skeletons, both burnt and unburnt, were found, as well as varieties of sea-shells, but there was no pottery.

The Scilly Isles have a number of notable monuments, the passage grave at St. Mary's being among the best preserved.

Among others, Cornwall has Lanyon Quoit, in the parish of Madron, between Penzance and Morvah; Zennor Quoit, in Zennor, near Land's End; and Trethevy Quoit, near St. Cleer, East Cornwall, which are the remains of barrows. The Devil's Den, Marlborough, and Chagford, in Devon, may be mentioned.

Dolmens [1] are sepulchres constructed of two, three, or four stones on which a capstone is placed. There are hardly any in Scotland, they are frequent in Wales, and there are at least 800 in Ireland. New Grange, a great chambered round barrow, is perhaps the most famous stone monument in the Irish series. It is a great corbelled tomb with much fine engraving, the spiral being a conspicuous element which betrays a connection with Mediterranean art, and it is considered that there is a connection between it and Gavr'Inis in Brittany. These two, with Maes Howe, in Orkney, are the classical examples of round barrows; while Houge Bie, in Jersey, is of the same type.

The Standing Stones at Boroughbridge, Yorkshire, are of importance. They are sometimes called the Devil's Arrows —one is 22½ feet in height and 18 feet in circumference, while another is 18 feet in height and 22 feet round.

[1] See p. 278.

10

Maiden Castle, in Dorset, is the subject of investigations under Dr. and Mrs. Wheeler, which will be continued over a period of years. So far, the published newspaper accounts say the Roman building (which was known to exist) is a temple and not a villa, as previously supposed. Dwelling pits of the Iron Age have been found. The site, which covers an area of several acres, is expected to produce most interesting results.

Silbury Hill is not far from the Avebury monument and is the largest artificial mound in England. Several attempts to date it satisfactorily by excavation have been made, the last by Flinders Petrie, but no evidence was produced to make a pronouncement possible.

METAL : THE GREAT DISCOVERY

ONE writer says it was a good thing the Beaker people came to Britain to overlord these Megalithic people who were wasting their energies in a senseless cult of the dead, and cites Brittany as an example of an area where this cult was not checked. There it is estimated there are 4458 dolmens and passage graves, Carnac being one of the most important, with its long avenues of standing stones. So, perhaps, it was not so disastrous that the poverty-stricken Beaker people, whose only possessions, beyond their beakers, appeared to be barbed and tanged arrow-heads, came to England. Poor though they were, they brought another point of view, and the building of Megalithic monuments may have begun to decline during the Early Bronze Age which the Beaker people foreshadowed. Although it is convenient to use the terms Stone Age, Bronze Age, and Early Iron Age, there is no hard and fast line anywhere between the actual periods which they describe.

1900 B.C. is an important date to remember, for it was then that the Neolithic civilisation was destroyed by the Beaker people, who invaded Britain at this time, coming, it is believed, from the Rhine. They heralded the Bronze Age, but probably did not introduce bronze. This may have come in by peaceful penetration and trade to our south coast ports—in the shape of copper and bronze knives.

These people brought with them a characteristic type of pottery called Beaker pottery. They also built the round barrows and had round heads, as distinct from the earlier invaders with long barrows and long heads. " This invasion is

of special interest, in that it is the first of which we have any
definite and clear information, and because the Beaker people
are apparently the only round-headed people who have ever
entered Britain *en masse*." [1]

Beakers were not used exclusively for burying with the
dead ; evidence is accumulating to show that they were the
ordinary domestic ware of these invaders. Beakers are
usually very well made of fine paste ; they are thin and well
fired, and are very superior to the cinerary urns of the Late
Bronze Age. They were divided by Abercromby into three
main types, A, B, and C, according to form, but as type C
is a debased form of A, it is usual now to divide them into
two groups : the first group comprises A and C and the
second type B. It has been pointed out that the theory of a
single landing is now generally rejected.

It has also been shown that the majority of the A and C
beakers represent an invasion that landed in the Wash or on the
north-east coast and spread northward to Scotland and westward to Wiltshire and to Wales, and that the B beakers were
brought to the south-eastern shores of Britain. With the
A+C beakers are associated flint daggers, stone axe hammers,
bored buttons and riveted metal daggers, while with the
B group, archer's wristguards and tanged metal daggers
are found ; barbed and tanged arrow-heads are found with
both. Not only is there a difference in form of the beaker,
but there is a distinct difference in decoration—the A+C
group are richly and elaborately decorated, perhaps with
bird bones, in the way we have already described, while
the B group are altogether simpler. There are, of course,
beakers which are intermediate, and they are to be found
mostly at points where the two groups met.

Beakers of class B were decorated with a cog wheel or
short-toothed comb of bone or wood, whose square teeth,
when passed over the wet clay, left an almost continuous
series of little angular depressions ; sometimes, as in North
Britain, they were marked with a cord impressed upon the
damp clay, or with a simple-pointed instrument.

THE PEOPLE WHO STARTED THE BRONZE AGE

WHEN the Beaker people had arrived and settled in as
conquerors, the Bronze Age may be said to have begun.
Although bronze was a most important metallic substance,

[1] *Arch. Camb. Region*, p. 23 (Fox).

copper was the next one after gold to be used. Metallurgists have pointed out that there is no reason in the nature of things why iron should not have attracted some inventive genius at the end of the Neolithic Age. Its ores are more abundant and more easily reduced than any others, while in its meteoric form it requires no " reduction " from its ores.

In the British Museum *Bronze Age Guide* (p. 6), the literary evidence that bronze was known before iron is set out. It mentions an eighth century B.C. record, which speaks of a time when men wrought in bronze, but when " dark iron was unknown," and Lucretius (about 50 B.C.) distinctly states that iron was discovered later than copper.

It is most unlikely that if iron had been used before any other metal it would have fallen into disuse in any place where its ores could readily be obtained. This consideration disposes of the argument that primæval iron weapons may once have existed but have now rusted away. Iron may, then, fairly be eliminated from the general inquiries; there remain copper and bronze, the former a simple metal, the latter an alloy of copper and tin.

Metallic copper occurs " native " in nature, *e.g.* found in a pure state. By hammering, it may be shaped into imitations of the simpler forms of stone or bone tools. The American Indians of Ohio employed the native metal in this way, hammering it without the aid of heat. But such an application of Stone Age processes to native copper does not mark the beginning of the age of metals, and there is no reason to suppose that it led directly to their use.

The first smiths had discovered that a certain hard, reddish substance became malleable on heating, and that it could thus be poured like water into a vessel, but on cooling it became hard, and assumed the shape of the receptacle. The superiority of copper over stone lies in its plasticity. In regions where the metal had to be extracted from its ores by reduction, the change would seem still more marvellous. Copper ores are crystalline substances, greenish-blue, red, or grey in colour, found in metamorphic rocks,[1] and the change to a tough red metal was a startling one. The process of reduction is simple; heat in contact with charcoal will effect it, but it was a noteworthy act on the part of prehistoric man to connect green crystalline stones with the tough red metal. It is probable

[1] See p. 47.

that in most localities copper was first used for making implements.

This was followed by another wonderful discovery. Bronze Age Man found that his copper tools were much more serviceable than his flint ones, but they were not perfect ; they were too soft, and somehow, probably accidentally, he found that if he put some tin in his copper he produced a metal which was very much more serviceable.

The discovery of silver, lead, and tin were not so wonderful. He probably experimented a good deal with curious coloured stones and so discovered these other metals. A more remarkable fact is that nearly all his bronze tools have 10 per cent. of tin in their composition, which must have been the result of a great deal of experiment, 10 per cent. of tin being almost the ideal amount to make a serviceable bronze.

WHEN WAS BRONZE DISCOVERED ?

At present the piece of bronze for which the highest antiquity is claimed is the rod from Mêdûm, in Egypt, dating about 3000 B.C. Mesopotamia can show a statuette of Gudea, of 2500 B.C.

The important step of discarding bronze in favour of iron was taken by some peoples centuries earlier than others, although the distance between their territories may have been only a few hundred miles. The reason for this inequality of culture is to be found in geographical conditions. Those countries which were situated upon or near the main lines of commerce and intercourse were naturally the first to take advantage of the latest achievement of human ingenuity, while those that lay in remote parts of the world continued for a long series of years the use of a material which had already been superseded among their more progressive neighbours. In countries where the use of bronze was indefinitely prolonged, the artistic quality of the metal was developed in a higher degree than in those countries where iron was brought into use at an earlier date. Italy, southern France, and Upper Austria all offer examples of a bronze culture cut off before it reached full perfection. Italy had always been open to the civilising influences of the Mediterranean. Southern France and Upper Austria, situated as they were on the great trade routes for tin and amber, participated in the new inventions.

Eastern Hungary and Scandinavia were the latest to be affected by southern civilisation, the consequence being that the Bronze Age there is represented by a series of antiquities which for splendour and wealth of ornament have no parallel in other countries more favourably situated.

Child says, " All the vital elements of modern material culture are immediately rooted in the Bronze Age," and he recognises three important centres of Early Bronze Age culture in Europe : (a) Central Europe, (b) south-eastern Spain, (c) Britain.

It is not possible here to discuss in full the Bronze Age

LATE	
Villanova North Alpine Urnfield and Lake Dwellings Lausitz	} 1200–1250 B.C.
MIDDLE	
Hungarian Urnfields Terremare Bronze Culture (Po Valley) Tumulus Bronze Culture Teutonic Bronze Culture (Scandinavia ; In- humation, Tree Coffins)	} 1600–1200 B.C.
EARLY	
Adleberg Culture Rhône Culture Armonican Group (France) Galician Rock Carvings (Spain) El Argar (Spain) Remedello (Italy) Aunjetitz and allied groups	} 1900–1600 B.C.

25. BRONZE AGE CULTURES IN EUROPE

in Europe, but it is necessary to realise something of what happened elsewhere, in order that we may get the right perspective for Britain. By 1900 B.C., when our Bronze Age opens, the second city of Troy had fallen. Egypt was in her twelfth dynasty ; the second phase of the Middle Minoan period was in full swing in Crete ; and the Late Bronze Age of the Sumerians had begun. All these civilisations were rich and magnificent, with a demand for gold, tin, copper, and amber. These could be obtained from Europe, and prospectors went to Tran-

sylvania for gold, to Bohemia for tin, to Slovakia and northern
Hungary for copper, and to Jutland and the East Baltic for
amber. De Navarro has shown that the central amber route
was opened about 1800 B.C. (the Aunjetitz period in Central
Europe (see Fig. 25)).

The prospectors took with them goods of varying kinds ;
for example, from Cyprus they took knot-headed or roll-top
pins, and at Nienhagen in Saxony a clay copy of the gold
Vapheio cup from Troy was discovered. On the other hand,
at Biblos, in Syria, torques and spiral wire tubing from Central
Europe were found. In exchange for the goods they took
from the East these prospectors obtained their raw materials,
the Danube serving as a thoroughfare for most of its course.
This river leads to large tracts of land in Central Europe which
were covered with a fine wind-borne dust which is called
loess. Loess does not grow heavy timber, but is excellent for
agriculture, and ideal for settlers. But the Danube did more
than lead to lands fit for settlement. It led to the valleys where
the precious metals were to be found, and so it is not surprising
that the area was a favoured one.

A list of the principal cultures of Europe is given in Table
on opposite page.

In Scandinavia the Stone Age persisted till a late date, and
only a few metal objects were imported ; in fact, the Bronze
Age in Scandinavia did not open until 1650 B.C. Although
Scandinavia started late, she produced a marvellously brilliant
Bronze Age which was not equalled by any other country.

THE BRONZE AGE IN BRITAIN

BRITAIN has always obtained her culture at a later date than
her continental neighbours. She was at the end of the
world as then known, and after the Straits of Dover were
formed there was no reason why people should come, unless
compelled. There were two reasons for such migration :
(a) pressure, usually from the north of Europe, forcing people
to migrate ; and (b) the fact that Ireland possessed gold and
Cornwall tin. When people came to Britain for these products
she shared in the rich civilisations of Central Europe, developing
in her own way, and her inhabitants producing tools and
weapons of great beauty, but when this traffic ceased, as it did
at about 1100–1000 B.C.,—" Britain," says Fox, " now takes up
the relation to the Continent which is historically familiar as a
country on the edge of the known world, the last to receive

and absorb cultures moving transcontinentally from east and south-east to west and north-west."

Britain now entered upon a period of trouble and turmoil. She certainly produced weapons of war, such as rapiers, spear-heads, swords and bronze shields, and mighty cauldrons, but the unsettled state of the country is shown in the enormous number of hoards of the late Bronze Age which have been found.

It is thought by some that from about 1100 B.C. until the Early Iron Age about 500 B.C., Britain was invaded, not once, but several times. Among the invaders were the people who brought the socketed axe and the " U " type sword from which the " V " type is produced. Others brought the " Carp's Tongue " sword from the West Alpine region. The Urn-fielders (people who cremated their dead and buried them in urns in flat cemeteries) came from the Lower Rhine and occupied the Lowlands.

The divisions of the British Bronze Age are set out in Fig. 26. Emphasis is laid on the fact that now the period has to be considered as possessing two culture phases only. It has always been the custom to speak of the Early, Middle, and Late Bronze Age, but the thing to notice is that while those divisions are retained, there are only two *culture* phases.

THE CRAFT OF THE WORKMAN IN BRONZE

BRONZE Age Man had many more possessions than his Stone Age ancestors. He had tools, weapons, vessels, and ornaments in great variety. The number of them that have come down to us gives us a very vivid picture of that phase of his life.

Ireland is important in the Early Bronze Age. In the rich copper deposits in County Wicklow, one of the earliest weapons—the halberd—is found, which shows that the copper age commenced in Ireland as early as in any other country in north or north-west Europe, but, though it may be admitted for Ireland, there is no evidence of a true copper age for the rest of Britain.

Simple flat axes and daggers of bronze are made in stone moulds. The shape of the object was carved in the stone, and the molten metal was poured in. Elaborate moulds, however, made in at least two pieces were necessary for most things. The *cire perdue* method was much employed. In this method a wax model was made, which was then dipped in a bath of clay

DIVISIONS OF THE BRONZE AGE IN BRITAIN	
Phases and Dates (Approximate)	**Characteristic Metal Form**
SECOND PHASE **Late Bronze Period** (1000 B.C.—600 or 450 B.C.)	Sword Spear Head Socketed Axe (Two Views)
FIRST PHASE **Middle Bronze Period B** (1400 B.C.—1000 B.C.)	Palstave Rapier
Middle Bronze Period A (1700 B.C.—1400 B.C.)	Flat and Flanged Axes Dagger
Early Bronze Period (2000 B.C.—1700 B.C.)	Flat Axe (Rare) Dagger (Rare)

26. *The division of prehistoric time into " Ages " has been greatly helped by the evidence of early man's weapons, tools, and utensils. This table shows the weapons typical of the Bronze Age, the later periods being shown towards the top of the page.*

whipped to the consistency of cream, and this was allowed to dry, when it was coated with a thicker clay. After the wax had been melted and allowed to run out, the molten metal was poured into the cavity where the wax had been.

The earliest bronze flat axes (or celts) are evidently copies of stone implements of the Neolithic period. A little later it was discovered that when the edge was hammered it expanded sufficiently to make a serviceable tool, and to economise in metal the width at the top was reduced. These were hafted in a cleft stick, but it was found in practice that the axe-head could be more firmly fixed in a cleft stick by beating up the edges to prevent side slip, and by making a ridge half-way down to prevent the axe splitting the handle. Later, the flanges became shorter, and the stop ridge merged into them. The top of the axe covered by the prongs of the handle was made thinner and thus provided deep grooves. The handles were bound on, and later a loop was added for a cord. This form is called a palstave, which continued in use till late in the Bronze Age.

THE BRONZE AGE SOLDIERS' TOOLS OF WAR

DAGGER BLADES are numerous, and it is sometimes difficult to distinguish between a dagger and a knife; indeed, some may have been used for either purpose. Rapiers are elongated daggers, and are sometimes very beautiful. There is a transitional form between the rapier and the sword, which partakes of the character of both. The Bronze *sword* is the ancestor of the later Hallstatt (Early Iron Age) type. It was evolved in Central Europe while Britain was still using the rapier.

The *Spear-head* is another descendant of the dagger, and its evolution is best studied in the British Isles. The dagger first had a tang to push into a wooden handle, then a bronze collar was added, attached by two rivets, then the tang was discontinued, and the socketed spear-head appeared. At first the socket was nearly as long as the blade, and two bosses represent the pair of rivets as in the Snowshill (Gloucestershire) specimen, which is an important example of one stage of the spear-head evolution; the Arreton Down specimen from the Isle of Wight is a little later. Loops appeared at the end of the socket, and one often reads that these were for securing the head to the shaft by means of a thong; but a distinguished archæologist has pointed out that the loops were useless for this purpose. Nevertheless, there the loops are, and they gradually move up towards the base of the blade and then eventually become openings in the blade themselves. These openings vary in size and outline and may have served merely to reduce the weight of metal.

A hoard found in the Heathery Burn Cave, County Durham, is important because it shows us what the possessions of a family towards the end of the Bronze Age were like. These people had lived or taken shelter in this cave, and disaster overtook them when the stream was in flood. The objects found can be described as contemporary, and among them there is a sword, spear-heads, bronze discs, a conical bucket of bronze, knives, a razor, a socketed axe and gouge and pin, all of bronze; a gold bracelet, cast bronze collars from the wheel hubs (nave collars), and a bronze mould for socketed axes. Bone was used for spindle whorls, prickers, skewers, jet for armlets, and there was a single amber bead and a single flint arrow-head, with barbs and tang.

Many other bronze articles are known, such as torcs (Latin *Torquis*, a collar), embossed bucklers made from sheets of bronze, razors, and sickles.

THE MOST FAMOUS PONY'S COLLAR IN THE WORLD

MANY gold ornaments were made in this period. They include bracelets, with " ring money," *i.e.* small pieces of metal, each forming almost a complete circle, which were probably used as currency. The most famous Bronze Age gold piece is the peytrel (French *poitrail*) or brunt for a pony, which is in the shape of a breast collar. It was mounted on a copper plate, and was found in a cairn called Bryn yr Ellyllon (Hill of the Fairies or Goblins) at Mold, in Flintshire, with over 300 amber beads and remains of coarse cloth. A romantic story is told of the discovery, which is said to be attributed to second sight, and several pieces, including the gold straps for fastening, were lost after the peytrel had been thrown aside as worthless. Many pieces have, however, been recovered. The thin gold plate is embossed in a style similar to the circular bronze shields of the late Bronze Age. A discovery of this kind demonstrates in a striking manner the abundance of gold at the end of Britain's Bronze Age period. It is obvious that before a warrior would decorate his horse with gold he would have sufficient for his own personal needs.

Gold articles are commonest in the south-west and in Wales, the areas nearest to Ireland. The significance of four gold discs and one of bronze from Ireland has been verified with the help of a notable find at Trundholm in Zealand (Denmark), where a bronze horse on wheels connected with a gold-plated disk, also on wheels, was found. The whole object stands for the solar chariot, and after it had been used in some pagan ceremony it had been " ritually slain," *i.e.* broken and cast into the " moss " whence it was recovered. It is dated about 1000 B.C. The ornament on the Irish gold discs is probably later than the Trundholm sun-car, and does not contain the spiral, but other details are similar.

Irish gold was apparently in general use quite early in the Bronze Age, for over thirty lunettes are in Dublin Museum, showing an early type of ornament, and two specimens were found in Cornwall with a bronze (or copper) axe of primitive form.

Reginald A. Smith says :

" Irish Gold Crescents (worn on the neck) were called lunulæ or little moons, and later called lunettes, which is French for telescopes, and though more manageable than lunulæ, is not so fitted for international use as ' crescents.' All three names suggest a connection with the moon and are certainly more fully justified than ' tiara ' or diadem, as the notion that crescents were part of the head-dress has long been exploded, in spite of the fact that the daughters of Zion, late in the eighth century B.C., wore ' round tires like the moon,' for which they were reproved by Isaiah (Isaiah iii. 18)."

The gold crescents may be said to represent moons ; and in the Swiss Lake Dwellings, of Bronze Age date, stone and pottery crescents occur, which show the close connection between moon worship and the sacrifice of bulls which is known to have existed. One opinion is that Bronze Age man saw in the crescent moon a glowing bull's head rather than the moon in a bull's head. Examples of these crescents have been found in France and Denmark, showing intercourse with Ireland either via England or direct by sea.

Among unusual bronze objects, the mounts of wheeled vehicles, such as nave-bands, from Heathery Burn, County

Durham, and a pole-ferrule from Cardiff, are important, as they suggest the chariot or the ritual carriage. The Swiss Lake Dwellings have produced evidence in the shape of bits and wooden wheels, which show that the horse was domesticated there.

The spoked wheel was known to the Assyrians, the Egyptians, the Greeks, and others. It is probable that spoked wheels reached the British Isles in the Bronze Age, *i.e.* after about 1800 B.C., along with the war chariot itself, but it is not known whether this was the first appearance here of the wheel in any form.

THE STORY OF POTTERY IN BRITAIN

As pottery now became a key industry, it is advisable to set out its course of evolution. We have already noted that Britain was but a part of the great West European zone of Bronze Age culture, but it possesses distinguishing features in its unique forms of sepulchral pottery. The Beaker people had, as we have observed, come *en masse* and overwhelmed the Neolithic population, but the native element reasserted itself, as is indicated by the food-vessels (Fig. 28) which were made solely for burying with the dead. These are found in considerable numbers in Ireland as well as in Britain, and they are quite unrepresented outside the British Isles, where they are the product of the fusion of two cultures. They are the most attractive class of all Bronze Age pottery in Britain, and are frequently found in round barrows and usually with *unburnt* burials. The ware is coarser than that of the beakers, but is very lavishly ornamented on the outside, and sometimes this extends inside the lip, while a cruciform design is by no means uncommon on the bottom. The Peterborough bowl is its predecessor. This familiar round-bottomed bowl underwent several changes, acquiring a flat base, an angular outline and lugs originally pierced for suspension and set on the shoulder or within a hollow moulding.

Cinerary Urns (Fig. 27) mark the beginning of the Middle Bronze Age. Abercromby derived the cinerary urn, which has an overhanging rim, from the food-vessel, which was a native production. It was used as a receptacle for the cremated remains of the dead. The series begins with urns that are structurally tripartite, *i.e.* in three divisions, and ends with those that are structurally bipartite, *i.e.* in two divisions. They are sometimes very large, and their size says something for the technical skill of the potter. They have an unusual amount of grit in their composition to prevent them from cracking in the process of firing. They lack any slip[1] or polish, but are usually elaborately decorated, with either a twisted thong, a pointed tool, or the finger-point and nail.

SOME LITTLE VESSELS WHOSE USE IS A MYSTERY

WITH the cinerary urns little vessels are sometimes found, which Colt Hoare called incense cups (Fig. 27), and though this infers a purely conjectural use the name is retained. Their use is unknown but they are frequently found inside the larger cinerary urns. They are very superior in quality to the urns themselves but are not so fine as beakers. In shape and decoration they vary considerably, and are often pierced as if to assist combustion. Sometimes the base is ornamented like some of the food vessels. As some specimens are unpierced, the incense theory is disqualified, even if incense was available ; and the same objection would lie against their use as braziers, in which fire could be carried from the family hearth to the funeral pyre. Some of these vessels are often called grape-cups, because they are covered with knobbly projections.

The Folkton Chalk drums from Folkton Wold, East Riding, Yorkshire, are important, as they are the only things of their kind in England. They were found in a barrow in a trench twenty-two feet from the centre, with unburnt burials, and their date is determined by their ornamentation rather than by their position in the barrow. Their ornament has Mediterranean affinities, and recalls the remarkable sculptures at New Grange, County Meath, and Gavr'Inis, Brittany.

Beads of jet, amber, and lignite, a fossil wood, jet buttons with V-shaped perforations, cylindrical loom weights, etc., go to make up culture at that date. Five cups made of shale and two of amber, making seven altogether, are known, all from Southern England. They have ribbon handles and simple flat bases and seem to have been turned on a pole lathe.

The famous gold cup of this age found in a cairn at Rillaton in Cornwall is of similar shape to the above, is hammered out of a single piece of metal and decorated with horizontal corrugations. These vessels, unique in north-western Europe,

---

[1] Pottery is sometimes finished by a coating (" slip ") of colour made of the same kind of clay, or clay of another colour, fired in the usual manner.

TABLE SHOWING THE EVOLUTION OF POTTERY

Urns of the Deverel Rimbury Type (Late Bronze and Early Iron Age)	Two Types of Deverel Rimbury Urns
Cinerary Urns and "Incense Cups" (Middle Bronze Age)	"Incense Cup"
Food-Vessels	
Beakers and Food-Vessels	
Beakers (Earliest Bronze Age)	
Peterborough and Windmill Hill Pottery (Native Neolithic Culture)	

27. *Native British Pottery was submerged early in the Bronze Age by the Beaker ware brought over by invaders from the Continent. It re-asserted itself later in food vessels. All these types of pottery were buried with the dead and are found in barrows.*

show that Britain had not lost her originality in the Middle Bronze Age. The British Isles retained their European trade, as amber was still imported from the Baltic and the rich finds in round barrows show that beads of blue faience[1] were imported from Crete or Egypt about 1600 B.C. It is declared by some authorities that these beads were manufactured in Britain from slag, but be that as it may, they imitate the eastern ones. It was possibly in exchange for such imports that Britain exported to northern France, tin, Irish gold torcs, looped spearheads and other British types of the Middle Bronze Age in considerable quantity.

Deverel-Rimbury pottery (Fig. 27) is shown to have come from the Low Countries at about 700 B.C., and it is proved that the distribution in England is confined to the south and south-east and suggests that the Cloven Way may have been used by the people of that time. This pottery is roughly divisible into three types : barrel, bucket, and globular. They are usually decorated with finger-tip impressions, and are often coarse, badly made and badly burnt.

In Cornwall they show variations, two or four strap-handles sit on the shoulder, and decoration takes the form of vertical or horizontal zig-zags. In the north, " the encrusted urn " is evolved from the enlarged food-vessel, which has bands of clay applied to the body of the urn, the bands then being lavishly decorated, very like pastry strips on a pie. Forty-eight of these interesting encrusted urns were listed in 1927, five being found in England, fifteen in Scotland, two in the Isle of Man, three in Wales and sixteen in Ireland. This is considered an excellent example of the principle that the Highlands *absorb* a culture, whereas it is *imposed* on the Lowlands.

HOW BRONZE-AGE MAN BUILT HIS HOME

HABITATIONS of the Bronze Age consist of circular huts very like the Neolithic ones. In Scotland, beaker sheds have been found in " hut circles," of which the foundations only (a circular bank of stone and turf) survive. They are also recorded from Yorkshire and Dartmoor.

At Park Brow, Sussex, a habitation site of late Bronze Age date was found, while at Hucclecote, near Gloucester, an occupation trench was discovered under a Roman Villa, with Deverel-Rimbury pottery and flint implements. Many

[1] Earthenware or porcelain.

important sites of this date are known, including one on the Lower Thames and one at Southchurch in Essex.

WORTHY WEAPONS BURIED WITH THE DEAD

THE invaders from the Rhine who brought beakers with them and apparently little else, appeared to have introduced the barbed and tanged flint arrowhead comparatively small in size, the barbs and tang terminating at the same level, as Reginald A. Smith has shown.   He notices tendencies : (a) for the tang to be lengthened at the expense of the barb and (b) the barbs to be prolonged into swallowtail curves when the tang is diminished.

Flint daggers in the Bronze Age period are linked with A + C beakers while plano-convex flint knives are found with food-vessels and are of Early and Middle Bronze Age date.

Discoidal polished flint knives have recently been studied, and it is shown that in the main they belong to the Beaker period.   Clark says : " First, however, it is necessary to point out that we cannot expect to find our knives buried with warriors, as we find the flint dagger, the bracer or the barbed arrowhead, associated directly with beakers, since the discoidal flint knife was on the analogy of the Eskimo knife, and in view of its domestic use, merely a woman's implement, unworthy of so high a purpose."

Perforated stone axe-hammers, strangely enough, belong to the Bronze Age.   Reginald A. Smith has shown that several have been discovered with bronze implements and as a basis for his study takes two grave groups 110 miles apart—Snowshill in Gloucestershire and Hove near Brighton.

The Snowshill implements can be closely dated, as in the centre of a barrow was an unburnt cist-burial and with the skeleton was a bronze spearhead (which is intermediate between the spearhead with a tang and one with a socket) ; a bronze dagger with three rivet holes ; a bronze pin and a stone axe-hammer.

At Hove, the cist was represented by a tree coffin in which was an amber cup and small whetstone, a bronze dagger and a stone axe-head of the same type as that from Snowshill. The stone axe-heads have a resemblance to a Danish type. These axe-heads were seldom made of flint, but usually of a hard, fine-grained stone which would take a polish.   The earliest stone hammers (perhaps Neolithic) were bored by placing wet sand on the stone in the required place and then twisting a stick on the sand until a hole was bored right through the axe-head. As this was done from both sides, the result was usually what is called an " hour-glass " perforation, the hole being constricted in the middle. Later a hollow cylinder of bone or metal was used and the perforation was itself cylindrical.

HOUSES BUILT FOR THE ANCIENT DEAD

ROUND barrows are very numerous and are invariably on high ground. Long barrows are not numerous, but they are more easily seen and are frequently impressive, and as we have already stated they belong to the Neolithic people who used them as ossuaries.

The round-headed Beaker people who built round barrows, buried their dead unburnt until the time of the appearance of the food-vessel, when cremation began to be used, and later still, with the overhanging cinerary urn, cremation was the usual rite.

There are round barrows and bell barrows, disc and saucer barrows, ring, twin, triple, and bowl barrows ; and there are examples of most on Salisbury Plain. In other places such as ploughed fields, we have to cast our eyes along the surface, and sometimes take the barrow on faith. The nature and date of the contents are always uncertain.

> It is said " The fascination of archæology consists in reconstructing the life of the past, but by a curious paradox we obtain most of our raw material from the graves of the dead. We profit by the superstition which ordained that the dead man should be supplied with tools and weapons and the dead woman with ornaments, to accompany them to the land of the shadows." [1]

In the Bronze Age both burnt and unburnt burials were found in round barrows, and in one case at Acklam Wold, Yorkshire, opened in 1849, both methods had been resorted to. A pile of burnt human bones was found there in close contact with the legs of a human skeleton buried in the usual contracted position, and they seem to have been deposited while yet hot, for the knees of the skeleton were completely charred. It has been suggested that in cases like this, or where an unburnt body is surrounded by a ring of urn burials,

[1] *Antiquity*, December 1932, Crawford.

the entire skeletons may be those of chiefs, or heads of families, and the burnt bones those of slaves, dependents, or even wives sacrificed at the funeral. The practice of *suttee*, the sacrificing of a Hindu widow on her husband's funeral pyre, in Europe, rests indeed on the authority of Julius Cæsar, who represents such religious suicides as having, in no remote period from his own, formed a part of the funeral rites of the Gaulish chiefs. It is possible that fire in certain cases was used for purification, or for other ceremonial purposes, and not to consume the body.

THE " ROUNDHEADS " OF THE BRONZE AGE

BRONZE Age immigration provided a remarkable contrast in racial type. The Bronze Age race was slightly taller than the Neolithic, with lighter hair and a fairer complexion. The head was shorter and remarkably flat at the back—the typical round head. It was definitely brachycephalic in marked contrast to dolichocephalic man of Neolithic days. The face was broad and relatively short, with prominent cheek bones.

The Bronze Age is the most epoch-making in the history of mankind. It is very difficult to realise what an enormous difference to life the discovery of metal must have made. To be able to produce, almost at will, a material with which to make an axe and then to-morrow be able to melt it down and make it into a knife, must have been a most thrilling affair for these early people, who had long realised that once a flint was made it could not be remade except by making it smaller. They saw the beauty of their metal, and soon produced beautiful things ; indeed, many of the productions of this period, apart from their age, are delightful things to possess.

IRON, THE MYSTERY METAL, APPEARS

THE Iron Age is divided into two parts, the first being called Hallstatt, after the famous cemetery in the Austrian Tyrol, while the second part is called La Tène (or the Shallows) after an excavated military post on Lake Neuchâtel in Switzerland. The latter is sub-divided by Continental scholars into La Tène I, La Tène II, and La Tène III.

Exactly when the Iron Age commenced is not known, and how iron was discovered is a mystery. As has already been suggested, this discovery may have been made accidentally on the domestic hearth, or Bronze Age man may have experimented with stones and eventually found a deposit of ironstone. The precise form of the earliest furnace has also not been ascertained, although more than one discovery of prehistoric iron works has been made in Europe. Crucibles found in Europe point to a primitive form of furnace like that used in Egypt up to last century. It is important to remember that the metal was never cast, but always obtained from the ore as a solid mass of malleable iron. Although there is proof that iron was produced in Britain in the Iron

---

(A) IN BRITAIN

CULTURES.	DATES.
(Native culture after 43 A.D.)	
La Tène III .	From 75–50 B.C. to 43 A.D.
La Tène II .	From 250 B.C. to 75–50 B.C.
La Tène I .	From 550–450 B.C. to 250 B.C.
Hallstatt . .	From end of Bronze Age up to La Tène I times.

(B) ON THE CONTINENT

La Tène III	
La Tène II	From 500 B.C. to 1 B.C.
La Tène I	
Hallstatt . .	From 1000–900 B.C. to 500 B.C.

28. *Divisions of the Early Iron Age in Britain (A) and on the Continent (B). The earliest division is Hallstatt.*

Age, no furnaces have been discovered, and it is probable that the ancient Britons used a simple low hearth resembling the Catalan furnace of the Pyrenees, which has been in use from remote times until our own day. Tin was already known, and possibly the same methods were used for iron.

Two of the earliest known ironworks in Europe are in the Upper Danubian region, within easy reach of the famous cemetery of Hallstatt, from which the first part of the Early Iron Age takes its name. There were famous salt mines there also.

THE TIN TRAFFIC IN ANCIENT BRITAIN

THE first mention of tin in Britain is by the Stoic Posidonius, who travelled in Britain about 90 B.C. He seems to be the authority for the statement " that the inhabitants of Belerion were very fond of strangers and were civilised in consequence. After smelting and purifying the tin, they beat it into masses shaped like knuckle bones and carried it to an island off Britain called Ictis, which at low tides was accessible to wagons. Here the merchants bought the metal from the natives and carried it over to Gaul." Belerion is known to be Land's End and Ictis is best identified with St. Michael's Mount, which is not twelve miles distant and only an island at high water. When this traffic began is uncertain. Reinach thought the Phrygians visited Britain about 850 B.C., even before the Phœnicians, but tin exports seem to have declined before the days of Strabo, who wrote in the first twenty years of our era, and enumerates wheat, cattle, gold, silver, iron, skins, slaves, and dogs as exports from Britain, but does not mention tin. For three hundred years before Cæsar, the east-coast districts of Britain had been given over to agriculture.

Trade in various commodities with the Continent was evidently of long standing, coinage being introduced by way of Gaul. Of the country north of the Thames, Cæsar can have had little personal knowledge, and his account of the natives and of the mining of tin is far from precise ; though his conception of the *inland* population as the first inhabitants who had been displaced by Belgic immigrants seems to be very near the truth. While the inhabitants near the Straits were the most civilised and resembled their neighbours of Gaul, most of those inland sowed no corn, but lived on milk and flesh, using skins of animals for clothing. All these, but presumably not the Southerners, stained their bodies with blue to frighten their enemies, wore their hair long and shaved all but the upper lip.

THE ADVENTUROUS AND CONQUERING CELTS ARRIVE

THE Celtic type is credited with great stature, fair or reddish hair, blue or grey eyes, and a long head (dolichocephalic). In origin the stock is presumably North German, Teutonic, or Scandinavian, but was located in Central Europe at the dawn of history. From that region successive hordes crossed the Upper Rhine and established themselves in Western

Europe, even invading Italy, Greece, and Asia Minor with varying success. The late Hallstatt culture may be Celtic. The occupation of the Rhine by the Celts seems to have been uninterrupted for some centuries, and this adventurous and conquering race may have distributed this civilisation through most of Europe. At about 250 B.C. the Belgae, who are known to be of Teutonic origin, crossed the Lower Rhine and founded Gallia Belgica between the Rhine, the Marne, and the Seine. These people cremated their dead.

Cremation is in itself an index of race, and its geographical distribution in Europe is of special interest. It is *northern and barbarian*, whereas " inhumation " is *oriental and classical* ; but there are exceptions both in time and place. In the Late Bronze Age cremation was general in Europe, and in the Hallstatt period the two rites were practised together in varying proportions.

The Celtic-speaking peoples are divided according to their language into P Celts and Q Celts, the latter being represented in Ireland, the Scottish Highlands, and the Isle of Man. This branch can be traced to Spain and Greece. P elements are characteristic of Brythonic folk, and to them belong the languages of Wales and Brittany, as well as the extinct Cornish tongue. Brythonic seems to have been the language of Britain when Pytheas of Marseilles visited these shores in the fourth century B.C.

It is quite in accord with their German origin that the Belgæ practised cremation ; and in spite of Ptolemy's evidence that in the second century of our era they occupied what is now Hampshire, North Wiltshire, and Somerset, it is possible to connect them with the pedestal cinerary urns of the Aylesford type in Kent and Essex and the bead-rim pottery elsewhere. It is assumed that the inhabitants of Kent (Cantii) and Essex (Trinobantes) were of the same stock as the Atrebates, with their capital at Silchester (Calleva), in Hampshire, who linked them with the West, and are known to have been a Belgic tribe. The native military force consisted of infantry and charioteers, but there was perhaps no cavalry in the strict sense.[1]

FASHIONS IN ART OF THE EARLY IRON AGE

IN the art of this period we find first the purely geometric style lightly engraved without embossing. This is followed

[1] British Museum, *Early Iron Age Guide*, p. 2 et seq.

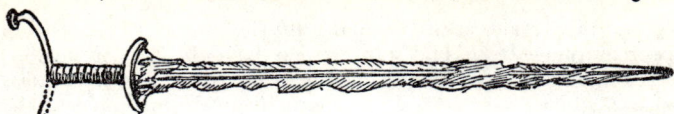

Sword of the
Hallstatt Type

Scabbard
(Early Iron Age)

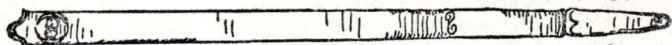

Socketed
Iron Celt

Iron Spear Heads
(from the Thames)

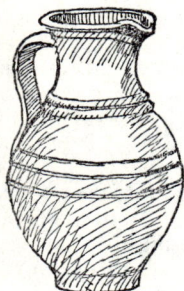

Bronze Brooches

Pottery Jug

29. FINELY WROUGHT WORK OF THE EARLY IRON AGE

*Lightly engraved geometric patterns and embossed work are
the two types of ornament characteristic of this period.
Bronze was still used, often in conjunction with iron, especially for making swords. Note especially the shapes of the
brooches, which now assume importance.*

by another style, seen on many of the broad belts of thin bronze plate from Hallstatt, which have bosses of various sizes and embossed linear ornament, sometimes with figures of men, birds, and horses. Ornament gives some clue to the date of Iron Age antiquities, but a more solid foundation for chronology is afforded by the successive changes undergone by the sword and the brooch.

Swords are recognised as being of importance for dating in Hallstatt times. The earliest phase is one of transition from the Bronze Age, when bronze swords of three types were in use—the *antennæ* type, the Ronzano type (which is similar, but has an angular expansion in the middle of the grip), and the leaf-shaped sword.

At first iron was scarce and valuable, but its cutting edge was quickly appreciated. Sometimes the blade was of iron while the bronze hilt remained, the pommel meanwhile increasing in size to balance the large blade of iron. In the seventh century B.C. this huge weapon went out of fashion, and a knife with a fish-tail scabbard came in.

WHERE THE FIRST SAFETY-PIN WAS FOUND

THE simplest and earliest brooch or safety-pin known is named after Peschiera, on Lake Garda (north Italy), where it was found in pile-dwellings on the shore. It was evidently evolved from the wire-pin, perhaps through the swivel-headed brooch of Scandinavia, and has been dated about 1400 B.C. This type has been found in Mycenæan graves on Salamis, near Athens, dating before 1200 B.C., where it is recognised as intrusive and characteristic of a more primitive dress than the Mycenæan.

In Britain the Celtic artist was unsuccessful with figure subjects, but was a master of line, and his gradual divergence from classical models towards eccentric scroll work of his own fancy can be appreciated by comparing two bronze shields. One from Witham, in Essex, preserves the palmette in a form easily recognisable, and has studs of coral from the south. The other, the Battersea masterpiece, has no obvious relation to classical art, and is decorated with enamel. In the interval between them British art had proved that it could stand alone. Pottery is now known to have developed locally ; and a marked improvement on the Late Bronze Age ware is noticed in several groups that go back to Hallstatt times, that is, the beginning of the Iron Age.

HOW THE IRON AGE BEGAN

Recent research has suggested the division of the Pre-Roman Iron Age into three broadly-distinguished cultures, within each of which there are probable or certain divisions. The three are as much *regionally* as *chronologically* distinct, and their dates in different areas overlap. They have been conveniently lettered A, B, C.[1]

The great Celtic expansion over Europe was much affected by the growing pressure of the Germanic peoples advancing southwards from the Baltic. It was the Celts of the Lower Rhine who first felt this pressure in the seventh century B.C., and a mingling of Celtic and Germanic features soon begins to be noticeable in the archæology of that region. The Germanic pressure increased; and while the mixed Celto-German culture persisted in the Lower Rhine area for many centuries and produced the Belgic culture of the British Iron Age C, a number of Celts were inevitably forced to disperse. In the sixth century this great dispersal reached its height, and those groups which crossed to Britain became her principal Early Iron Age immigrants. Others found their way to the Pyrenees and northern Spain. This happened just when the culture of La Tène was taking shape. With Scarborough as their northern limit, these immigrants occupied the whole of the south-east of England, reaching as far west as the Mendip caves, and passing into the Severn basin.

Habitation sites of the Iron Age A people are numerous, and Hengistbury Head, a fortified fort settlement, is important, as it was here that Hallstatt pottery was first recognised. The most important Iron Age A site is All Cannings Cross, near Devizes, Wiltshire, where seventy-five pits were found which were used for storage and rubbish, some of which had dome roofs of hardened clay, while the occupants lived in huts which were chiefly rectangular. The pottery of the Final Hallstatt period of the Champagne type can be linked with the All Cannings culture, and dated about 500 B.C. The pottery is of the greatest importance, and forty vessels have been restored from fragments found on this site. Objects of bone and antler were found, including two dog's teeth bored for suspension, eighteen bone needles, and knives made from rib bones. Ring-headed pins, which are rare in Britain, brooches, bracelets, beads, and a maple-leaf razor are also

[1] By C. F. C. Hawkes, *Antiquity*, March 1931, p. 62.

amongst the finds from this site, which make up this Iron Age A.

At Park Brow, near Worthing, Sussex, Bronze Age, Hallstatt, and Roman occupation was found. Hallstatt hut-sites, sixty feet long and forty feet broad, were explored, and typical pottery, thin and hard, sometimes gritty, but often smooth and covered with a lustrous red-brown coating which now perishes very quickly, was recovered. This site is remarkable, inasmuch as there were Late Bronze Age Deverel-Rimbury pottery people there who were replaced by Hallstatt Iron Age A people, and the later development of pottery was influenced, but not superseded, by the later Belgic forms.

THE FIRST IDEA OF COMMUNITY LIFE

THE camps, which we must now call Hill-forts, belonging to this period are very numerous. It was clearly the Iron Age A people who brought the idea of building these citadels of tribal groups. Practically all the hill-forts were built in this period, which shows that the immigrants desired to foster tribal traditions and to assist tribal development.

The forts were no doubt built from fear of invasion and attack. They were probably permanently inhabited by a fraction of the population, and they were essentially places of refuge in times of trouble. The people within them occupied pit-dwellings. Examples of hill-forts are on St. Catherine's Hill, in Hampshire; The Trundle; at Cissbury; and an unfinished one at Ladle Hill, Hampshire. The entrances have been closely studied and their development worked out.

Flint implements continued to be made, and comprise scrapers of all kinds, points, blades, barbed and tanged arrow-heads, as well as hammer-stones and pounders. Triangular loom weights, bone implements of all kinds (including weaving combs), shovels made of ox shoulder-blades, picks of deer antler, and spindle whorls of pottery and baked clay are also found. Spear-heads of wrought iron imitating late Bronze Age spear-heads were made, as well as iron-socketed axes.

There is distinct evidence of continental trade in the shape of imported brooches, chiefly of Italian design. Ring-headed pins date from the fifth century B.C. to our own era.

Brooches of La Tène type evolved in the following way : The earliest is a bow brooch in one piece common in the fifth century along the Middle Rhine and in other parts of Central Europe. At the head was a spiral coil on both sides to give tension to the pin, which was caught in the returned foot. In course of time the loose end of the foot was found to be inconvenient and was fixed to this bow. La Tène II brooches are generally long, with depressed bows. The next stage is marked by the complete junction of bow and foot which now form a continuous curve. A hollow space is thus left above the pin-catch, and this is gradually filled with openwork designs, generally crescents and step patterns. Finally in the early Roman period the foot becomes a solid plate, and the likeness of the bow to the La Tène pattern is more or less obscured. Examples of La Tène brooches are shown in Fig. 29.

As we have already mentioned, Britain's Iron Age A people at about 200 B.C. were being influenced by their neighbours, the Iron Age B people, and absorbing some La Tène elements from the Contintent. As a result, their pottery shapes alter. The Hallstatt shouldered form is modified into a saucepan shape. The paste improves and acquires a smooth " soapy " finish; the decoration begins to show the Celtic love of curves, and by the time the Belgæ arrive in 75 B.C. British potters have attained some proficiency.

As to burial rights, cremation and inhumation are present, and it is thought that cremations are the earlier. The upland country was still used for agriculture, and the embankments of the small rectangular fields formed by ploughing are now called Lynchets. They were discovered through air photography, and have been identified and mapped from aeroplanes. Ox, sheep, goat, pig and horse, and oysters were eaten, and the climate was damp—a sub-Atlantic phase.

THE BATTLE BETWEEN TWO IRON-AGE PEOPLES

WE have noted a Celtic migration from the Lower Rhine to the Pyrenees and northern Spain in the sixth century B.C.[1] This latter area was closely connected with Cornwall by the Atlantic tin trade which the Celts had dominated. Leeds considers that the hill-forts of Chun Castle, in Cornwall, are the work of some of these Celtic immigrants from north Spain. Brooches, pottery, and similarity of the forts form the basis of the argument. The stone hill-forts at Chun Castle have an inner and outer ditch, walls faced with granite blocks,

[1] See page 313.

and an elaborate entrance with a double turn. Inside each of them there are dry stone buildings, a furnace, and a well. These are extremely like the north Spain hill-forts, and it seems probable that some of these immigrants came from there, but our material has close affinities with Brittany.

Such movement, or movements, took place probably in the beginning of the fourth century B.C. These Iron Age B people spread all over the south-western counties, and although they mixed with the native population they also controlled them.

These Iron Age B people spread from Cornwall and Devon, over Somerset, and on to the Cotswolds, absorbing or driving out such Iron Age A people as might be on the fringe of the area occupied by them. Their pottery has been found at Hengistbury Head. Though they crossed the Severn they hardly penetrated farther westwards, but pushed up into the Midlands along the edge of the Iron Age A area. They went as far as Hunsbury, in Northamptonshire, where they met their kinsmen from Yorkshire.

Hunsbury is a hill site two miles south-west of Northampton, and it is most important. It was excavated by Sir Henry Dryden, and over three hundred circular pits were found. The majority of the finds are in the Northampton Museum. The interesting thing is that this was the point where the Iron Age " B " (the chariot burial people from Yorkshire) met the south-western Iron Age B people from Glastonbury, and there are items from both cultures present.

Their cultures lasted until the Roman Conquest, and during its prevalence the flourishing Cornish tin trade ensured contact with Gaul, for the Mediterranean currency bars (slats of iron something like unfinished swords to look at) were used for exchange. Some of these currency bars have been found on Iron A sites, which proves contact between the British Isles and southern Europe. The iron to make them was probably obtained from Dean Forest. Such a primitive form of currency agrees well with their primitive culture. They lived in clusters of round huts of dry masonry, the sort of building which went back to the Bronze age and which in Ireland and the Scottish Highlands persisted into our own era. At Chysauster, in Cornwall, a village of this period was excavated. The houses consist of oval enclosures of dry masonry clustered together, forming an irregular courtyard, with massively built entrances in which great blocks of stone that remind us of the Megaliths, were used. They can be connected with the tin industry, and

Iron Age pottery is found which can be dated to A.D. 200; there was hardly a trace of Romanisation in this district.

These settlements previously had an underground retreat called Fogou or Souterrain; many others are known in Western Britain and in Ireland. Agriculture was practised, and these Iron Age B people built or reconditioned forts, such as Hembury, in Devon; Dolbury; Ham Hill and the two Cadburys, all in Somerset; while at Worlebury it is thought a massacre took place when the Belgæ came later on.

BEAUTY AND INDUSTRY IN IRON AGE LIFE

THE Glastonbury site, in Somerset, is the best in Britain of Iron Age B times. The site was surrounded with a palisade, and had artificial understructures of prepared timbers, brushwood, stones, and earth for a firm foundation for dwelling huts. It is now only eighteen feet above sea-level. Over ninety dwelling huts of circular or oval design, varying in diameter from fourteen to thirty-eight feet, were excavated. Each hut contained a central hearth, and when a new floor was added a new hearth was made too; five or six of such hearths was a common number, but nine or ten are met with. It is estimated that two hundred to three hundred people lived there; and although the site is naturally fortified, these people augmented the fortifications, but it is not considered it was in any sense a military station, although a skull with a deep sword-cut speaks of an attack.

Their social and industrial equipment was on a high level. There is much evidence of weaving; such as spindle whorls, weaving combs, bone spools, loom weights, and the framework of one or two looms. There is also evidence of smelting metals and of carpentry, as wooden tubs and tools to make them with were found. Personal possessions include needles and pins of bone and bronze, beads of glass, amber, and jet, brooches of the safety-pin type, finger-rings and bracelets, and a bronze mirror. There is some evidence of cremation, but the burial place has not been discovered.

The domestic animals include ox, sheep, goat, pig, horse, dog, and the domestic fowl. Wild animals include stag, roe-deer, beaver, otter, cat, boar, and a number of birds. Agriculture was practised, and the horse was used for riding and driving, as harness ornamented in the British La Tène style was found. Flints were still used and rotary and saddle querns occurred, proving that the former, which is typical of

La Tène III period, was introduced while the latter was still in use. The site ceased to be inhabited prior to the Roman Conquest. Many other interesting objects were discovered from this site, among them being a riveted bronze bowl, forty-five brooches, knives—some of them still retaining their handles—a boat eighteen feet long, and much interesting and beautiful pottery.

The aristocracy of this period owned beautiful things, such as a sword scabbard in bronze from Meare Heath, Somerset, and bronze bowls which are thought to have been used as water-clocks. A water-clock appears to have worked in the following manner. A small bowl with a hole in the base was placed on the surface of some water contained in a larger vessel, and the water was allowed to percolate through the aperture. In a definite time the vessel sank, and was then replaced on the surface of the water by an attendant, who perhaps then rang a gong or in some way announced the lapse of a certain time unit. They have been found in many places. The Standfordbury bowl was used for this purpose.

A beautiful hanging bowl from Cerrig-y-drudion, Denbighshire, is a lovely work of art, and was found in a rifled stone cist. The ornamentation is derived from the classical palmette. The alternate hatching of the ground at the top of the drawing is a common feature in Early British art, but here probably made its first appearance in England. The bowl was suspended by four chains, and is dated about 250 B.C.

A bronze bowl beaten out of sheet bronze and finished on a lathe was found at Launceston in Cornwall ; on one side it has a grotesque escutcheon which resembles a ram's head. It is very like the larger of the two bowls from the famous burial at Birdlip, Gloucestershire, where the skeleton of a woman was found with two other skeletons, probably of men, together with bowls used as water-clocks, beads, brooches, and, above all, the bronze mirror. The whole group is in the Gloucester Museum. Twenty other mirrors are known.

THE IRON AGE PEOPLE'S IDEA OF A FUNERAL

INHUMATION was the rule at Harlyn Bay cemetery in Cornwall where the skeletons were contracted. Other finds of the same kind have been made, and it is considered that there is enough evidence to say it is the typical Iron Age rite.

About 250 B.C., Celtic immigrants from Gaul, who practised inhumation, and particularly chariot burial, appeared in eastern Yorkshire. They are identified with the Parisii, located in Yorkshire by Ptolemy ; there is a great resemblance between their chariot burials and those at Nanterre in the territory of the Gaulish Parisii, so migration from the Seine Valley may reasonably be affirmed. This folk can be traced as far south as East Anglia on the fringe of the A area, as the important burial at Newnham in the Cambridge region resembled that of the Yorkshire Group.

The Santon Downham hoard in the Cambridge Archæo-logical Museum was found in a large Celtic bronze cauldron ; it is late in this period. The hoard consisted of bronze harness plates, decorated with red enamel (in this case, sunk enamel, which is called " champleve ").

At Dane's Graves, four miles north of Driffield, Yorkshire, which best represent Iron Age B in the north, there are still two hundred barrows to be seen. Hand-made urns were usual with the contracted skeletons, and many bones of pig were found. Among others, a brooch with a broken back (called involuted) was found. This is an entirely British type.

At Stanwick, seven miles north of Richmond, North Riding of Yorkshire, there are earthworks which enclose about five hundred acres. In a pit there about five feet from the surface, some extremely fine harness and chariot trappings were found. They are in the British Museum.

INVADERS BRING THE POTTER'S WHEEL TO BRITAIN

WHILE the Iron Age B culture lasted in the west and north until the Roman Conquest, its influence on Iron Age A was curtailed in about 75 B.C. by the invasion of the Belgæ, who appeared in Kent, and spread over south-east England, north of the Thames ; a second invasion took place in 50 B.C.[1]

Aylesford is the chief site for evidence of the first invasion, the pedestal urn of the Marne type being the most important item. It was made on the wheel, evidently now first intro-duced. The key to the history of these invasions is to be found in Belgic Gaul, which was divided by the Ardennes into two cultural regions. One remained a backwater, and

[1] Hawkes and Dunning, " The Belgæ of Gaul and Britain," *Archæological Journal*, lxxxvii. 1930.

in the other the La Tène Marne culture flourished, but
was brought to an end by invasions from the north and
east, and the heirs of the latter were the Belgæ who invaded
England in 75 B.C.

Essex was not conquered by the Belgæ in Cæsar's time,
and the Iron Age A people (the Trinobantes) put themselves
under Cæsar's protection against Cassivellanus, but at the
opening of the Iron Age C era the Belgæ conquered it, and
the capital of the dynasty was transferred to *Camulodunum*,
the British predecessor of Roman and of modern Colchester
on the adjoining hill.

The Belgæ invaded Dorset early in this period, and
Somerset is believed to have been invaded by them just
before the Roman Conquest. In Sussex only the west of
the country came under them—elsewhere the Iron Age A
people continued in occupation. There are settlement
sites showing that the new people lived side by side with
the Iron Age A people already in possession, such as those
at Broadstairs, Walmer, and Margate. The hill-fort of
Bigbury, near Canterbury, now being excavated, is believed
to have been stormed by Cæsar. The Belgæ have been
detected in Gloucestershire, Hertfordshire, the Nene Valley,
and on the edge of the Fens.

The second Belgic invasion of 50 B.C. is characterised
by bead-rim pottery as opposed to the pedestal urns of the
first invasion. The second is associated with the name of
the Atrebatic Prince Commius, who is known to have fled
to Britain with a following in about 50 B.C., when he struck
Britain's first coinage. Silchester (Hampshire) was apparently
a Belgic foundation. The small tribal units of Iron A were
now merged in larger kingdoms, and their local tribal hill-
forts abandoned, but some sites continue into the Roman
period, and some hill-forts were then deserted for a valley
site; for instance, St. Catherine's Hill was replaced by
Winchester, and The Trundle by Chichester. A number
of camps have been excavated which show these Iron Age C
people (Belgæ) occupied, and in some cases altered hill-
forts on the fringe of the country occupied by Iron Age B
people.

The burial rite was cremation, but extended inhumation
or burial in a stretched-out position has been found with
bead-rim jars. A notable cremation burial in a barrow,
evidently of a Belgic chief, was discovered at Hurstbourne

Tarrant, Hampshire. Among the grave furniture was a wood-bucket mounted with iron and bronze, a thistle type brooch, a bronze bracelet, glass, and a dozen pottery vessels. It is dated A.D. 30–40.

WHAT BRITAIN WAS LIKE WHEN THE ROMANS CAME

THE Belgæ boasted of their German blood. It is a Teutonic trait to use the loess or similar plains for agriculture where not too thickly covered with trees, and so these people occupied the lowland sites hitherto unused. The Iron Age A people appeared to keep to their upland sites, and they farmed side by side with the Belgæ.

Corn and cattle were imported to Gaul, and it was through this trade that the Roman provincial character was brought to Britain, and as Gaul became more Romanised so more Romanisation came to Britain, even before the coming of Claudius in A.D. 43. Among the imports, articles of luxury are prominent. The British princes and nobles took the lead in developing Romanising tastes, and diplomatic relations were encouraged by Augustus, with the British as well as with other native rulers, who lived on the fringes of the Roman Empire. [1]

Tasciovanus, who ruled at Verulamium, minted coins with classical designs. Pottery was imported from the Continent in abundance, and this, with other imports, belongs chiefly to the first part of the first century A.D. After Essex was conquered, Tasciovanus's son, Cunobelinus, took over an old capital at Camulodunum, by Colchester, which was made the centre of the import trade about 5 B.C. In fact, Camulodunum became the capital of all South Britain. The coins of Cunobelinus are found nearly all over the country, and he must have been the supreme ruler for some time before his death in A.D. 40.

In the realm of La Tène art, the Battersea shield, to be seen in the British Museum, and the bucket-handle from Harpenden (Luton Museum), are leading examples.

As in the other periods, it is the burials of the great that produce the finest things. At Stanfordbury, Bedfordshire, two large vaults were found which contained Roman pottery, bronze bowls used as water-clocks, and glass. In one vault there were two fire-dogs, four spits, and a tripod with six hooks, while in the other there were pieces of iron, which

[1] Hawkes and Dunning, "The Belgæ of Gaul and Britain," *Archæological Journal*, lxxxvii. 1930.

may have formed a sacrificial table like one from Welwyn in Hertfordshire. The Welwyn find contained remarkable amphoræ (earthenware vessels) and imported objects, including two silver cups and three bronze masks, wooden tankard handles, and three pairs of iron fire-dogs measuring 42 inches between the uprights, and terminating in knobbed horns, and an iron frame which may have been a sacrificial table or altar. It is unique in Britain.

THE GREAT INVASION : ROME THE BUILDER ARRIVES

W E have already seen that Romanisation had been going on for some time before the Conquest of Britain by Claudius in A.D. 43. Across the narrow seas was a flourishing Roman province, and the Gauls were in touch with Britain through trade and diplomatic relationships. It is to be remembered that both in 75 B.C. and in 50 B.C. there were Belgic (Iron Age C) invasions into the south-east of England, the territory which had previously been occupied by Iron Age A. Further inland, the Iron Age B occupation was undisturbed.

The Lowland Zone of Britain was quickly conquered by Claudius, and later both the towns and the country estates were peacefully occupied. The highlands remained almost entirely unoccupied by civilians ; but the military certainly were there at times, and the situation became such that later the Highland Zone demanded military occupation.

The Romans in A.D. 43 had to fight their way across Kent and the Thames to capture Camulodunum (Colchester), and there was much fighting in Wessex. Sussex was occupied by a tribe called the Regni, and Norfolk and Suffolk by people called the Iceni. Neither of these offered any resistence to the Roman soldiers, so the native rulers in these places were left alone. Apparently it was the Belgæ, the last comers to this island, who resisted the Romans. There was a good deal of friction between the Belgæ and the older Iron Age people who now emerge as Britons with pro-Roman tendencies. Cunobelinus, as we have noted, established a capital at Camulodunum, and there is no doubt that he was a great ruler. On his death in A.D. 40, the Belgæ quarrelled among themselves, and the position was very much the same as it had been in Gaul before Cæsar entered it. This was, of course, exactly the moment for the Romans to come. The second, fourteenth, and twentieth legions (between forty thousand and fifty thousand men) under the command of Aulus Plautius, crossed the Channel, and most of what is now England was subdued in a few days. Cunobelinus's only surviving son, Caractacus, was forced to fly into South Wales, a part of the Highland Zone.

The main landing-place for the army has been discovered under the later forts, at Richborough in Kent. The occupation material, especially the pottery, is important; and the Richborough reports published by the Society of Antiquaries gives this information in great detail. The companion site to Richborough is at Camulodunum outside Colchester, where the winter-quarters of the army were discovered in 1931. This area was occupied while Roman Colchester was being built.

Camps were built in many places, often within the earthworks of the British people. Hod Hill in Dorset and Bury Hill in Gloucestershire, are examples. On the Fosse Way, which runs from Exeter to York, there is the Claudian fort of *Margidunum*, near East Bridgford in Nottinghamshire, which covers 6½ acres. Its wooden buildings were rebuilt in stone after a fire, apparently during the rebellion of Boudicca (incorrectly spelt Boadicea) in A.D. 61.

Caractacus attracted Belgæ, men without lands, and other native tribesmen. With them he formed an army. Ostorius, the governor, who arrived in A.D. 47, was faced with the stubborn resistance, under Belgic leadership, of the whole of Wales. The Second Legion was brought up, and a pitched battle was at last won by the Romans in A.D. 51. Caractacus's family was taken prisoner, and he was reduced to doing what he scorned to do before, namely, seek refuge with his British enemies. He fled to a tribe called the Brigantes, who lived in the York area, but they had strong feelings about the domination of the south by Cunobelinus (Caractacus's father), and the queen, Cartimandua, received him only to hand him over in chains to the Roman Governor, Ostorius. The story of the appearance in Rome of Caractacus, in A.D. 51, is well-known. When led captive through the magnificent streets of the greatest capital in the world, Caractacus expressed astonishment that the possessors of wealth so vast should envy him his thatched cottage in Britain. The Emperor, struck by his intelligence and free and noble bearing, spared his life, and granted him an " honourable freedom," but Caractacus never returned to Britain.

In the south the bulk of the Belgæ, when they saw resistance was useless, had abandoned the struggle, and the Romanisation which was begun under Cunobelinus made headway. We have noted that the native ruler of the Iceni was allowed to remain in Norfolk and Suffolk. On the death of this ruler, however, the kingdom was annexed. The British population revolted under their queen, Boudicca, and sacked Verulamium (St. Albans), Colchester, and London, with enormous slaughter of those in favour of Rome.

Agricola was given command in A.D. 78 and, according to Tacitus, his son-in-law was bent on spreading civilisation. He provided a liberal education for the sons of British chieftains. There certainly was a general spread of education, as Roman dates, names, and short phrases, which are scratched on a number of things, have been found in Great Britain, but not one word of the Celtic language. It has been said that the level of education was higher than anything attained in England until the nineteenth century. As far as religion was concerned, the Roman gods were welcomed, Mars being the most popular.

ENGINEERING PROBLEMS FOR THE WALL-MAKERS

HADRIAN arrived in A.D. 122, and it was about this time that the great Roman Wall was built, stretching from Newcastle-on-Tyne to Solway Firth—a distance of 73½ miles. Bede, writing from Jarrow about A.D. 720 to 730, says " it is eight feet in breadth and twelve feet in height," and a description written as late as about 1572 gives the height as twenty-one feet. The general height can be taken as twenty feet, and it was defended by a fosse and rampart, *i.e.* a ditch and defensive mound of earth. This wall constituted the frontier except between A.D. 143 and 180, when the Antonine Wall of turf, between the Firths of Forth and Clyde, formed for thirty-six miles the northern limit of the Roman province.

This wall was completed in A.D. 143. Regiments normally encamped on Hadrian's Wall were transferred either wholly or in part to the Antonine Wall. It is much simpler than Hadrian's, and is built on a fourteen-feet foundation, finished by massive kerbs on either side. In front of the wall there is a ditch normally forty feet wide and twelve feet deep. The ditch is separated from the wall by a berm (a ledge between the ditch and the base of the parapet), generally twenty feet wide. The width of the berm is remarkable, as in Roman work such ledges are usually narrow.

About the time of Hadrian's arrival the native tribe centred in York (the Brigantes) were giving trouble. They were probably responsible for the entire destruction of the ninth legion, which is known to have been in York, and which was never heard of after A.D. 107. The sixth legion was sent there in A.D. 120.

A legion of five thousand to six thousand men was nominally composed of Roman citizens, but cavalry and auxiliary troops were recruited in the provinces. These did not possess full civil rights. Full citizenship was sometimes given while on service as a reward for some meritorious action. Infantry were divided into cohorts of five hundred to one thousand men. The officers were Roman citizens. The Roman army in Britain did not include any native soldiers, as these were sent abroad to fight. The composition of the armies is shown by the diplomas of honourable discharge, which took the form of engraved bronze plates joined together like writing tablets. They conferred civil privileges upon the veteran soldier, including Roman citizenship for his wife and children. The originals were filed at Rome on the wall behind the temple of Minerva (goddess of wisdom), copies being sent to those concerned.

Some of the legions remained in Britain for at least two hundred years. The Second legion had its headquarters at Caerleon, three miles from Newport (Monmouthshire), while the Twentieth legion was at Chester. The Ninth legion had been at Chester also before it was sent to York.

THE " VICAR OF BRITAIN " TAKES COMMAND

THE functions of government were concentrated in the commander-in-chief, who represented the Emperor, and had the title of Legate, three years being the average term of office. At the time of Diocletian, A.D. 284–305, the government was altered, civil and military power being divided. Britain now became one of three dioceses under the Prefect of the Gauls, and formed a political unit under the Vicar of Britain, who was called *Vir spectabilis* (which may be rendered "his Excellency"), and who probably resided at York. Under him were five governors or presidents, and the country was divided into parts, the limits of which cannot be traced, but a fair deduction from a local inscription

is that Cirencester (Corinium) was in the province of
Brittania Prima. Little is known of local government, but
from names which survive it is clear that the provinces
were divided into cantons as in Gaul, and the capital of
each retained the name of the tribe who lived there before
the Roman Conquest. The *civitas* (canton) of the Silures
is the only one mentioned in an inscription, which was
found at Caerwent (in Monmouthshire), the site of their
capital. Each canton had its magistrates and senate, while
there are four of the more Romanised colonies—Colchester,
Lincoln, Gloucester, and York. Verulamium was of superior
rank, but all the towns in Britain now ranked as *municipia*,
as Caracalla (A.D. 211–217) extended the franchise so that
every free provincial became a Roman citizen.

The military affairs under the new regime were handed
over to three officials, with the rank of *spectabilis*, who were
known as the Count of Britain, the Count of the Saxon
shore, and the Duke of the Britains, Count being the superior
rank (contrary to mediæval practice). The Duke commanded
in the north, guarding the Roman Wall, with his headquarters at York. The Saxon shore command included
the forts of Brancaster, Burgh Castle, Reculver, Bradwell-
on-Sea, Dover, Lympne, Pevensey, and Porchester. Richborough formed the backbone of this defence, but the headquarters of the fleet had been removed to Gaul, probably
Boulogne.

In the third century things went smoothly and conditions
gradually improved until the reign of Constantine the Great
(A.D. 306–337), the first Christian Emperor. The Romans
permitted all religions except Judaism and Christianity,
which were regarded as upsetting to law and order. It is
not known at what date Christianity found its way to Britain,
but Constantine was converted in A.D. 312, and Christianity
became the State religion of the Empire in A.D. 323.
Mithraism was a rival to Christianity, and underground
temples for its rites have been found in Britain.

The Picts broke through Hadrian's Wall about A.D. 343,
and apparently burnt Corbridge on the Tyne (Corstopitum);
and as there were a large number of " hoards " buried
between A.D. 350 and 360, the people must have been uneasy.
Invasions by the Picts from Scotland and by Scots from
the north-east of Ireland (the Scots did not occupy Scotland
in force until 498) took place in A.D. 360 to 364. There

were also other attacks, and the Count of the Saxon Shore and the Duke of the Britains were slain. Valentinian sent Theodosius to Richborough in A.D. 368 to take charge and restore law and order, but the relief was only temporary; the army could not be relied upon, and in 383 the pretender, Magnus Maximus, took most of the picked troops to the Continent to fight the Emperor Gratian, who died at Lyons in the same year. The Picts, Scots, and Saxons seized this opportunity, but were checked by Stilicho, who had the Sixth legion at his disposal in 385. In 401–402 the Sixth legion was recalled from guarding the northern frontier to fight in Rome, and five years later the island was cut off from Rome by a great barbarian invasion from Gaul.

OUR SCANTY LEGACY OF ROMAN ART

THE Romans left little of permanent value behind them in Britain. Their system of government, their laws and institutions, religion, language and writing, science and learning were all but ruined during the next two centuries. Compared with the Continent, the Roman remains in Britain are poor and unattractive. We have nothing comparable to the grandeur of Rome, but we have Hadrian's Wall and some pieces of town walls, those of Caerwent being an excellent example, and remains of fortresses and country houses, which are usually called " villas." Bath, with its local building stone, shows what could be done in Roman Britain with suitable material. Yet we have to admit that there is very little to show for the four hundred years of the Roman occupation except their roads. These are good ; they were generally made straight in spite of obstacles, and a round stone was placed at every Roman mile, which was about 1618 yards—1000 paces.

The Romans mined lead, which they exported, and there were silver refineries at Silchester, Wroxeter, and Hengistbury Head, Hampshire. Coal was used at the North Wall, but there is no evidence that it was mined, though found on sixteen other sites in England. Iron-working was in operation in Dean Forest and in the Weald of Sussex, and copper was extracted from North Wales and Cornwall. Gold was dug at Dolaucothy, in Carmarthenshire. Oysters were exported as far as Italy, where they were fattened in a lake. Juvenal, writing soon after A.D. 96, records that the Roman gourmet could distinguish by the flavour those which came from Richborough. It was Hadrian who first used the figure of Britannia on British bronze coins, a constant reminder of the Roman occupation.

Collingwood commences his book with the dictum, "Transportation is civilisation," and no one ever knew this better than the Romans. Their roads are not all alike. The great highways were certainly laid out in straight lines, but the lesser roads to villas and to farms had little or no definite design. A Roman road is usually made with a foundation of large stones on which gravel is placed, and later repairs can be traced if a section is cut through. These roads are in straight lengths, and a change of direction is angular and not curved. Roman roads have often been used as parish and other boundaries. Stanegate, which runs perhaps from Corbridge to Carlisle, was used in this way. This road dates back to Agricola, and was possibly one of his frontiers. Hadrian certainly made use of it for his frontier and further fortified it.[1]

There is little doubt that these roads were first made for military use, but they were soon also used as means of peaceful communication. A system of relays of posting carriages was organised by Augustus at an average distance of twenty-five miles apart ; a day's journey was about fifty miles, but in emergencies these distances were exceeded. The inhabitants of the country through which roads passed were forced to assist in this postal service, and local roads were kept up by local money and labour, whereas the military road and those which the State required were apparently maintained by the State. The great Roman roads are shown on the Ordnance Survey of Roman Britain. The roads include such well-known names as the Fosse Way, Ermine Street, and Watling Street, but on the above-mentioned map the numbers from the Itinerary of Antonine are used.

The posting stations tended to develop into villages or small towns provided with a hotel, baths, and shops, and these form a definite class of Roman settlement. Bridges were built, of course, but we have no certain remains of this kind in England. They were sometimes wooden structures on stone piers, such as those over the Tyne at Newcastle and Corbridge, but the majority were of timber throughout, and so nothing remains except the piles driven into the river bed.

[1] " The Archæology of Roman Britain," by R. G. Collingwood.

THE "BARRACKS" THAT THE ROMAN SOLDIER KNEW

COLLINGWOOD restricts the use of the word "camp" to places where troops were temporarily accommodated, forts being reserved for small places where troops were permanently quartered, and fortresses for large sites. A camp is a recognisable class of earthwork with a ditch; it was usually rectangular, with rounded corners and a gate in each side. The commanding officer's tent was in the centre, and the rest of the tents were laid out according to invariable rules. Though the shapes vary, the sides are approximately straight (curved earthworks are not Roman), and gates are usually in the sides. Semi-permanent camps have better defences, Cawthorn, Yorkshire, being a good example.

After the conquest of Britain, the fortresses of York, Chester, and Caerleon in Monmouthshire were occupied by the legions. The fortress at York was the successor of an earlier fortress at Lincoln, and Chester may have succeeded one at Wroxeter. Gloucester may have been the predecessor of the fortress at Caerleon, but we do not know. The fortress at York occupied over fifty acres, at Chester fifty-six acres, and at Caerleon fifty acres. Caerleon is a rectangle in plan, and is the best known in the country. The amphitheatre here, which was excavated by Dr. and Mrs. R. E. M. Wheeler, would have seated about six thousand spectators. It has eight entrances, which include four wide processional gateways, one at each of the sides, and the ends including a waiting-room for performers, with perhaps a box above and intermediate entrances.

The purpose of a fort was to house a unit which was acting as a police force in a small district. As such a force was not strong enough to fight a pitched battle, they needed defence against attack as well as protection against the weather. A fort in lay-out follows the main lines of a camp.

There are an enormous number of forts of all types in Britain, but we name only three. They are Carnarvon, in Wales, of the Flavian period, as is Templeborough, near Rotherham; and Newstead, the most remarkable Roman site in Scotland. There are also signal stations and light-houses.

NEATER TOWNS AND VILLAGES TAKE SHAPE

THE Romans considered it desirable that towns should be formed in Britain, as elsewhere, as part of the normal classical civilisation. The shapeless straggling settlements of the Belgic princes were replaced by those of Roman plan, and the tribal hill-forts of the Britons were abandoned and peaceful market towns and provincial centres were set up. These towns of the Roman period are small by our standards, and were of two classes. The larger ones were those which were deliberately planned with the streets crossing each other at right angles, and the smaller those in which there were groups of houses where two roads meet or where a road crosses a river.

Although Londinium is a Celtic name, London is only important after the Roman Conquest, and that is because of its position with regard to its river and roads. At most it could only have been a small post established by traders from within the Empire in the dozen years or so before the Conquest. It was after the Conquest that London Bridge was built. The geographical position of London is unique, and accounts largely for its unrivalled advance. The area of Roman London was 330 acres ; Cirencester comes next with 240, Verulam 200, Colchester 108, Caerwent 44 ; while among Roman Continental towns Nimes covered 790 acres, Milan 329, Lyons 314. It is estimated that the population of Roman London was probably 15,000 people. London, Verulam (St. Albans), and Colchester were all unwalled at the time of their destruction by Boudicca in A.D. 61. Walls were built round London about A.D. 100, in Colchester before A.D. 185, and at St. Albans before A.D. 150, while the Silchester walls date from the late first or early second century.

The walls of the colonia of Gloucester (Glevum) were probably built at the time it received its municipal charter as a *Colonia* from Nerva about 96–98 A.D. Its south-east angle tower has been excavated. Caerwent, Wroxeter, and Caistor, next Norwich, have been excavated, and all have interesting features. There were also small towns, but only a few have been excavated. They include Alchester, Oxfordshire, and Weston-under-Penyard, in Herefordshire. The occupation of both of these seems to range from the first to the fourth century.

There are very few public buildings in Romano-British towns in England. The chief ones are fora, amphitheatres, and baths. The forum at Silchester is a rectangle surrounded by a portico measuring 310 by 275 feet. In the centre is a courtyard about 140 by 130 feet surrounded on three sides by a colonnade from which open rooms that may have been shops. The fourth side was formed by the basilica, a great hall 240 feet long internally (apart from the apses) and 58 feet wide, with a central nave, with an apse at each end and side aisles with columns, perhaps 27 feet high. The nave may have been 60 feet high.

Bath owes its existence to its famous springs, and the baths are among the best Roman remains in England. The Romans inherited from the Greeks the habit of bathing in what we call " Turkish " baths. Every civilised community in these times possessed public baths which were the centre of its social life. Villas were often provided with complete sets of baths, the simplest of which included three rooms heated to different degrees. They were called the *frigidarium* (a plunge bath with cold water), the *tepidarium* (warm), and then the *caldarium* (hot), but additions were sometimes made to the scheme.

STYLES IN HOUSEBUILDING FAVOURED BY THE ROMANS

VILLA, in Latin, means a farm, and any house of the Roman period may be called a villa provided it was occupied by people who farmed a plot of land. They are of three main types : the corridor house, the courtyard house, and the basilican house. The majority are of the corridor type with wings. The one at Chedworth in Gloucestershire is an excellent example of the courtyard type ; it is open to public view. Brading, in the Isle of Wight, North Leigh, Oxfordshire, Folkestone and Bognor have villas which are left open. A town house in its simplest form is a strip house. It is long, narrow, and rectangular, like a barn. The larger ones are of three types, the commonest of which is L-shaped.

Temples of classical type have been found in Britain ; one of the Goddess Sul (or Sul Minerva) was at Bath and the temple of Claudius was at Colchester. Others are known which approach this type, but at Lydney in Gloucestershire there is a remarkable temple based on the plan of a basilica. It was built in the fourth century, and was the centre of the cult of the god Nodens. There are also temples of Romano-Celtic type, of which Caerwent is an example. The only Mithræum, a temple where Mithras was worshipped, is at Housesteads, and Silchester has the only Romano-British Christian church.

The Romans always buried their dead outside their settlements. Cremation is general before A.D. 150. Inhumation was introduced about A.D. 150, and by the end of the third century was general.

The Bartlow Hills in Essex are barrows of the Roman period, forming two parallel rows running north and south. The western row probably consisted of five barrows, of which two remain. The eastern row consisted of four steep-sided mounds, the largest barrow being 40 feet high and 145 feet in diameter. They are imposing monuments and are very steep and difficult to climb. There are many other barrows of Roman date known.

Tombstones are numerous and varied. Inscriptions are plentiful, the great inscription from the gateway of the Wroxeter forum being the most striking. They are extremely common in the first and second centuries. These inscriptions become rarer in the third and almost cease in the fourth century, but the use of inscriptions on tombstones is continued. They are most important because they are contemporary and authoritative, and their value as historical material can hardly be exaggerated. Roman inscriptions are always cut in capital letters, words are abbreviated, and stops inserted or omitted. A large proportion of the inscriptions in Britain are the work of unskilled workmen.

Pigs (blocks) of metal were stamped, seals bearing the owner's name are sometimes found impressed on them, and brooches, knives, and pottery frequently have the owner's name scratched on.

Tiles are often stamped by their makers and sometimes bear unofficial inscriptions by the workman such as " *Fecit tubulum Clementius*," *i.e.* " Clementius made this box-tile." The " Chi Rho " or Christian monogram has been found in a few places, but archæological evidence for Christianity in Roman Britain is scarce.

Coins as archæological evidence are of great importance, but the life of a coin, the rate of travel, and the proportions of the numbers in any one group must be considered. Roman coins almost entirely ceased to come to Britain after 395 A.D. Hoards are important, as every hoard consists of the coins possessed at one time by one owner who normally broke it up. There were no banks and hence money and other valuables were often buried.

POTTERS WHO HANDED DOWN THEIR NAMES WITH THEIR WORK

TERRA Sigillata or Samian ware, as many prefer to call it, is important because it has been so closely studied. It is known where and when a great number of its makers worked. A piece of this ware frequently bears its maker's name, impressed as a rule in the centre of the base of the inside of the vessel, but sometimes the piece is decorated and the name may be stamped in the decoration. The decoration, shade of colour, paste, etc., are important and help to distinguish the unmarked pieces.

The forms of Samian pottery were studied by Dragendorff and others, and were distinguished by numbers. They are commonly referred to in this way and about thirty forms are found in England. Coarse pottery has been closely studied by Collingwood and Hawkes during the last few years. From a number of scientifically excavated sites, where other datable material has been found, it has been possible to fix several points. Attention is concentrated on the shape of the vessel. These shapes differ enormously, so when the types selected by Collingwood are examined it must be remembered that while there may be a general likeness there is no slavish copying. Conditions were against uniformity, either of pattern or of quality.

BROOCHES OF BEAUTY THAT REVEAL THEIR AGE

METAL objects are the most important items to the archæologist, because they can usually be dated with some degree of accuracy. Brooches are particularly important and Collingwood has worked them out into 26 groups distinguished by the 26 letters of the alphabet, the most beautiful being Aesica in X-group and the next best is the R-group, which is not found outside Britain and which was developed in the north. This group includes the famous Backworth brooch.

Glass was used in windows, for bowls for the tables and for jugs in which were buried cremated human remains. Horn was also employed, while pewter was used for the table. At Icklingham, forty pieces of a large table service were found in 1840, and are now in the British Museum. Spoons are of three types. Forks were not used. Knives are in great variety and whetstones were employed to sharpen them. Cooking was done chiefly on an open hearth. Spinning and

weaving were common. Jewellery included finger rings, the
silver gilt brooch, already referred to, silver spoons—one
of the *cochlea* type which were used for eating snails that the
Romans bred for the table—and a gold chain and ornaments.
Part of a snake bracelet was found in a hoard at Llandovery,
and the gold find at Corbridge of 1908 included a ring and
a number of gold coins deposited about A.D. 385–7, while
the important find of 1911 included 160 gold coins deposited
about A.D. 160–162. Kimmeridge Shale from Kimmeridge
in the Isle of Purbeck was also used for bracelets, pins, etc.
Buckets, skillets, statuettes, jugs, and canisters are found
and add to the picture of the Romanisation of Britain.

People at this time rode horses and drove chariots and
they wore leather shoes and sandals, the soles of which were
studded with domed hob-nails. Writing was done on paper
and parchment with pen and ink, but the commonest method
of writing was with a stylus on tablets. Tablets were made
of small pieces of wood with raised edges which prevented
the wax running away when it was spread over the wood
in the hollows. Very often two of these pieces of wood
were hinged together. If the writer pressed too hard with
the stylus the message was imprinted on the wood, where
we sometimes find it thus preserved.

Tools of all sorts are common. Lighting was done by
lamps and candles. There were keys to the doors and bone
was used for pins and spoons.

The houses were plastered. In many Roman villas
to-day the colours with which their walls were painted can
be seen in a remarkably fresh condition. Sculptures in marble
from the luxurious Roman villas in Gloucestershire are in
the British Museum, notably the Luna and the Cupid and
Psyche groups, from Woodchester, Gloucestershire, where
there are remarkable mosaic pavements which are uncovered
at varying intervals.

LAW AND ORDER IN ROMAN TIMES

OF the population in the Roman period, Keith holds
that those in the southern part of England, from Kent
to Cornwall, were of the same racial stock throughout the
centuries immediately preceding the landing of Cæsar and
during the four centuries of the Roman occupation. In the
east of England there is a variant ; a skull with the same
dimensions as in the west, but with a flatter, less ridged

vault, with a wider more upright but less lofty forehead, and with a wider and rather shorter face. In the eastern country, round heads are sometimes found, but no round heads were found at Harlyn Bay or in the cemetery at Barnwood, Gloucestershire.

The law and order upon which Roman rule depended must have been at times extremely irksome to our British ancestors. But the Romanisation which was fostered even before the conquest paved the way for the development of this ordered government. The Celtic feeling which is expressed in curvilinear ornament was not suppressed, and we are now being taught that many of the later artistic triumphs belong to the British people rather than to the foreign invaders.

The villa system and the town system were the principal features of Romano-British life. Town life was considered essential for the furtherance of the fine arts, and the public buildings were its centre. " Villas " were self-contained units, housing a well-to-do owner and his slaves. The military were confined to the camps and to the north.

As the years passed and the Saxon raids on the East Coast increased, the danger zones had to be fortified and defensive walls built. Later still, when the Roman Empire was threatened elsewhere, the army was steadily withdrawn from Britain. In A.D. 410 Honorius said that Britain could no longer look for help from Rome. The Roman occupation of Britain had come to an end. At this point the archæologist leaves the stage : it is the historian's turn.

GLORIES OF ANCIENT CIVILISATIONS : MESOPOTAMIA

THE archæology which has been discussed has been confined largely to England, and it has already been pointed out that our civilisation was definitely behind that of the Continent and far behind the great centres of civilisations in the East ; much controversy has raged over these civilisations, especially on the question of which began first. In the following sketch of the greatest Eastern civilisations, however, we have adopted the chronology given by Professor Gordon Childe.

The centres of civilisation were places eminently suitable

both geographically and climatically, for their purpose. They were places where there was a good supply of water all the year round, plenty of food for animals and human beings, sites on which houses could be built, and materials with which to build them. All these necessities the Mesopotamian and Egyptian centres possessed. Each centre would appear to have developed on its own lines, although contact between them was probable.

The rivers Tigris and Euphrates produced the delta land of Mesopotamia, and it is to be remembered that Mesopotamia is one of the only two places where wheat has been found growing wild. [1] Here palms and fruit trees flourished, and there was clay for bricks. These conditions were exceedingly favourable for food production, organised industry, and commerce. The latter spread outwards very slowly, but the early centres of civilisation had a profound influence upon the succeeding cultures of the world. It is upon the written records of these early civilisations, which begin about 3000 B.C., that the chronology of prehistoric Europe rests.

Egyptian civilisation is the one best known, because that country has a delightful winter climate, and excavation is an easier matter there than in many other countries. Moreover, the soil is such that antiquities are well preserved. Mesopotamia, on the other hand, has only been seriously explored since the War.

A DESERT CITY DESTROYED BY FIRE

OF the many towns in Mesopotamia, Kish is the oldest. (Damascus is the oldest living city, but Kish began earlier.) It is thought that Kish existed seven thousand years ago in what is now an uninhabitable desert. It was a vast fortified place with temples and palaces. Even to-day there is a huge mound of baked red bricks, 90 feet high, which is one of the most prominent objects to be seen across the open plain. Visible proof of a great flood has been discovered, which shows that this city was submerged about 3300 B.C. The same thing was observed at Ur. When the Euphrates changed its course, about one thousand years ago, Kish lost its importance and sank into obscurity.

THE GLITTERING TREASURES OF UR

UR of the Chaldees is also a familiar name, but its splendour was not known until excavations after the War revealed

[1] The other is on the slopes of Mount Hermon.

its most amazing treasures. Its earliest cemetery is dated by its excavators about 3500 B.C. In it gold vessels, which are fine works of art, were discovered. They denote a high level of civilisation which must have taken a considerable period to develop, and so the discovery of four lyres, proving the existence of music, is not so surprising. One harp, that of Queen Shub-ad, was a true harp with a single upright beam from which the strings were brought down transversely to the sounding-box.

A great feature of Ur is the mighty Ziggurat, the "Mountain of God," which was built about 2,400 B.C., probably on the site of an even earlier temple. It measured 200 feet long, 150 feet broad, and 50 feet high. A royal tomb, which had been rifled in the dim past, produced much treasure. In a wide trench, close to the tomb, were the skeletons of five men, and further on, those of ten women, with elaborate head-dresses of gold, lapis lazuli, and carnelian. There was also a harp inlaid with gold and precious stones, and, in another place, a sledge ornamented in the same way. In front of the sledge were the skeletons of two asses and their grooms, and nearby a very large number of gold and silver cups. Still further on were the skeletons of six royal guards with copper spears and helmets, and beyond them were two four-wheeled ox-wagons. Other human skeletons were found, and the whole gave a graphic picture of the ceremony which involved the death of seventy-four people, six of them armed men-servants and sixty-eight women.

ELABORATE RITES OF A ROYAL BURIAL

THERE was a great difference between the ritual that characterised the burial of a reigning king, who was deified in his lifetime, and that of a person of high, or even royal, descent. In the latter case, the funeral ceremony as visualised by Sir C. Leonard Woolley, the excavator, was as follows.

In one grave shaft was found the smallest royal tomb, which measured internally 2·50 metres by 2·00 metres; the low door was blocked by masonry, the domed roof was formed by corbelling, and the floor was of loosely laid mud-bricks. The principal body was that of a woman with a gold ribbon head-dress, wreath of gold leaves, crescent-shaped ear-rings, and necklaces of gold and carnelian beads. Her cloak was fastened by a long curved pin of gold with a carnelian head, and she had a gold cylinder seal. In her hand was a fluted gold tumbler. With her were the bodies of four male attendants, and scattered over the floor were other offerings, a silver drinking-tube with gold mouthpiece, a large limestone table of offerings, large copper vessels, strainers, etc., some weapons and stone vases.

FUNERAL BANQUETS OVER THE TOMB

WHEN the bodies were laid in the tomb and the door sealed up, a sheep was sacrificed and laid on the threshold against the blocking of the door; clay vessels containing food or drink were leant against the tomb wall, and the bodies of two more sacrificed animals were laid in the little forecourt. Then the grave was covered with earth to the base of the dome of the roof where a shaft had been formed. Fires were lit, and, judging from the broken clay vessels found mixed with the ashes, a kind of funeral feast was held, libations being poured down the shaft or drain to the under-world; then more earth was laid, and a new phase of the ritual took place. Just below the surface a dedication bowl was placed, and a piece of matting spread on the ground on which were laid clay saucers containing food, meat, dates, and bread or grain, and over all this a great bowl was inverted which kept the earth away from "the table of the Lord." This was the proper rite for the dedication of a building.

On the hard floor, deep in the grave shaft, were the foundations of a building of mud-brick. The lower part of the walls were buried in clean earth, and a clay floor had been trodden down on which were placed clay vessels with food offerings. This ceremony was repeated many times with the addition of copper vessels, animal bones, and the bodies of men, presumably sacrificed to the dead woman under the dome.

Among many beautiful objects found are two statues, each representing a "ram of the goats," standing upright on his hind legs behind a tree, to the branches of which his forelegs are fastened by silver chains. These statues are made of white shell, silver, gold, lapis lazuli, and red and white mosaic.

THE GRAVE OF THE ORDINARY CITIZEN

IN the case of ordinary graves (which vary only in detail) a rectangular shaft is sunk into the ground, measuring about 2 metres by $1\frac{1}{2}$ metres. A piece of reed matting is stretched over the bottom, and the body—which may be wrapped in matting or have a coffin of wood, wicker-work, or clay—is placed against one side of the pit. Personal ornaments are placed with the body, and a cup made of clay, stone, or metal, and containing drink for the dead person, is usually placed between the hands.

The offerings of the mourners consist of food and drink, weapons, tools, and such things as the dead person may be expected to require, and they are placed at the bottom of the shaft. In later times a boat, roughly modelled in bitumen and loaded with a cargo of food-stuffs, may be provided, perhaps for the actual conveyance of the soul. More matting is spread over the top, and the grave shaft is filled level with the ground.

In one cemetery in this stoneless land there were no fewer than six hundred and sixty cups, bowls, and vases of limestone and other stones. The stone must have been brought from a distance, the vessels being made on the site. Beads were varied and beautiful, the favourite material being carnelian. Usually beads were worn as necklaces, but sometimes they were worn at the waist, on the wrists, and, very rarely, as bangles on the legs.

Gaming boards of steatite (a kind of soapstone) have been found, and, before the Flood, the Chaldeans had painted pottery. Chariots have been found showing that the uses of the wheel were discovered before 3000 B.C. Houses were two-storeyed, the temples were the centres of the cities, and writing was usually done on clay tablets. Nebuchadnezzer built temples and houses on the site of Ur in the sixth century B.C., and these are almost its latest monuments, for in about 400 B.C. the city was deserted.

THE RISE AND WANE OF "TROY'S PROUD GLORIES"

THE site of Troy, the city sung by Homer, had nine successive cities. The second city, built about 2400 B.C., was rich and powerful, and at this time ranked next to Knossos, the great city of Crete. Metal work and jewellery from Troy was taken up the Danube to Europe, and these objects are used for dating purposes. The city was razed to the ground shortly after 2000 B.C., but the inhabitants found time to bury much of their treasure which was only rediscovered between 1873 and 1879. The excavator was H. Schliemann.

The third, fourth, and fifth cities were unimportant, but the sixth is shown by architecture and pottery to have belonged to the Mycenean age—that is, to the period of a brilliant civilisation which flourished round the Ægean Sea from 1500 to 1200 B.C. This sixth city of Troy had walls 14 feet thick, and the wall of the great north-east tower is still 30 feet high.

The seventh and eighth cities are of the historical Greek period, while the ninth was built in Roman times. Troy was small according to our idea of towns. Professor Sir Flinders Petrie has observed that it could all have been comfortably accommodated in Hanover Square—one of the smaller of the London squares.

THE SPLENDOURS OF THE EGYPTIAN CIVILISATION

In Egypt, on the banks of the Nile, which is a river without parallel on this earth, graves have been excavated and studied, with the result that we have some knowledge of the progress in industries and arts of the peasant communities from a time (about 3400 to 3100 B.C.) when a king of Egypt, traditionally known as Menes, united the whole land into a single kingdom.

In a remote period, known as the Badarian Period, beautiful pots were made, vases were ground out of hard stone, linen was woven, baskets and superb flint knives were made, stone beads were glazed, and ivory was carved into figurines, combs, and pins. This was followed by the Early Middle and Late Predynastic Period, when Egypt was in contact with the great civilisations in the Tigris-Euphrates valley. Abydos, which commanded a main caravan route, grew from a village into a town, and its ruler was eventually powerful enough to master the whole land to the Mediterranean Coast. He founded the First Dynasty about 3100 B.C. From this point written records are available to check the archæological material.

The old Kingdom Dynasties III–VI witnessed the building of the Pyramids, and then collapse came through internal exhaustion and Asiatic aggression. The Middle Kingdom Dynasties XI–XIII, B.C. 2000–1780, fell beneath the onslaught of the barbarian invaders known as the Hyksos or Shepherd Kings. Then came the greatest period of all : it followed the national revolt against the invaders in the seventeenth and eighteenth Dynasties, began in 1580 B.C., and is known as the New Kingdom.

PROVIDING FOR A LIFE BEYOND THE GRAVE

THE religion of the Egyptians included the belief that life beyond the grave differed little from life on earth. They believed it was still a physical life, only perhaps more ethereal, and that a dead king would therefore need much the same in the way of possessions in order to be happy as he had on earth. That is why food and drink, tables, chairs, chariots, clothes, jewels, and furniture were placed in the tomb. Then the body had to be preserved, first, against decay, by mummification, and, secondly, from destruction by robbers who would wish to steal any personal ornaments left on the body of the king.

As it was known that the vast pyramids which had been built in previous times had not prevented violation of the graves of earlier kings, in Tutankhamen's Dynasty, tombs were cut out of a solid rock in the Valley of the Kings at Thebes, and the usual chapels, where the daily supplies of food and drink were to be brought, were built several miles away in the plain, where they could give no clue to the position of the tomb. But, in spite of these precautions, the tombs were all rifled in antiquity with the exception of that of Tutankhamen.

THE MIGHTY TREASURE OF A BOY-KING

TUTANKHAMEN came to the throne shortly before 1350 B.C. He was a boy of perhaps only ten years, and reigned no more than nine years. His reign was a period of Egyptian history without any great event. He was not a great soldier, and was buried in one of the smallest and poorest of the royal tombs in the Valley. Yet the treasure found in his tomb is of immense intrinsic value, many of the art objects being of superb quality. The treasure that was buried with the really great kings of Egypt, such as Rameses the Great, who had a tomb many times the size of Tutankhamen's, must have been colossal. In fact, their religious beliefs must have cost the Egyptians immense sums of money. The tomb of Tutankhamen was discovered by Lord Carnarvon and Howard Carter in 1922. The inner coffin was not opened until 1925.

RICH TRAPPINGS OF DEATH : TUTANKHAMEN'S GLISTENING TOMB

THE peak of Egyptian art was reached between 2800 and 2500 B.C., in the Old Kingdom, but many of the objects found in Tutankhamen's tomb are very beautiful. The gold inner coffin and the mask of beaten gold which lay over the head of the king within the coffin are marvellous. There are portraits of the king formed of metal, though there are but few of these in ancient Egypt. The throne with the figures of the young king and his queen inlaid in glass faience and precious stones on a background of pure gold is wonderful, and so is a casket painted with scenes of war and hunting. A chair of plain cedar wood is exquisitely carved, and a wooden box inlaid with ivory is beautiful in design and proportion.

The " funeral barque," made of alabaster, is 27 inches high and 23 inches long. In the prow is the squatting figure of a charming girl, while a Sudanese dwarfish slave girl is at the helm. The walking-sticks, with crooks of ebony and ivory, are considered to be the finest pieces of decoration in the world.

A ROYAL VAULT'S TREASURE : THE THREE GOLDEN COFFINS

THE actual sepulchral chamber was almost filled with an enormous sarcophagus of yellow quartzite. Inside it were three golden coffins, very closely fitted to each other, and each containing a sculptured effigy of the king holding the crook and flail—the royal emblems. The inner coffin was more than 6 feet long. It was made of solid gold, $\frac{1}{4}$ inch thick, and the value of the metal alone is said to be £50,000. The note that these objects strike is one of brightness, the wealth of precious stones, such as carnelian, amethyst, turquoise, and lapis lazuli, together with the gleaming gold, make a deep impression on the visitor to the Cairo Museum, where everything from the tomb is housed.

A feature of an Egyptian burial is the mummy, the result of an attempt to preserve the body from corruption. The earliest actual mummy known to exist is in the Museum of the Royal College of Surgeons in Lincoln's Inn Fields, London, and is said to belong to the Fifth Dynasty (2750–2625 B.C.), but attempts at mummification go back to 3400 B.C., or even earlier.

Another well-known object is the great Pyramid, which was built at Gizeh by Cheops and Chephren in 3733 B.C. It is 450 feet high, and its side is 700 feet long. It has been calculated that it weighs 4,883,000 tons. A statue of Chephren, made of diorite, is considered to be one of the finest things in Egypt.

HOW THE EGYPTIANS WORKED AND PLAYED

IN Egypt the people of all classes had regularised habits of life, houses were comfortable and well furnished, meals were served at stated hours, and there were regular times for work and play. They worked hard, and they knew how to enjoy life. The craftsmen were well trained, the laws were of a humane character, and were administered without fear or favour. The best type of landowners and officials had a high sense of duty, but it was the priests who were all-powerful, and it was they who encouraged elaborate burial customs.

THE PRACTICE OF ARCHÆOLOGY

THERE is an enormous amount which individuals can do in Archæology. To train themselves to observe is the most important. When they go into a commercial excavation of any kind, such as a gravel pit, they should observe if there is evidence of disturbance to be seen in the exposed section; if there is, they should try and see if they can discover why it was made.

Readers can, and ought, to find clues, and then consult experienced archæologists. Articles which are discovered by promiscuous digging really have no value; it is only when their association is properly recorded that they are important.

In looking for flints in gravel it is important to observe the layers in which they are found. The local geology must be studied—see what the *Memoirs of H.M. Geological Survey* have to say about the district—find out what the levels are from a contour map. Keep your eyes open for bones and teeth of animals—shells are valuable too.

By working in a gravel pit, if your photographs and observations are careful no harm is done; whereas if inexperienced people begin to excavate a barrow or camp, valuable material which can never be replaced may be lost.

If the reader wishes to go further along these enchanting

pathways, he should ask to take part in scientific "digs" which are going on during the digging season (August to September usually) in several parts of the country. He will have to assure the director he will be punctual, obedient, industrious, and above all pleasant—even on wet days. After a few seasons of this he will realise how much there is to know about any period and how ignorant we still are, but nevertheless archæology remains, and will always remain, one of the most interesting and delightful studies in the world.

Archæology as a career has little promise, but there are a few posts to be obtained. Some universities include archæology in their subjects and to study it at those centres is undoubtedly the best method of approach. Facilities for work in the field are to be obtained while at the university, and contact with other important organised excavations is rendered possible by introductions.

The posts which are available are those of Museum assistants and curators, assistants on the Staff of the Board of Ancient Monuments, H.M. Office of Works, and the Historical Monuments Commissions. The competition for all of these may be severe, but archæology has now obtained a footing in the teaching profession and special knowledge may be used to advantage. There are, of course, a few posts in the universities themselves, for which in these days excavating experience is an important qualification.

SOME BOOKS TO READ NEXT

IT has not been possible to do more than touch the fringe of any period, and the Romano-British period has received least attention because it is the one about which most is known. For further details we can recommend *The Old Stone Age*, by Burkitt, published by the Cambridge University Press ; for the Palæolithic period, and for ancient man, Keith's *Antiquity of Man* and *Fresh Discoveries relating to Prehistoric Man* are excellent. Both are published by Williams and Norgate. A good introduction to British Archæology is provided by *Prehistoric Britain*, by Dr. Robert Munro (Home University Library, Thornton Butterworth Limited).

Miss D. A. E. Garrod's *Upper Palæolithic Age in Britain* is the classic work for that period. It is published in Oxford at the Clarendon Press. For the Mesolithic Age the student must have Clark's *Mesolithic Age in Britain* (Cambridge University Press).

Our Early Ancestors, by Burkitt, published at Cambridge, covers the Neolithic period ; and for the Bronze Age, Childe's *Bronze Age* is the simplest and best. His *The Dawn of European Civilisation*, published by Kegan Paul, is useful except that the British chapter now needs revision. As regards the Early Iron Age, several volumes are needed, and much has been written about Roman Britain. Collingwood's *Archæology of Roman Britain* (Methuen) and his *Roman Britain* (Oxford University Press, 1932), are excellent, but to know what has happened in archæology since 1914, one must read *Archæology in England and Wales, 1914–31*, by Kendrick and Hawkes (Methuen). Particularly good in this magnificently illustrated volume is the chapter on the Early Iron Age. The British Museum publish invaluable guides to the Stone Age, the Bronze Age, the Early Iron Age, and Roman Britain.

The great and wealthy civilisations of the East are dealt with more fully in books such as *The Early History of Assyria*, by Sidney Smith, London, 1927 ; *New Light on the Most Ancient East*, by Childe (Kegan Paul) ; *The Ancient East*, by D. G. Hogarth (Home University Library, Thornton Butterworth Limited) ; *Egypt*, by Sir Wallis Budge and *The Byzantine Empire*, by N. H. Baynes, both in the Home University Library, Thornton Butterworth Limited, provide a comprehensive picture of Egyptian and post-Egyptian civilisation.

There are two good quarterly publications called *Antiquaries' Journal*, published by Humphrey Milford (Oxford University Press), and *Antiquity*, which can be obtained from " Antiquity," 24 Park End Road, Gloucester. Both deal with recent discoveries in archæology, and by studying these the reader can keep up to date with what is happening in many parts of the world.

All those who are interested in archæology should at once take the necessary steps to become members of their own County Archæological Society, whose members are always ready to nominate keen and useful workers. For those living in London there is The Archæological Institute, with a very wide membership covering most of Great Britain. It holds winter meetings, and its summer excursions are of an attractive nature. Information can be obtained from the

Secretary, Lancaster House, St. James's, London; the subscription is £1, 1s. a year. The Society for the Promotion of Roman Studies deals principally with that period. The subscription is £1, 1s. a year, and the Secretary is Miss M. V. Taylor, Ashmolean Museum, Oxford. The Royal Anthropological Institute deals with man in every stage; Secretary, 52 Upper Bedford Place, London, W.C.1; Subscription, £2, 2s. a year.

THE CHILDHOOD OF THE HUMAN RACE : THE STUDY OF PRIMITIVE MAN

by M. R. MITCHINER, B.A. (Cantab.)

WHEN Adam delved and Eve span, who was then the gentleman? So runs the old rhyme, pointing out that society has not always worked according to the rules that we use in our corner of the earth. Nevertheless, even when there were no gentle and simple, there were some divisions, for Adam worked the agricultural and Eve the industrial portion of that small and far-off community. Indeed, wherever men live together in however primitive a society (perhaps no more than a handful of mud-huts in a clearing of some vast jungle) there will be divisions. Even in the most backward races there is some division of labour, although, unlike the rhyme, in primitive agricultural communities it is often Eve who both spins and delves, while Adam hunts or fights, or sometimes just loafs. There will also be a division of authority—some sort of headman or council of elders. But the earliest and most fundamental division of all is that concerned with marriage and kinship.

All over the world are to be found strict and important rules dividing communities into smaller groups within themselves, between which marriage may be compulsory or forbidden. In all societies there will be rules concerning the divisions and regulating individual conduct. Communal life, even for the simplest savage, is a complicated thing. The difficulties are many and varied, according to the type of men and of physical environment, but through them all run certain broad similarities. Equally, the solutions, such as they are, are many, but they, too, show certain lines of family resemblance. There is to-day a modern science which sets out to study the intricacies of social life, both in its material and spiritual aspects all over the world. This science is Anthropology.

WHAT DOES THE ANTHROPOLOGIST DO ?

ANTHROPOLOGY—it is indeed rather a forbidding, to some people almost a monstrous, word. Yet if we conquer our initial shyness sufficiently to make a more intimate acquaintance with the word, we find it is derived from the Greek *Anthropos*, which means simply *man*, i.e. just the general conception of all the John Smiths of the world. But what does the whole word mean? Let us look at the dictionary definition. There are three given. The first is : " The whole science of man." This, a complete knowledge of man, would mean learning : (*a*) all there is to know about man as he is now including all medical science, psychology, and sociology ; (*b*) all the history of mankind, including written history out of history books and unwritten history from stocks and stones and monuments, and geological history, telling us of man's environment, and helping to date the prehistoric eras ; and perhaps (*c*) a forecast, from the given data of the past and present, of man's evolution in the future.

After the breathtaking comprehensiveness of this definition, our dictionary gives us two abruptly narrowed alternatives : (1) The physiological and psychological study of man ; (2) the study of man as a nanimal. Obviously neither of these adequately explains what is covered by the term anthropology ; the former is dealt with by the sciences of physiology and psychology respectively, and the latter is usually considered a branch of biology. Yet both these define a part of anthropology. Since the first definition is too wide, and the other too narrow, and somewhat beside the mark, what then is anthropology ?

Let us ask, "What does an anthropologist study?" He investigates certain aspects of all those studies that would be included in the whole science of man, those aspects which will help him to build up a knowledge of man from two main points of view : (1) From the point of view of the development of man from the stage of the anthropoid ape to the present day ; (2) from the aspect of the classification and description of man as he exists to-day. This is done according to physical and cultural characteristics—that is, division into races on biological lines, into types of social organisation, and into linguistic groups.

In actual practice, anthropologists are concerned mainly with the study of what we call " primitive " peoples, partly because we know less of their life than of the life of what we are pleased to call the civilised world, and partly because the study of simpler forms of society can throw some light, though how much light is one of the problems of the science, on our own past development. By a method of unbiased comparison, this study can be used to reveal the broad underlying principles of human society, common to all men, be they black, white, or yellow, and so help us to understand better the place of our own civilisation in the whole social world.

There is another reason why anthropologists concentrate mainly on primitive peoples, and that is the fact that Western civilisation is making contact with, and rapidly changing the aspect of, all other cultures. But it should be made clear that anthropology is not necessarily confined to Africa or the South Seas ; there is scope for anthropological research in Washington or Surrey or Spain. Research has in fact been carried out on the physical characteristics of Europeans, particularly in Germany and America, and the intermingling and disentanglement of racial types is an anthropological problem that has found its way into the arena of politics.

THE LITTLE SISTER OF MANY SCIENCES

IT must be remembered that anthropology, like other biological sciences, is indissolubly linked up with its sister sciences. It cannot be abstracted from every other branch of knowledge and studied entirely alone. It is a separate science for purposes of convenience, and it justifies separate classification because it is a synthetic study of man and society. It is also a very young science, not by any means fully fledged. Although the study of different types of man was not unknown to the Greeks (Herodotus and Aristotle touched on ethnology), it was not until the second half of the nineteenth century that anthropology really took its place as a recognised study.

The work of Darwin and Huxley opened up a new conception of man ; no longer a creature unique and utterly apart from the rest of the living universe, he was now shown to be a member of the Animal Kingdom (much to the horror and indignation of many good people) and ripe for study as such. The new outlook finds its most brilliant and lucid expression in a famous essay by Thomas Huxley under the significant title : *Man's Place in Nature.* Just what exactly is his place in nature, and how he arrived there, is still one of the most fascinating and one of the most thorny problems of the physical and archæological sides of anthropology.

A little later, in the works of Herbert Spencer, social anthropology came to the front as a part of his comprehensive philosophy of universal evolution. But anthropology did not leave the fireside arm-chair until the first anthropological expedition led by Haddon of Cambridge went to investigate the natives of the Torres Straits in Australasia, and put field-work right into the forefront of anthropological research. About the same time the publication of Sir James Frazer's *The Golden Bough* brought the romance and beauty of anthropology vividly home to the reading public.

Since then there has been much arduous field-work and acrid argument (for anthropologists are academically the most quarrelsome of people—they disagree profoundly and bitterly). There have been three main schools of thought. The psychological school, mainly German, sets out to explain all the phenomena of social culture in terms of individual psychology. The best example of this is, of course, the psycho-analytic school of anthropology (Freud published an important treatise on Totem and Taboo). The point of view of individual psychology is also prominent in writers such as Frazer who, besides *The Golden Bough*, wrote a big work on *Totemism and Taboo*, and Westermarck in his monumental *History of Human Marriage*.

The sociological school apply the theories of group psychology to anthropology. They explain society and its differences and similarities by assuming some type of collective consciousness. This has led to a conception of primitive society as living an almost undifferentiated collective mental life with little individual activity. Rivers in England, Durkheim in France (particularly the latter who, bein primarily a sociologist an l not an anthropologist, was much more extreme in his vie vs on the collective consciousness,) belonged to this school. Both these schools are cross-divided into evolutionists and diffusionists. The former maintain that similarities of culture in different parts of the world can be explained by a similar but independent evolution, while the latter, or diffusionist school, maintain that all culture and civilisation has spread from a single source.

WHAT LIES BEHIND THE HABITS OF MEN ?

THE accepted modern method of study is that named by Malinowski, its most prominent exponent, the " functional " approach. This means investigating all sorts of anthropological facts with a view to finding out their object or function. The anthropologist asks himself what rôle does such and such a thing play in the life of the society he is studying, how is it related to other social activities, and how is it influenced by physical surroundings. The " functional " method aims at the understanding of the nature of culture, rather than at conjectural reconstructions of its evolution or of past historical events.

What, then, does this nebulous creature, the anthropologist, study ? If he is interested in the history of man before the period of written history, he studies prehistoric archæology. If he is a physical anthropologist, he is interested in the description and classification of racial and physical types. He studies what is known as " Anthropometry." This is the science of comparative measurement of the human body. He makes a number of standard measurements, particularly of the skull. For this he has a special instrument, known as " callipers," something like a large pair of dividers. Skulls are classified into broad, or brachycephalic, medium or mesocephalic, long or dolichocephalic. These classifications are based on figures obtained by dividing the length of the skull by its breadth. Different races of man tend to have characteristic types of skull. The physical anthropologist also attempts classification according to the colour of eyes and skin and the texture of hair. Types of hair are the most important and are usually divided into straight, wavy, curly, frizzy, and woolly.

But we are mainly concerned with the social anthropologist. He is trying to find out how different human societies live. He divides his work into three main categories—social life, material culture, and the study of language. Investigation of the social life of a community includes the study of the social structure—that is, the divisions into tribes, clans, groups of families, and so forth ; the complexities of law and custom, religion, economic and family life, and inter-tribal relations. An inquiry into material culture concerns itself with, first, the material necessities of life, such as agriculture, crafts, houses, and weapons ; and, secondly, with the arts—music, dancing, painting, and all kinds of decoration. Literature is represented in primitive communities by legend, story-telling, and mythology.

WHAT THE ARM-CHAIR ANTHROPOLOGIST CAN DO

SOCIETY is constantly changing, and the causes which produce change come both from within and without.

The way in which institutions, customs, language, and material objects are modified by external contacts and internal variations is one of the main theoretical problems of modern anthropology. Facts have not only to be collected but to be explained in the light of general theories. Here the problem of anthropology is that of all science—the framing of theories to fit the facts. Here the arm-chair anthropologist is at his most useful and most dangerous. With data ready collected from wide and varied sources, it is easier for him to sift and classify and form generalisations than it is for the field-worker, whose vision necessarily tends to be somewhat distorted by an enormous mass of detail and by an inclination to explain all things in terms of experience in his own particular field. On the other hand, the arm-chair anthropologist, since he is not up against facts of his own experience, but only paper records, is only too ready to jump to conclusions right over the heads of unaccommodating facts. The best approach is undoubtedly a combination of both methods : practical investigation of actual conditions at first hand, combined with the widest study of similar work in other areas.

The work of a practical field observer is beset with pitfalls. Imagine yourself going with a few white men of academic life to some remote savage island, as Haddon and his companions from Cambridge University went to the Torres Straits, or alone, as Malinowski went to the Trobriand Islands, to live among an unknown people alien in every aspect of custom, language, and manners. The anthropologist is a self-invited guest and risks a very hostile reception. His first concern is to establish friendly relations, for without them nothing can be accomplished. The natives must be convinced of the peaceable disposition and purposes of the investigator ; it is a great mistake to make any show of arms with a view to impressing the people ; if it is deemed advisable to carry weapons they should be concealed until the confidence of the natives has been won, or, of course, until it becomes imperative to use them.

It should be remembered that " savage " peoples have had embittering experiences of white men in many parts. Unscrupulous traders have robbed and cheated them, carried on a slave trade or enticed labour away to virtual slavery in distant plantations. Ill-advised missionary zeal has sometimes caused spiritual havoc and misery by trying to stamp out, instead of to adapt, old ways and beliefs precious to the community. Ruthless colonisation has broken the organisation and sapped the vitality of many of the original peoples of Africa, America and the Pacific. The Red Indians are fast disappearing ; the Tasmanians are wiped out altogether— the last died in 1876. The disappearance of the latter race is a great loss to anthropology, for it was probably the most backward and primitive race in the world.

MAKING FRIENDS WITH THE NATIVE

FRIENDLY relations are often helped by gifts and by rendering successful first-aid or medical help, but the fundamental necessity is a real sympathy and friendliness on the part of the investigator. He must learn to enter the life of the natives with sympathy and great tact. He should treat all their laws and customs with respect and particularly he should keep a strict observance of native taboos and prohibitions. He should take care neither to shock nor to offend, and especially to cast no ridicule. He should participate with friendly interest in everything to which he may be invited, however distasteful or undignified by his own standards.

It is useless to approach the study of any lower culture with a rigid European outlook. The anthropologist must learn to see things from the point of view of the people whom he is studying. This is not easy, for he should first learn to know himself—his own prejudices and limitations—so that these may not distort his view. An anthropologist is concerned primarily with facts and not with ethical values. He is not concerned to judge right or wrong, good or bad, in the ethical sense. His business is not what ought to be, but what is.

This does not mean that anthropological knowledge is not of great value in the formation of practical administrative policy, when judgments of value must be made. An anthropologist well versed in primitive ethics and the needs of the savage mind is better able to advise on native administrative policy than either a Whitehall official who has never seen a native, or a settler on the spot to whom the natives are only a menace or a source of cheap labour. To-day entrants into the colonial administration services are provided with special courses in anthropology at the universities. The practical value of anthropology has been officially recognised.

12

THE DIFFICULTY OF EXPLORING THE HUMAN MIND

YET even the investigator with the most sympathetic, unbiassed tactful approach possible, finds innumerable obstacles in the way of probing deeply into any primitive society, and of getting a really profound understanding of its life and habits. It is not easy to get at the reasons of other people's conduct, even when they are willing to explain them to you, for the reasons are often inadequate to an outsider. We know ourselves how much of our own habits are due to custom and convention for which we should be hard put to it to find adequate rational explanation. Why, for instance, does a man salute a lady in the street by the method of raising his hat a few inches from his head with one hand ? A savage society is usually hidebound by the most rigid and unquestioned customs, and the difficulty of explanation is further complicated by the fact that what seems logical to a Bushman or an Andaman Islander may seem at first sight utter nonsense to a European. Different habits of life lead to different habits of thought ; to understand one custom one must understand many others.

Frequently, however, natives will not be willing to reveal their more precious and sacred customs to the white man's eye. The more sacred a rite, custom or object, the more secret it is usually kept. Moreover, much primitive law and custom is surrounded by a mist of fear and awe, and fear is a great tongue-tier. Besides general customs the anthropologist needs also to investigate all sorts of details of daily life in order to gain a complete picture of the community under study. He needs to learn many things connected with very intimate sides of life, for instance details of sexual behaviour and family life. It may take months of patient questioning and waiting and watching to ferret out all that the investigator need to know. The first difficulty is to find some one among the people in question who is both willing and able to show the field worker round and to give him the requisite explanations. Sometimes it may be an intelligent and enterprising young man, sometimes perhaps an elder of the tribe. It is always advisable to ask two or three different persons for the same information and then to compare accounts.

Needless to say, language is the first difficulty. Some sort of working knowledge of the language of the people he is living among is of the greatest importance to the field worker. Material of untold value may be lost through ignorant interpreters and inaccurate translation. People living very different lives in very different types of society are apt to think in rather different categories. A savage groups ideas and objects in his mind in a different order from a European or indeed from another and different type of savage. Consequently, the words he uses will sometimes have no equivalent in another language. In many primitive societies, for instance, the word that would be translated as " father " will designate in practice a number of other men besides the true parent. The same word has often to be used in translation to imply two quite distinct types of object. To take an example close at hand : the word *loaf* and the French word *pain* imply distinctly different types of bread to the Englishman and Frenchman respectively. An English loaf is different in appearance, weight, and flavour from a French loaf, but the same word has to be used.

Besides purely linguistic difficulties of this kind the use of an interpreter confines the field worker to one or at most two or three informants, who may not be the most reliable or accurate. The way is open for any amount of deception, conscious or unconscious, on the part of the interpreter. Then it is obvious also that it is twenty times more difficult to establish friendly relations and enter into the life of a people unless you can to some extent converse with them.

LISTENING (WITH DISCRETION) TO THE "MAN-ON-LEAVE"

IT is important to emphasise that all persons who have lived in areas inhabited by primitive races and have had some dealings with them are not anthropologists. An anthropologist is not necessarily a professional scientist ; he may be a government official or a planter or a missionary, and study anthropology as a side line, but unless he has really studied the subject, that is, read widely and gone among the natives himself with his eyes well and sympathetically open, he cannot talk about anthropological questions with any scientific authority. This means that persons back from the tropics, or on leave from the outposts of this or other Empires, who lay down the law on native questions, should not be accorded an entirely credulous and uncritical ear merely because they have been on the spot. Their interests are fairly certain to lie in another direction from those of the natives—they may be diametrically opposed to them. Prob ably the native population comes into contact with such persons either as domestic servants or as industrial and agricultural labour, or as rebellious insurgents.

The white settlers are very unlikely to be able to look at any native question with a disinterested eye. A tradition of race prejudice exists in all white colonies in the midst of coloured peoples, a tradition of dislike, contempt and exploitation of the native, mixed with varying degrees of fear. So universal is this atmosphere of race prejudice in such places that it is very difficult indeed for the ordinary settler or visitor not to become permeated by it. Naturally it robs their observations of most anthropological value.

The same caution should be exercised in listening to the opinions of that type of missionary whose one idea is to get as many converts as he can in order to impress his financial supporters at home. He is trying to christianise at all costs, and to a uniform pattern ready-made at home. Everything native, therefore, is likely to be " heathen " and therefore bad. Much of importance also will pass unnoticed or be forgotten.

We have now a rough general idea of what an anthropologist does, of his aims and methods. Let us now turn to the work he has done, and find out something of what anthropology can tell us about ourselves.

HUNTER AND HUSBAND: MAN'S TWO PRIMITIVE NEEDS

TWO great needs dominate our whole lives — food, to sustain the life of the individual, and sex, to sustain the life of the race. Strong impulses to act in such a way as to satisfy these needs are inherent in us and may be called instinctive. When hunger makes itself felt there is an urge to seek food. When sexual desire is felt there is an impulse to court the nearest desirable woman. Hunger and sex are the two prime mainsprings of man's activity all the world over. Most people who read this book will have had little direct conscious experience of the first motive in their ordinary day to day lives, for it has become disguised under the developments of civilisation and shows itself more as the desire for money than for food. But in the simple societies procuring food is one of the main activities of the community. The lower the level of culture (" culture " is a word used to sum up the material and spiritual achievements of a society where

they are too simple to merit the term civilisation), the larger
looms the place of food-seeking activity. This is because
the less perfect man's instruments are, the longer time and
greater energy he will have to spend on satisfying his most
immediate needs. Therefore in the very early days of mankind, before the time of agriculture, we must imagine that
the main occupation, at least of the able-bodied males, was
hunting. This is still true of the simplest types of culture in
the world to-day, known as the " Lower Hunters," such as
the Andaman Islanders, the Australian Aborigines and the
African Bushmen.

HUNTERS WHO LEFT US PORTRAITS OF THEIR PREY

THE cave men of the end of the Great Ice Age (who
lived actually more in shallow rock shelters than in
caves, as far as we can judge from the remains they left
behind them) and later peoples right up to the coming of
agriculture in the New Stone Age, must have lived mainly
by hunting. We know there were no crops, although
probably wild fruits and vegetable foods were gathered.
Numbers of animal bones, often charred or burnt, have
been found round prehistoric hearths, with an enormous
quantity of flint implements, such as would have been used
for knives and axes and skin scrapers.

Even more interesting, and finally conclusive as to the
importance of hunting in the life of early man, are the remarkable series of cave paintings to be found in France and
North Spain. These beautiful representations of animals
are often depicted with wounds and indications of weapons in
their flesh. The paintings are usually explained as being a
type of magic painting to ensure good hunting, by a process
of what is known as " sympathetic " magic. The principle
is the same as that of the old custom of making an image in
wax of an enemy and then piercing it through the heart with
a pin, whereupon the enemy would (it was believed) die
forthwith. Equally, if the hunter drew a good likeness of
the animal he wanted to kill and put in the wounds, he hoped
the original would follow the fate of the image and be wounded.

Not only, however, did the cave men want good hunting,
but they also wanted a good stock of game. We find among
the cave art (which includes engravings and bas-relief
sculpture as well as paintings) several examples of the male
and female beast portrayed together, as if to induce them by

magic to breed prolifically. There is in one cave an engraving of a bull following a cow, and a pair of bisons, male and female, beautifully modelled in clay as a bas-relief on the wall of another.

We may pertinently ask why these paintings and carvings should be considered to have been " magical " and not simply decorative or even just a casual method of self-expression in leisure hours. The answer is that the pictures are frequently found painted one on top of the other, until there may be three or four different pictures over each other—not exactly over the one underneath, but just painted across it anyhow. It is unlikely that any one who wanted to decorate his cave home, or even merely to scribble on the wall with a lump of charcoal would choose a spot already drawn upon and not a nice blank piece of rock. Also the pictures are sometimes found at the end of deep and obscure caves, difficult of entry, where it is highly improbable that people either lived or came very frequently. There is a cave at El Pendo in North Spain with a large vestibule at the mouth, where plenty of signs of habitation, such as the remains of hearths, bones, implements, etc., have been found, but no pictures, while right at the back in the farthest and most obscure parts are a series of paintings The explanation usually given is that the art had a ceremonial significance of a mysterious and magical, perhaps almost religious kind.

DROWNING FEARS IN MAGIC RITES

WE can imagine a band of these prehistoric hunters clad in rough skins, armed with stone axes and knives, being led by some ancient medicine-man into the depths of a long cave, where at the bottom, eerily lit up by primitive torches, the bright-coloured images of animals shone strangely on the walls in the fitful light. These caves are creepy enough to-day, when we visit them with bright electric torches and modern sophisticated minds—how much more so must they have been to early man with his dim flickering lights and untutored savage brain ! There, before the life-like paintings some magic rite was probably performed, perhaps with ceremonial dancing and mime, until care and oppression changed to wild excitement. Then, filled with half-mystic elation, they streamed out again into the dazzling sunlight, fully confident now that the magic powers would ensure the success of their hunting.

The magic must have worked, we can be sure of that, for the archæologist can tell us from the evolution of the styles of painting checked by other data of associated implements, that this art continued over a long period of hundreds and hundreds of years. If the explanation of ritual magic be a true one, it is impossible to think that men would have continued believing in the magic and creating new animal figures for it unless it appeared to bring them success. No man, however savage and superstitious (or even, let it be said in a discreet undertone, however civilised and superstitious), or however conservative, will continue forever to practise a thing which does not produce the results for which it is designed. If the matter concerned is of as vital an importance to him as the matter of procuring food, he is less likely to continue out of conservatism and habit a usage which brings him no help where help is so urgently needed.

What then was the secret of the magic power of the paintings ? We shall never know for certain, just as indeed we shall never know for certain that they were magical, for do not forget that it is only a probable hypothesis ; but the likelihood is that the psychological effect of the ritual and the complete faith in the reality of the physical connection between the images and the real animals armed the hunters with such courage and confidence that their "hunting efficiency," as we of this industrial world would call it, was definitely improved. Besides, we may be certain that the medicine-men made sure that whatever success there was in the day's hunting should be put down to the effect of the magic.

HOW THE HUNTERS "SCREWED UP" THEIR COURAGE

CONFIDENCE would have been a necessary asset when out hunting in a world of which man had not one-fiftieth of the knowledge or of the physical control that he has to-day, and where mammoths and rhinoceroses, elephants and bison, bears, giant-deer, and "sabre-tooth" tigers walked the earth as commonly as sheep do now. Some kind of spiritual stimulus would have been a great help to success for even the hardiest spirit in that terrifying wilderness. Something on the principle of :

> "But screw your courage to the sticking place
> And we'll not fail."

THE HUNTING PEOPLES OF TO-DAY

BUT who were the " we " among the cave men hunters ? Did they hunt in great gangs or packs or did they go out alone, each after his single prey and risking his single life ? Again here is something which we can never know. We can only guess at probabilities. It is unlikely that under the conditions of primitive weapons and enormous and dangerous game described, a lone hunter could accomplish very much, while the risk to life would be excessively great. He is almost certain to have gone out in large groups or in twos and threes, perhaps all the males of a family together. Let us leave speculation and turn to the habits of existing hunting peoples to see what light they can throw on the question.

There are few purely hunting peoples left in the world to-day. They have been nearly all pushed to the wall by the more advanced types of pastoral and agricultural societies. Hunting and food gathering is always a precarious and uncertain method of procuring subsistence. Game and wild vegetable foods may become scarce, the hunters may fail through loss of life and limb. Tilling the soil and keeping herds obviously provides a much more stable source of food supply. Most hunting peoples to-day eke out their supplies by other methods, the Eskimo, for example, by trading, and many Central African peoples by a little primitive agriculture.

There still remain, however, a few peoples who rely entirely on hunting, but they are confined to remote unsettled areas, except where they have been deliberately " preserved " by white authorities, as, for instance, the Red Indians of North America and the Australian Aborigines. In the depths of equatorial Africa, in the remotest steppes of Asia, and in the jungles of South India and Malay purely hunting types are still to be found. Theirs is the simplest and most primitive type of culture known.

With all of them we find that hunting is carried on in groups of varying sizes, although naturally this does not preclude a certain amount of individual hunting, particularly in trapping and fishing. But most large animals are caught by methods of beating with a cordon of hunters who frighten the beasts with noises and drive them in an opposite direction to where a number of men await to kill them. Yet nowhere do we find anything resembling the animal hunting pack, although it has been suggested that early man hunted in packs.

The organisation of the hunting group may be of a greater or lesser strictness. Obviously a certain co-ordination is necessary in beating wild and dangerous animals, and there are generally one or two acknowledged leaders remarkable for their courage and skill (primitive mythology is full of great hunting leaders of fabulous strength and cleverness). The main rôle of organisation is in the dividing of the spoils. Usually there is some method by which the man who actually killed the animal, or whose weapon first struck it, has the largest and choicest portion and the rest may be divided equally, or according to some system of priority. In the Andaman Islands, a pig belongs to the man whose arrow first strikes it, unless he is a bachelor, in which case the pig is distributed by one of the older men who gives all the best parts to the other elder members.

HUNTERS WHO RUN THEIR PREY TO DEATH

Hunting methods are many and various, according to the type of game, the ingenuity of the hunters and the materials at their disposal. Perhaps the simplest, though most arduous method is that of the Bushmen of the Kalahari Desert, who merely keep a spring-bok continually on the move during the hottest part of the day until it sinks exhausted. The Australian Aborigines rely on very simple traps, stone and bone-tipped spears, and clubs. They use also the special kind of wooden throwing club well known as the boomerang. The Eskimos have various quite ingenious types of harpoon for seals and fish.

Everywhere, except in Australia, the bow and arrow is to be found, though there are many different kinds both of bow and of arrow. The deadliest method invented by the primitive hunters is the poisoned weapon. Poisoned arrows and spears are widespread and poisoned darts propelled from a blow-pipe are used in South America, Borneo, and Malay. Everywhere, however, that white men have penetrated in any numbers the old weapons tend gradually to be superseded by firearms, sometimes of very old-fashioned types, that the natives manage to procure from our civilisation. (Flint, for flint-lock guns for African natives, is still prepared at Brandon in Suffolk. Let us now leave hunting and turn back to the second vital need that governs man's behaviour—sex.

MARRIAGE OR FAMILY : WHICH CAME FIRST ?

IT was rather fashionable among anthropologists at one time to assume the original type of community to be a primæval horde with little conscious organisation, but acting together as by instinct and holding all things in common. Among the property held in common would be woman. Those writers who, as was explained in the introduction, were partial to the theories of group consciousness, maintained that there was a sort of " group marriage " by which all the men married all the women. Others, who believed the horde to have been more of a complete anarchy, considered that there was no kind of marriage at all in the primitive group, but utter promiscuity. These views have latterly fallen into discredit.

There is no community living to-day, and none of which we have any historical record, which has not some form of marriage as one of its basic institutions. There are several forms of marriage—monogamous, polygamous, and polyandrous—and many different usages in the regulation of sexual intercourse before and after marriage. Many peoples all over the world permit, or condone, pre-nuptial relations, though sometimes only of a modified character and sometimes only so long as there is no pregnancy as a result ; some even encourage it. Many others, however, even very primitive people, like the Andaman Islanders, expect strict continency before marriage, particularly on the part of girls.

Rules concerning marital fidelity vary very widely, from the absolute faithfulness demanded by the Maoris of Oceania, several Indian tribes of America, and many others, to the " wife lending " or " wife exchange " custom of many Polynesians and some Asiatic and Australian tribes. " Wife lending " is usually a form of hospitality, and the opinion of the wife is not asked, as it is largely an affirmation of the husband's complete right of disposal of her body. Somewhere between the two extremes lies the custom of making the girl sleep with some other man than her husband just before or at the time of her marriage, a custom which lingered on in Europe throughout the Middle Ages under the name of *jus primæ noctis* (the right of the first night).

Nowhere, however, do we find anything resembling

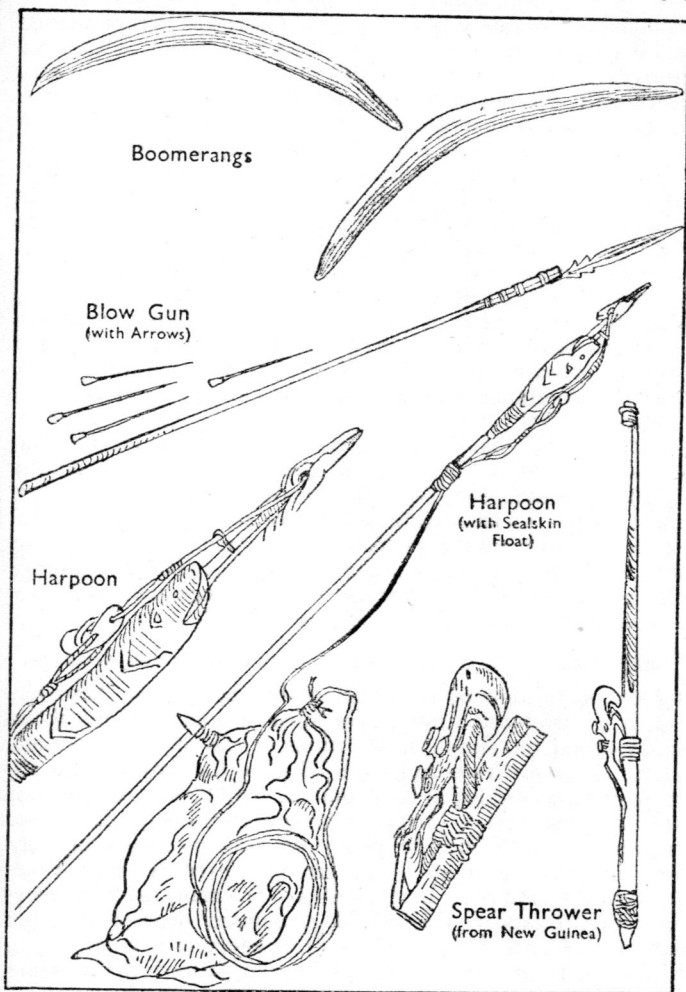

30. THE SAVAGE HUNTER'S WEAPONS.

Throwing-sticks, harpoons, spears, and bows and arrows, are used in some form by most primitive peoples. The handle of the spear-thrower, from New Guinea, is here shown enlarged.

established promiscuity in lieu of marriage, except among some peoples on certain special occasions, such as seasonal festivities when wholesale orgies of a ritual nature may take place with the object of inducing fertility in cattle and the land.   There is then absolutely no evidence to go upon that such a state of sexual anarchy as envisaged by the " group marriage " theory ever has existed.   It is possible, but it is unlikely, for biological facts and needs are against it.   In Man, not only is the period of pregnancy very long compared with that of animals, but the child when born takes from twelve to fifteen years to grow to maturity, so for the first six years at least it is utterly dependent on its parents. Primitive marriage does not consist so much of love-making as of the bearing and rearing of children, the protection and support given to the mother by the father during pregnancy, and the combined care of the two parents from birth to maturity.

" Marriage," as Westermarck, the greatest authority on the subject says, " is rooted in the family, rather than the family in marriage."   Marrying in this sense is a biological, more than a social institution ; there seems to be a natural tendency, both in the animals and in man, for the male to stay with the female at least during pregnancy and during the babyhood of the offspring.   Social usage then probably followed and confirmed a biological habit.

MARRIAGE RULES OF THE WILDS : THE PROHIBITED DEGREES

THE institution of marriage in the social sense, however, has introduced a number of intricate complications above and beyond the simple implications of the physical relationship.   In every race and tribe all over the world there are very important rules as to whom the members may or whom they may not marry.   In Christian countries the list of persons whom it is forbidden to marry consists nowadays entirely of very near relations.   We are permitted to marry our " in-laws " and our first cousins.   In many savage communities, however, the list of prohibited degrees contains a much wider and a very different category of persons.

Incest is nearly always prohibited, although in some societies it may be the custom among certain classes. In Ancient Egypt, for example, the reigning prince used to marry his sister.   Among the African Ashanti also it is the custom for the Chief to marry a woman whom he calls sister, although, owing to the fact that savages reckon their kindred differently from the way we do, as will be explained later, she may not actually be his sister. The custom arises from the desire to keep the ruling stock pure. Generally, however, there seems to be a universal abhorrence of incest, which has given rise to a number of different types of marriage regulations and prohibitions, extending far beyond the immediate family.

The most common type of prohibition outside the family is bound up with the clan system. There are various types of clan among different peoples, but they are all based on marriage regulations and laws of descent. The most usual regulation in vogue in many parts of the world is that members of a clan may not marry inside the clan—they must find a woman outside. This is known as *Exogamy* (a useful term to understand, as it is constantly cropping up in anthropological writings). It may be supported by other rules designating precisely into which other clan one may marry. Among the Australian Aborigines, for example, there is in many tribes a very complicated group system by which a man from Group A must marry a woman, say, from Group C, and a woman from Group B must marry a man from Group D, whereas a woman from Group D must marry a man from Group C, and so forth on those lines. A less common rule is the contrary prohibition—the forbidding of marriage outside the clan or group. This is known as *Endogamy* (the word is derived from the Greek *Endon*—within, and *Gamos*—marriage). The best example of this custom is the very strict marriage rules connected with the caste system in India, whereby a woman may only marry a man of her own or superior caste.

WHERE A MAN MUST MARRY HIS BROTHER'S WIDOW

BESIDES these rules forbidding marriage with certain classes of persons, there are others in usage among many peoples which oblige them to marry certain classes of people. There are rules of " injunction," as opposed to rules of " prohibition." A well-known type of injunction refers to second marriages ; this is called the *levirate*. By this custom a man is obliged to marry his brother's widow. Usually it is the elder and not the younger brother's widow. Sometimes the son is obliged to marry his father's widow (when she is not his own mother), although if there are several

widows left one may go to the deceased man's sister's son—
in other words she must marry her nephew-in-law, if she
cannot get a stepson.   The object of the levirate is to provide
for the widow, the responsibility for this naturally falling
on the next of kin to the deceased, and also to keep in the
family any property, such as a dowry, which the widow
possesses.   Among the Old Testament Hebrews, it was
the duty of a man to marry his brother's widow if his brother
died childless and the first born of this union succeeded to
the brother's name in order " that his name be not put out
of Israel."

The *sororate*, on the other hand, a custom of marrying
the deceased wife's sister, is a means of providing the husband
with a second wife from the same stock as the first.   Among
some peoples a second marriage may be made with the
wife's sister during the wife's lifetime, if the first wife prove
barren.

Another common type is that of " cross-cousin " marriage,
when the custom is for a young man to marry either his
mother's brother's daughter, a very usual form, or his father's
sister's daughter.   Sometimes he may marry either one or
the other of the two possible cousins, or he must marry only
the one kind of cross-cousin, *i.e.* either his maternal uncle's
daughter or his paternal aunt's daughter.   This cross-cousin
marriage leads to very complicated kinship relations, as
anybody will appreciate who cares to make a genealogical
table of two or three families, putting in imaginary cross-
cousin marriages.   A further complication is that persons
may count as cousins who are not in reality cousins at all.

THE FAMILY RELATIONSHIP : FATHERS WHO ARE NOT PARENTS

THESE complicated degrees of relationship arise from the
peculiar systems of kinship that are recognised in
uncivilised societies.   At least they seem very peculiar at
first sight.   We of the civilised world reckon kinship according to a particular system of relationships, and we imagine
that to be the only way.   If we call a certain relationship
that of uncle, we laugh at anybody who calls the same relationship that of father, as in fact many savage societies do.   On
the other hand our word " cousin " would convey almost
nothing to many a savage.   Is this cousin, he would ask,

the son or daughter of your paternal uncle or of your paternal aunt, or is it the son or the daughter of your maternal uncle or of your maternal aunt ? You may think I am mad, he would say, because I call a number of men " father " who are not my parent, but I think you are mad because you use the same word to describe the brother of your wife and the husband of your sister.

The civilised world uses a relationship system based on the immediate family, father, mother, brother, sister, uncle, aunt, etc., and the in-laws are brought into line. Most primitive societies, however, use what is called the " classificatory system," a method of reckoning kinship by which certain classes of persons, irrespective of direct blood relationship, are called " father," " mother," " brother," " sister," etc. The classificatory system or systems, for there are many different kinds, are at once more vague and general, and more accurately descriptive than our family system. On the one hand large classes of persons are called by one kinship term, but on the other, different types of kinship are more accurately differentiated.

A savage may call " father " all his father's brothers or all men of the clan in the same age group as his father. Consequently if he is bound to marry his " father's " sister's child he may have a wide choice, especially if his " fathers " call " sister " other women besides their blood sisters. The Hawaiian Islander classes together with his father all persons of his father's generation with whom he is related by blood (not by marriage) ; all relations of his own generation he classes as brothers and sisters and all of the next generation as sons and daughters.

The classificatory system of relations is based not on blood but on forms of social conduct. A certain type of behaviour is due to all those whom you call maternal uncle, who may include all the men whom your maternal uncle calls " brother." In primitive societies there are strict and well-defined rules of etiquette to be observed in behaviour towards the different relations, and these rules apply to all those to whom the kinship term applies.

THE LAWS OF ETIQUETTE IN THE FOREST

R ULES of etiquette commonly take the form of avoidance. It is very often a rule for the son-in-law to avoid his mother-in-law, and perhaps all women whom his wife's mother calls sister. Among the Berber tribes of Morocco a bridegroom refrains from speaking to his father-in-law or brothers-in-law for some time after the marriage, and even later he never eats with them, nor is he ever seen together with them in public ; should any of them come where he is sitting with other persons he at once gets up and leaves the company. If a man meets a friend whom he has not seen for a while he jokingly says, " Why have you been running away from me ; am I your brother-in-law ? " On the other hand, familiarity is often permitted only to certain relationships, such as perhaps between a man and his father's brother. Only between persons of express relationship may joking or free conversation on sexual matters be entertained. Sometimes joking is even obligatory. Among some Red Indians brothers-in-law should never meet without joking and making obscene remarks at each other's expense.

Not only etiquette, but duties are determined by kinship. The duties are often of a ceremonial nature—different relatives have a definite rôle to play in the ceremonies connected with birth, initiation, marriage, and death. Duties may also be of a more permanent and arduous nature, as in the obligation we have already noted to marry the widows of deceased relatives.

Kinship also may carry its privileges, usually connected with inheritance and property. Among some peoples a man may purloin the property of his maternal uncle or grandfather or certain relatives of his wife without their permission. Kinship terms among savage peoples are the labels denoting appropriate behaviour rather than terms expressing family relationships. Nevertheless the actual family relationships remain and do not go unrecognised.

It would be a great mistake to suppose either that the classifactory system of kinship terms signifies complete anarchy in family relations (as if, for example, because a man called all his paternal uncles " father " it were assumed that they all stood in the position of husband to his mother, and might therefore any of them be the actual father), or that the savage is simply incapable of differentiating between the family and the classificatory relationships. He is perfectly aware of the distinction and is not troubled by any confusion between the two, such as one might think would arise.

Ambiguity in conversation is avoided in the minds of both

speaker and hearer either by the context or by different
linguistic devices, such as a change in form of the word or
of the tone of voice, or descriptive additions or circum-
locutions, as it might be " my parent father " or " the father
who begat me." Nevertheless, when customs of intermarriage between the generations exist, as for example, when
a man marries his father's, or sometimes even his grandfather's
widow, the actual family relationships themselves grow very
complicated. In the former example the man will be both
stepfather and half-brother to the widow's children by his
father. The choice of kinship terms in this case will be
according to the behaviour expected of them towards each
other, according, that is, to the social rather than to the
blood relationship.

DIVIDING THE CHILDREN AMONG THE PARENTS

IT must also be borne in mind that although the family
relationships exist and are recognised, the actual family
organisation may be different from that with which we are
familiar in our own society. With us a woman takes her
husband's name and the children their father's. Descent
is reckoned mainly through the male line, and family property
goes rather to the sons than to the daughters. Children, at
least until this century, were considered to belong to the
father. Nowadays, divorce court decisions by which the
custody of the children is granted to either parent on the
merits of the case indicate that the child is considered to
belong equally to both parents. The chief authority in the
family is still, however, nominally the father. This kind of
family organisation, where the sons are heirs to their father,
is known as " patrilineal."

In many primitive societies, however, descent is organised
on different lines. The children, or especially the sons,
sometimes belong by birth to the mother's clan or group,
which would be equivalent to taking the mother's surname.
This is called " matrilineal " descent, or descent traced
through the mother's line. Among the African Ashanti there
are two separate descent groups for different purposes, one
reckoned through the father and one through the mother.
Some peoples, on the other hand, like the Eskimos, have no
descent groups at all, and children are just born into the world
as isolated and rather haphazard entities.

Sometimes, too, the daughters will belong to the mother's

group and the sons to that of the father, as happens among certain tribes of Assam. This system, of course, splits up the family into membership of two separate groups. It is as if when Miss Smith marries Mr. Brown, all the daughters are the Misses Smith and take part in the Smith clan ceremonies, while the brothers are the Masters Brown and go to the Brown clan festivals and meetings.

Succession and inheritance do not necessarily follow the line of descent. Where descent is patrilineal a man's heir is nearly always his son, as in our civilisation. There may be variations, as there are in Europe, where in some countries the custom is for the main property to go to the eldest son, and in others for the inheritance to be divided equally among the sons. Where descent is matrilineal, a man's normal heir is usually his sister's son, because descent is traced through the mother and therefore his own children belong to his wife's group and succeed to their maternal uncle. This is true both of the inheritance of property and of the succession to titles, such as chieftainship or to special privileges and duties, such as those connected with priestcraft or medicine. Very often in both types of inheritance, patrilineal and matrilineal, the brothers of the dead man are his first heirs and successors, and the property or office reverts to the children in the direct line only after the death of the uncles.

In the family where descent is reckoned through the mother, the father is in a sense a kind of intruder, a stranger in the group. He does not, therefore, usually have the authority accorded to the patriarchal type of father in the patrilineal family. The paternal authority is often in the former case vested in one of the maternal uncles, probably the eldest. This is so among the Trobriand Islanders, where the maternal uncle rules his sister's family, while his own, in turn, is regulated by his wife's brother. An interesting result is seen in the attitude of the children towards their father. Where he is the supreme family authority he is treated with respect and reverence, or even awe, but not with affection, for this would imply too great a familiarity. This is especially true of nomadic tribes, where the patriarchal family is most often found. We see it exemplified many times in the stories of the nomadic Hebrews of the Old Testament—in the attitude, for instance, of Jacob to Isaac.

Where, on the other hand, the main authority lies with the mother's brother, the attitude of obedience and respect is transferred to the uncle. We see this very clearly among the Trobrianders, where the uncle is treated with respectful formality, while the father is treated familiarly and affectionately, and gains in love what he loses in authority. According as the children are divided, so we get the building up and continuation of group, clan, tribe, and ultimately, on the civilised plane, national organisation. We can now turn our attention to the general organisation of societies.

RACE, CLAN, AND FAMILY : THE SOCIAL CODE

THE first great division of mankind is into races. The difficulty here, unfortunately, is that no two anthropologists ever agree on a definition of race. Consequently all the race experts (the physical anthropologists) divide up the races differently, and it is quite impossible to say how many races there are in the world, and what is their distribution, with the certainty with which we can say how many species of cockroach there are and where they are to be found. In popular speech the term " race " is used very loosely, and is often merely another word for nationality. We speak, for example, of the British " race," although the English alone are composed of at least three separate races (as European races are generally understood by anthropologists), while the word " British " covers groups of people as alien from each other as French-Canadians and West Indian negroes. The term " race " should be used to denote " a group of people who have certain well-marked physical characteristics in common," but it must be remembered that race names, such as Nordic, Alpine, or Mediterranean, are merely working conventions that help us to appreciate broad facts.

There are generally considered to be three main races in Europe : the tall and fair " Nordics " from North Europe ; the " Alpine " from Central Europe, short and broad and round-headed ; and the Mediterranean race, short and slight and dark. Each is characterised by a number of detailed physical attributes, such as types of skull, nose and hair, and various different mental qualities have also been attributed to the three races.

It might be noted in passing that the expression " Aryan race " should at all costs be avoided. The word was originally coined to describe a hypothetical extinct language which was supposed to have been the original of that whole group of languages known as the " Indo-European." All European languages, except Hungarian, Finnish, Estonian, Lettish, Lithuanian, and Basque, belong to this group, along with Hindustani, and they all have much in common. It has been assumed that there was one basic original language of them all, and therefore that there must have existed a people who spoke this language, and who, probably coming from Central Asia, invaded India and Europe and founded European civilisation. This hypothetical people was called the " Aryan " people, and the term has passed into common speech and even got mixed up in politics as a synonym for " Nordic " or even for non-Jewish rather than with its original linguistic meaning.

HOW THE RACES SPREAD OVER THE EARTH

OUTSIDE Europe there is a most bewildering complexity of races and peoples. Very roughly we may say that north and east of the Himalayas, Asia is peopled by a mongol stock which has somehow spread, probably by way of the Bering Straits, into Arctic and North America, where we find it again in the Eskimo and Red Indian. South of the Himalayas and the Caucasus is the Dravidian or Brown Race in India, spreading eastwards into South China and westwards into Europe and even as far as the British Isles, where a few people of the Dravidian type are still to be found. India, however, is an absolute hotch-potch of races, owing to successive waves of invasion from the North. There are at least four distinct racial types and a far greater number of peoples, including Turkish, Arab, and Assyrian elements. The oldest indigenous stock in India is a very black-skinned people of much the same type as the Australian Aborigine, sometimes called the Veddaic-Australoid type. The Veddahs and jungle tribes of South India are typical of this race.

To the south-east of the Himalayan line we find the tall dark negroes of eastern Pacific islands, generally known as the Papuans. It is as yet unknown whether the African and the Papuan negro evolved separately in Africa and the Pacific, or whether at some prehistoric time they spread from one centre to the other. If the latter supposition is correct, how is it that we do not find negroes in between the two areas ? Actually there are traces of a negroid race in India, but so there are in the Mediterranean. The question adds itself to the already considerable pile of unsolved anthropological problems.

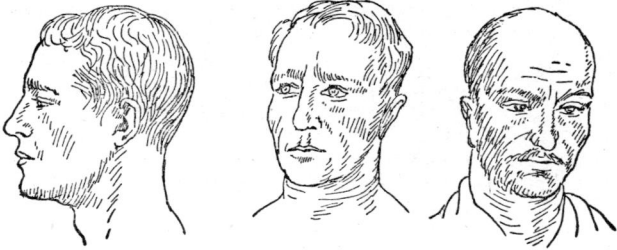

Three Aspects of Nordic Man

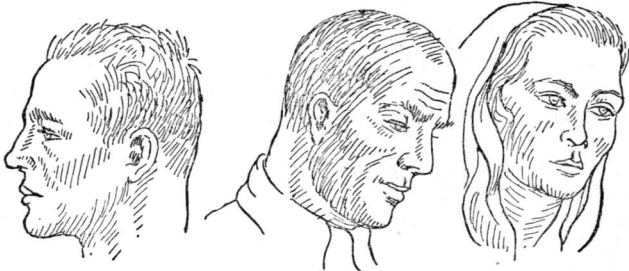

Alpine Men and a Woman

Typical Mediterranean Men

31. THE THREE RACES OF EUROPE.

It is generally considered that there are three main races in Europe, the tall, fair Nordics, the Alpine race (short and round-headed, and the Mediterranean (short and dark).

There is another East Pacific race beside the Papuans and Melanesians (the latter a hybrid people of Papuan stock). This is the Negrito race, a very small and dark people to be found in isolated groups in the East Indies. These groups— the Andaman Islands, parts of Malay, Sumatra, the Philippines, and parts of Dutch New Guinea—lie on the circumference of an imaginary and rather irregular circle. It is possible that this race once occupied a much larger area, including the whole area inside the circle.

In Australia we have the aborigines, a black-skinned, woolly-haired race resembling, as we have noticed, the primitive Veddahs of India. Africa is the home of the true negro, but it contains also several other peoples. The true negro area is Central and East Africa, centring round the Guinea Coast. In the North there are the Arabs. From the East came an invasion of Hamites or Ethiopians (the nominal descendants of Ham). They spread in a south-westerly direction, intermingling with the Bushmen and negroes, until they now cover most of Rhodesia, Nyasaland, and South Africa. They are known as the Bantu peoples. The southerly spread of the Bantu took place quite recently—they crossed the Zambesi River about a hundred years ago. The original peoples of South Africa were the Bushmen and Hottentots, racially akin, a people of small stature and many primitive characteristics. Then, lastly, there are the Nilotic peoples, very tall, dark, and slender negroids, who live in and around the basin of the Upper Nile.

In America we have already noted the North American Indians and the Eskimo. There is almost no reliable information about the indigenous peoples of South America. They would make a fine field for investigation for some enterprising physical anthropologist.

This is a very rough sketch of the geographical distribution of the main races of the world. When we come down to smaller units we must remember that we cannot divide the primitive world into nations. Savage societies have not reached a sufficiently high level of culture to be able to weld themselves together on a wide enough basis to obtain the solidarity of a nation. The widest organisation is that of the tribe. " A tribe is the largest body of people inhabiting a specified territory who speak the same language, have a common name for themselves, and feel a sense of solidarity among themselves, regarding all outsiders as foreigners."

THE CLAN : KEY TO SAVAGE SOCIETY

Most primitive societies are organised more in detail into sub-divisions of the greatest importance in the life of the community. The clan is the key to primitive social organisation. Primarily a group of kinsmen, it comes to have a wide political and religious importance in the community, and great power over the individual. He receives membership of a certain clan as his birthright, and after his initiation at puberty he becomes a full member of a closely united fraternity.

The bond that unites the clan is a bond of kinship, but, as we have had occasion to notice before, not necessarily kinship in the narrower European sense. Members of the same clan will usually call each other by kinship terms, and will use towards each other the proper behaviour appertaining to such terms, although there is no blood relationship. In North America many clans have a special series of personal names belonging to each clan, which no member of another clan may use, so that a man's clan is known immediately by his name. If his name were John or Tom, for example, then he would belong, say, to the Smith clan, because no other might use those names. If it were Dick or Harry he would belong to the Robinson clan, and so on.

Membership is determined by blood descent from one parent only, either through the mother or through the father. The fictitious kinship which unites the members arises from a belief, common to most clan systems, in a common ancestor from whom the whole clan is descended. This ancestor is usually wholly imaginary. He may be some legendary hero connected with the stories of far-off times, or he may be a mythical figure related rather to religious beliefs. He may be what is known in mythology as a " culture-hero," that is, a person who is said to have introduced some branch of knowledge or useful art to mankind. (Prometheus is a good example of a " culture-hero," for he stole fire from the gods and gave it to man.)

Often the imaginary ancestor is some animal or plant, and then all the members of the clan consider themselves related, or connected in some mysterious way, to all the living examples of the ancestor animal. The animal is then known to us as a *Totem*, after the word used by the Ojibway Red Indians. The thing to remember about totemism in this connection is that the half-mystic connection between men and animals is not between any individual person and individual animal, but between whole groups of people, such as a clan, and a whole species of animal. The totem is by no means always an animal; it is often a plant. Sometimes it is just part of an animal, like the Buffalo Tongue totem of the Omaha Indians; or sometimes it is the part and not the animal that matters, like the totem of a Bengal tribe which is the ears of any animal. Occasionally, too, we find an abstract totem, such as the colour red, of another Omaha clan, or " pride," the totem of a Madras caste of weavers.

THE TOTEM : " OLD SCHOOL TIE " OF THE WILDS

THE possession of a totem adds greatly to the solidarity and unity of the clan. Sometimes when clan members are very scattered, one member may recognise another by his behaviour towards the totem—some ceremonial conduct when he sees the totem animal perhaps, or a refusal to partake of its flesh owing to a taboo laid on all the totem brothers—and immediately he will be treated with the utmost cordiality as a near relative and fellow-member of the clan. In some places the members of a clan are even supposed to resemble their totem in character.

Thus among the Red Indians the members of the Ojibway Bear Clan were reputed to be surly and pugnacious, and were the acknowledged war chiefs of the tribe. Members of the Crane Clan were supposed to have the loud ringing voice of the crane, and they were the official tribal orators. Totemism has also a religious as well as a social aspect, which in its turn also helps to weld the clan together in a common sense of unity.

Sometimes the clan has a definite function of a political or economic order. Certain clans may have the duty of providing certain goods or certain foods for the community. There may be a hunting clan or a fishing clan or a pottery-making clan. Certain clans, too, may take over the government of the community—there may be a ruling or a war leaders' clan. The relations between the clan and the tribe in regard to social organisation vary very much in different parts. In some places the clan, in some the tribe, is the chief administrative unit. Sometimes it is the one or the other, according to the function concerned.

A further grouping occurs in some societies, particularly in

Australia and Melanesia, where within the tribe the clans are arranged in two groups known as moieties or halves. These moieties are nearly always exogamous. A very usual form of marriage among tribes divided into this " dual organisation," as it is called, is the " cross-cousin " marriage, of which we have already spoken. Since membership of the moiety is determined through one parent only, a cross-cousin, that is the child of the father's sister or of the mother's brother, must belong to the other moiety, and thus exogamous marriage is secured.

Very often the moieties are separated from each other at feasts and ceremonials, and will sit on different sides of the meeting-place, and each perform different parts of the ceremonial. Sometimes there arises an elaborate system of reciprocal duties and obligations between the two moieties. Reciprocal gifts are common. Persons among moiety A find, as it were, partners among moiety B, and supply them with certain goods in return for services or other articles supplied to them. Or persons of moiety B may have certain duties to perform in the case of death among their partners of moiety A and *vice versa*. On the other hand, however, in a few Melanesian tribes the two halves are hostile and suspicious, and avoid each other as far as possible. The whole structure and working of the dual organisation is very interesting, and would repay further investigation by field workers.

THE EXACT MEANING OF A "CLAN."

A word should be added concerning the term " clan," which, loosely used in everyday language, has a rather narrower and different meaning in anthropology. The main feature of the clan when the word is used by an anthropologist is that it is " exogamous "—that is, that its members must marry outside it. If this rule does not apply, then a group is not a clan. Now the Scottish " clans," to which so much glamour and romance has become attached, did not use this rule of marriage. They are, therefore, not " clans " in the anthropological sense. So when the unwary reader, glancing through the chapter-headings of a book on anthropology, sees a chapter on clans, he will be sorely disappointed if he reads it through expecting romantic stories of highland feuds. Nevertheless there are stories of feuds and love among the clans of black, brown and red peoples that are no less romantic.

" NOW THAT I AM A MAN . . ."

ANOTHER form of grouping within the tribe or community is that of age-groups. It is very common among most primitive societies to find the people grouped together as elders, middle-aged men, young men, and children (or perhaps more commonly elders, married men, young bachelors, and children). These groups, which usually cut right across the clan divisions, are held together by the many interests common to people at the same stage of life. Like the same sort of groups among school-children, the age-grades tend to become sharply separated cliques.

These cliques are not the same as the secret societies so prevalent all over Africa. The essence of a secret society is that only a restricted number of people may join, or the " secret " will soon be out, whereas the age-group consists of all members of the community of the same age. Both types of association have, however, many features in common. Entry into each is through initiation or by a payment. In the case of the age-group the payment is small enough to come within the means of all, and is in the nature of a small contribution towards expenses ; but the purchase price of the right of entry into a secret society may be very high indeed. Secret societies may be without any apparent purpose, or they may play some definite part in the religious or political or economic life of the community. Age-groups are most prominent among warlike tribes, where they often control the organisation of society. The younger grades act as training grounds for courage, skill, and endurance ; the middle grades provide the warriors, the elders, the administrative and political power.

Birth is always an event marked with ceremony, although there are many different kinds of celebration. Some tribes, for example, take no notice of the actual arrival of the baby, but reserve their ceremonies for the naming of the child (as indeed is the custom among ourselves). This will not take place until a few days after birth, as meanwhile there is no knowing whether the child has really come to stay—whether, that is, it will live. The African Ashanti scarcely look after the newborn child at all for the first few days, considering that for the first week it is only a ghost-baby, and may easily go off again to the land of spirits whence it has come, so that it is scarcely worth bothering about.

CHILD INTO MAN : THE CEREMONY OF INITIATION

CHILDREN, in most primitive societies, are left very free to occupy and amuse themselves according to their own devices. With the onset of puberty, however, the situation changes. The child is now about to become a man, when he must take his place as a member of adult society, with its duties and responsibilities and privileges. He must, therefore, put away childish things and learn the ways of his new estate. In all primitive societies the child is considered to become an adult as soon as he reaches puberty, and the adolescent stage seems to be neither so long nor so difficult as it is in our maturer civilisation. Nevertheless, the change is momentous, and not accomplished without some difficulty. The savage realises its importance and dangers, and deals with them in his own way by initiation ceremonies. Initiation into the adult group is generally the most outstanding event in the individual's life. Marriage, which usually takes place within at most a few years of initiation, is really just the final stage, and is not accompanied by nearly such an elaborate ritual, nor has it so great an emotional significance as the rites of initiation.

These rites that mark the passage from childhood to adult life all have a definitely biological basis and trend. The child is about to enter a period of sexual activity new to him. There are many things that he should be taught, concerning both his own health and the sexual code of the society in which he lives. These things are not, in " savage " communities, left to chance or to literature.

Initiation often includes a period of segregation varying from days to months in which the initiates are kept away from the rest of the community in special huts where they are taught by appointed persons, often elders, while they are undergoing various forms of training. The training is designed to emphasise the difference between the care-free life of childhood and the duties and responsibilities of manhood, and takes the form of intensified discipline along various lines. A very common mode of discipline is abstention from certain foods, usually staple articles of diet, in order to stress the fact that food will not, as heretofore, just appear at meal-times, but that it has to be obtained through the united efforts of the individual and the community. Instruction in hunting may be given at the same time. Seclusion, too, may be very strict—the initiates may not be allowed to see their families or to go beyond certain limits or even to leave their special hut.

A further form of discipline is provided in the tests of endurance which are so prominent a feature of many initiation rites. These often take the form of what seem to us to be very cruel practices. Many rites demand not only hardship but ordeals of intense pain and include various degrees of mutilation. Among a number of Australian tribes, for instance, the initiate has one of his front teeth knocked out. The most well-known ceremonial operation at puberty is circumcision. Among the Jews, of course, circumcision takes place in infancy, and is a most important occasion of great religious significance. Among most savage peoples, however, circumcision, and the corresponding operation on girls, forms a part of initiatory ritual.

These and other operations of the same nature, such as scarifying, are normally performed by skilled persons, probably a medicine man or an elder, and although in most cases the instruments are of the crudest—sometimes just a stone knife—and there are no disinfectants—nevertheless little harm seems to be done, and deaths are rare. In some places, however, missionary activity has discouraged or forbidden the performance of initiation rites with the result that these operations are done secretly by any one who can be prevailed upon to undertake them. Consequently the operators are often unskilled, the operation performed hurriedly, and the result is too often infection, permanent injury or death.

Ordeals, hardship, and seclusion form the main theme of the disciplinary side of initiation. The significance of the change, however, and the difference between child and manhood are also brought home by gentler means. The initiates often have to wear special dress, or some distinctive mark such as a particular style of hairdressing or design of paint. Formal instruction is also often given by the elders of the tribe in the laws and customs of the community, and in morals or religion. Tribal laws and regulations seldom extend to children, but after initiation all customs must be followed, all taboos kept, and all etiquette observed without excuse.

Often, too, a new name is conferred at initiation to emphasise the new estate of manhood. With the name go the new duties and privileges. After initiation is completed, the young man will no longer consort with his former playmates, the younger children who have not yet been initiated, but only with those of his own age-grade. As initiation often takes place in large batches of youths, the initiates of each year or season form a clique or group of their own.

WOMAN'S PLACE IN THE PRIMITIVE WORLD

So far we have been considering the life of the individual in society almost exclusively from the man's point of view. In describing the rites of initiation we have referred mainly to boys. Girls also, however, have their ceremonial initiation into womanhood, although the custom is not so universal nor are the preparations and ceremonies usually so elaborate. Among the Andaman Islanders as soon as a girl has her first menstrual period she tells her parents and they weep over her.

" She must then go and bathe in the sea for an hour or two by herself. After that she goes back to her parents' hut or to a special shelter that is put up for the occasion. . . . All ornaments are removed from her, only a single belt of *Pandanus* leaf being left with an apron of leaves. Strips of *Pandanus* leaf are attached round her arms near the shoulders and round her wrists, and others are placed as bands crossing her chest. . . . These are so attached that loose ends hang down at the girl's side. Bunches of leaves . . . . are fastened beneath her belt before and behind. . . .

" Thus covered with leaves the girl must sit in the hut allotted to her, with her legs doubled up beneath her and her arms folded. A piece of wood or bamboo is placed at her back for her to lean against, as she may not lie down. If she is cramped she may stretch one of her legs or one of her arms, but not both arms or both legs at the same time. . . . She may not speak nor sleep for twenty-four hours. Her wants are attended to by her parents or their friends, who sit near her to keep her from falling asleep.

" The girl sits thus for three days. Early every morning she leaves the hut to bathe for an hour in the sea. At the end of the three days she resumes her life in the village. For a month following she must bathe

in the sea every morning at dawn. At the ceremony
the girl is given a new name, a flower name after any
plant or tree in flower at the time. From then until
the birth of her first child she may only be called by the
flower name."

THE PERPETUAL FEUD BETWEEN THE SEXES

ALL over the world women play a less conspicuous part
in public than men. Their position and status in society
vary very widely. A certain degree of hostility, mostly sub-
conscious, between the sexes seems to be part of the common
psychological make-up of mankind. It is sometimes referred
to as " sex antagonism." It often shows itself in primitive
society under the guise of a belief that the two sexes are
mutually dangerous, and more especially that women are
dangerous to men. The danger is usually believed to be more
acute at some periods than at others ; pregnant women or
women at their menstrual periods are commonly supposed
to bring bad luck or evil of some kind. Not only this, but
women in these conditions are also often credited with magic
powers, it being commonly believed that then they are
possessed by spirits. At such periods women are often sedu-
lously avoided, and not only the women themselves but
contact with anything belonging to them. Sometimes men
will not enter the house of a woman in childbed, nor eat food
prepared by a pregnant woman, nor touch anything she has
touched for fear of something akin to our " evil eye."

Something of the same feeling of danger accounts for the
practice of debarring women from important ceremonies.
Shrines and holy places are often forbidden to women in the
East, while among primitive peoples women are often strictly
debarred from attending the initiation of boys, or rites connected with hunting or war. Sometimes so strict are these
prohibitions that infringement, even unwitting, may be
punishable by death. In many primitive communities, too,
it is the custom for all the young men to live together in a
big man's house, a sort of men's club, and it is often strictly
taboo for any woman to enter such a house. (This taboo
still survives in many of the men's clubs in Piccadilly and St.
James's in London.) Among many African cattle-keeping
tribes, whose sole wealth lies in their herds, which also play a
most important part in their social life, women are never on
any account allowed to tend the cattle. On the other hand,

among agricultural peoples women usually do most of the work in the fields. Polygamy is supposed to be common in agricultural communities for that reason, for the more wives a man has the more free labour is there at his disposal.

In very few societies are women allowed a voice (at least an official voice), in the government of the community and the administration of public affairs. Nevertheless women rulers are not altogether unknown. The status of the wives of chiefs or kings is largely influenced by the rule of descent. If descent is through the mother, then the ruler's wife, or chief wife is likely to be a person of greater importance than if descent is traced through the father. If, however, the heir to the throne is not the king's own son, but his sister's son, as we mentioned further back is often the case where descent is by the mother's line, the king's sister, or that sister who is mother to the heir, may be accorded the greatest honour.

Magic, rather than politics, seems to be woman's sphere. Although in most savage societies important magic seems to be mainly performed by men—medicine men and sorcerers and rain-makers—minor magic in the way of small spells, and making magic foods and potions, is often practised by women ; while in Europe, as we know, magic practices were attributed almost entirely to women, and witches were burnt for their evil arts right up to the beginning of the eighteenth century.

A WOMAN IS RESPECTED ACCORDING TO HER PROPERTY

WITHIN the family circle the position of women is again very varied. In China and among the nomad tribes of Asia, woman is of little account, and if she does not bear a reasonable number of men children she is absolutely worthless. On the other hand, women of some African peoples have considerable voice in family affairs and are treated with respect. The status of women within the family largely depends on her economic status in the community as a whole. If she may hold property, and especially if she may hold any form of property and dispose of it independently of her family, her position will be much higher than if she is debarred from ownership. Her position is lowest of all when she herself is merely a form of property belonging to her father or her husband ; when she can be sold or bartered or even pawned like any other chattel.

In this connection it should be mentioned that the payment

of a bride-price by the groom does not necessarily imply that the wife is " purchased " like a sack of oats. The payment is often more in the nature of a substantial gift, either of money or more usually in kind, made by the bridegroom to the bride's family. It very often acts as a sort of guarantee for the marriage, for unless the bridegroom is both in earnest and fairly well established, he will not be likely to produce the requisite sum. The payment is also sometimes regarded as a kind of compensation to the bride's family or clan for the loss of a member. Such a custom does, however, sometimes degenerate into marriage by purchase, just as the dowry system degenerates into purely financial matches.

Outside the family women sometimes organise themselves into clubs or associations of their own along the same lines as men's societies. Just as there are bachelors' houses where they all live together, so there are sometimes communal houses for girls of marriageable age. Where there are girls' initiation rites, the initiates are sometimes segregated like the boys in special club houses to which no man is allowed access. Women's associations are very much rarer than men's, for in all societies except our own, marriage is the almost universal career for all women, and except in cases of sterility the bearing and rearing of children takes up most of their time and energies. Combined with the duties of preparing food and of making cloth, pottery, and household goods, this allows the woman little leisure or energy to pursue interests and occupations outside her biological and domestic sphere.

LAW AND ORDER AMONG THE TRIBES

LAW grows out of custom ; indeed in the lowest cultures we may say that custom is law. It is only at a higher stage that authority is sufficiently well-organised for laws or regulations to be definitely made by a ruling power. The Jews had become a closely organised tribe before Moses gave to the people the famous Mosaic code. Even, so that code must have been largely a resumé and definition of existing customs. Moses was said to have received the tablets of the law from God, for among the Ancient Hebrews religion and law were inextricably bound together—there was no division between the law of God and the laws of man.

Similarly in all the simpler societies, religion, using the word to cover the whole complex of mystic beliefs and practices among primitive people, is an integral part of law. An offence against a deity or a spirit is punishable just like an offence against a person or property. Very likely, however, the punishment will be administered according to a different procedure from that employed in other offences. There is a distinction made between different categories of law, such as we would call religious, civil and criminal laws, and they work in different manners. There is also in all societies, a moral code outside the law, trespass against which is punished by public opinion rather than by legal means.

Primitive laws are, as we have seen, embodied in actual customs ; there is no way of drawing a hard and fast line between the two. It is the law that a man must marry outside his clan ; it is the custom that he must make a gift of, say, so many cows to the bride's family. Can this latter be said to be a law ? Without the bride-price there will be no bride, but yet if a man did manage to procure a wife for, say, one cow instead of two, would there be any punishment ? This is rather a case of civil law.

If the husband won his bride on what might be called the hire-purchase system, with one cow deposit " cash down " and perhaps two calves to pay in instalments, and then never delivered the instalments, he would be proceeded against by his father-in-law according to the customary procedure in the case of debt. His father-in-law might come and carry off the livestock by force, perhaps with a few extra as interest, or he might reclaim his daughter, or he might distrain on other property or persons connected with the debtor.

On the other hand, if the woman was willingly given on the understanding that only one cow would be forthcoming instead of the customary two (and let it be said in parenthesis that according to African standards, where such payments are commonest, two cows would be a very small sum for a woman), there would be no state law laying down that all brides must be given only in exchange for the customary sum or more. Custom regulates the conduct of affairs between individuals and has the force of law. If the individuals agree among themselves to modify the custom (which would be a very rare occurrence), then so long as the deviation affected no one but the individuals concerned, society would let it stand. The parties might be scorned or ridiculed, but they would not be punished.

If, however, the deviation affected, or was believed to be

13

likely to affect, society as a whole, then custom would have all the primitive force of law. If, for example, two families agreed to a marriage which was forbidden by custom, then the law would forbid the match and punish the parties. When an unlawful marriage takes place among the Eskimaux, the community comes in a body and stamps in the roof of the snow hut on the guilty pair and that is the end of them.

"THOU SHALT NOT—": THE POWER OF TABOO

PRIMITIVE law might be divided into two parts: the category of " Thou shalt," and the category of " Thou shalt not." The former is included under much that we should ordinarily term custom. It is impossible to say whether many types of behaviour, in regard to property, trade, personal conduct, etiquette, and ceremonial, are prescribed by law or by custom. When we come to the " Thou shalt nots," however, we are on firmer ground. A custom that habitually forbids any action, and punishes any transgression of the order, may well be deemed a law. Primitive law in this sense is mainly composed of a formidable series of prohibitions and taboos. A prohibition is the simple forbidding of a thing under penalty for whatsoever reason. A taboo is a prohibition for magical and religious reasons. The mystic and supernatural element in the taboo surrounds it with an aura of fear and mystery which ensures such strict observance that the word has passed into our language to describe anything that is absolutely and unexceptionally forbidden.

The word was first introduced into England by Captain Cook, who met with it in Tonga in 1777. He says, in the account of his voyage, that taboo " has a very comprehensive meaning, but in general signifies that a thing is forbidden," being " applied to all cases where things are not to be touched." A genuine taboo, however, among a savage people, may vary considerably in extent and strictness. Many taboos refer only to certain times, such as seasons of the year, or to certain individuals, like chiefs or sorcerers; or, again, only to groups of persons, such as warriors or young people going through initiation. Others are permanent and universal for every member of the community.

The reasons lying behind a taboo may be quite simple. Many taboos are just precautionary measures—there may be, for example, a taboo on plants known or believed to be poisonous. There will, however, be some other reason of a magico-religious character beyond the mere fact of the poison ; otherwise the plant concerned would just be known to be poisonous and avoided as such, and that would be all. There will be some extra feeling attached to the plant, connecting it, perhaps, with evil spirits, before anything so serious as a taboo is placed upon it.

Another more subtle type of precaution commonly lies behind the sort of taboo that forbids a pregnant woman to tie knots, for fear of childbirth difficulties. Then there is the desire to propitiate the mysterious spirit powers by avoiding certain objects to which this spirit power (often called *Mana*, from the Polynesian name for it) is particularly attached. Other precautions are more difficult to understand. The king of a certain tribe in West Africa, for instance, was never allowed to leave his chair, nor touch a woman, nor certain foods, for fear of evil befalling his people.

Taboos may in general be considered to be either inherent in a thing—an action or object that has always been taboo since the memory of man—or imposed temporarily or permanently by a definite order from some individual such as a chief or priest. It is the latter kind of taboo that is most akin to what we would call law-making. In some tribes the tribal authorities have considerable power to impose taboos at will. When Captain Cook wished to set up an observatory in the Sandwich Islands, the priests laid a taboo on the place for him by setting up wands made of a particular kind of wood. These " imposed " taboos lie rather on the borderland between kingly and priestly authority, for though they may be imposed by the will of a chief, they are nevertheless made effective mainly by the magico-religious quality attached to them.

WHAT HAPPENS TO THOSE WHO BREAK THE LAW

WE have discussed savage law and how it cannot be distinguished from custom, but is composed of the more hard-and-fast and important rules of custom, and how it is re-enforced by religion and magic. What, now, of those who break the law ? How are primitive laws enforced ? Crime may be roughly divided into two classes, offences against individuals and offences against society. In the first class would be considered theft, murder, violence, adultery, and so forth. These are actions which would be generally regarded as criminal all the world over. Crimes against society, however, such as we should consider forgery and bigamy, include all sorts of offences, varying in different societies, many of which we should not consider offences at all. Among the Andamanese, for instance, laziness or the refusal to marry are considered quite as bad as theft or damage to property. The most serious crime against society in any community is infraction of the marriage rules—marrying within the prescribed degrees. Next would come infringement of taboos, particularly of taboos connected with sacred things. Misbehaviour at, or refusal to take part in, public ceremonials would also be a grave offence. Boys who refuse, or attempt to refuse, to go through initiation are committing what is tantamount to a criminal act, and are punished accordingly.

WHEN VENGEANCE IS TAKEN BY THE FAMILY

ALL offences against individuals are, of course, ultimately offences against society, since society is only an aggregate of individual persons. On how far this fact is understood depends the method of procedure in cases of crime. In the very simple primitive societies, although what are held to be offences against the community will be severely dealt with by the community, crimes against individuals, like murder and theft, will very likely be left to individual vengeance. Custom will settle what form this vengeance shall take and who shall wreak it. It if is murder the relatives may take charge. If it is a case of crime against property, probably the injured party himself will direct operations against the offender. He will very likely enlist the help of his relatives if the offence was at all serious, while on the other side the culprit will fly for help to his family. In this way blood feuds are started. The relatives of the murdered man demand blood for blood and kill the murderer, or one of his family. Then his relatives retaliate, and so the cruel story goes on, spreading beyond the family to the whole clan.

Sometimes, however, the culprit or his friends are willing to admit the wrongfulness of his action and to give compensation. The compensation that custom demands may be " an eye for an eye, a tooth for a tooth," or more often this simpler method has evolved into a more complicated and less savage system of compensatory payments. Such is the custom of " blood-money," the exaction of a payment, probably, among the lower cultures, in kind, as compensation and atonement for murder. In some cases " blood-money " takes the form of ceding a woman to the family or group of the victim, and thus compensating them for the loss of one of their members by giving them one who shall bear them new lives. It even happens that such a woman, after bearing a son, returns to her own group.

Both vengeance and compensation, however, in the more complex communities, are exacted, or at least controlled, by some other agent rather than by the injured party himself. There will be some sort of court from which justice is dispensed or some recognised power, such as the chief medicine man, through whom the punishment will be carried out. The Andamanese are about the only people in the world who have no system whatsoever of organised punishment for crime. In these islands individual crime is avenged by private means, but, the people being generally of an amiable and peaceful disposition, this seldom leads to bloodshed or feuds. Very often the culprit runs away into the jungle and waits until the affair has blown over. If he is a much-feared man, then as likely as not no one will dare to seek revenge upon him.

Social offences are dealt with simply by public opinion, by disapproval, contempt, or ridicule. The Andamanese, like most other savages, are very sensitive to anything which touches their vanity, and the fear of ridicule is often quite enough to maintain and enforce social laws. This ultra-sensitive vanity of the savage may be considered childish and absurd, but we should call to mind that in England there is a law by which any person may prosecute another for slander for saying anything, true or untrue, likely to bring the plaintiff into " hatred, ridicule, or contempt."

MYSTERIOUS RETRIBUTION FROM AN INVISIBLE SOURCE

IN slightly more advanced societies, social crimes will be the first to be dealt with on a systematic basis by the community or by those in authority. The breaking of marriage rules might be punished, on the advice of the elders of the tribe, by death or expulsion or some less severe penalty inflicted by the men of the village in a body, or by the clan leaders. Many taboo infringements however, which would count as offences against the community are not punished by open action on the part of any one. But punishment, often of the direst, nevertheless ensues. The offender is " unclean "; he knows himself to be so and others know it too. He is shunned by all. Then he falls ill and perhaps dies, or he is overtaken by a terrible injury or some tragic misfortune. The horror that surrounds the breaking of a taboo is largely due to the fact that punishment overtakes the wrongdoer in an utterly mysterious manner, without any overt move from elder, chief, or priest.

Cases have been known in Australia and elsewhere of natives falling ill after breaking a taboo, and dying within two or three days without a sign of any known disease. Fear, remorse, and suggestion act so potently upon their nervous systems, that savages do in fact die because they think they will. Every time that such a fate befalls one who is known to have broken a taboo, the sacredness and mystery of the taboo, and the certainty of punishment for those who disobey, is reinforced a hundredfold in the minds of the natives.

Another form of punishment by magic, which can be equally deadly, is to employ the medicine man or magician of the community to deal with the culprit by magical means. This is often done in cases of death by violence, whether murderous or accidental. Murder, in the primitive mind, often includes other forms of death than homicide with intent. This can be explained by the primitive attitude to death. Death in many communities is not considered the natural inevitable end of man, but as something quite abnormal and accidental. This is not usually the attitude to all death, for certain forms are common enough to be believed normal, perhaps old age, or a sickness that is very frequent, or in a warlike community death in war. Accidental death, however, for instance in some hunting misfortune, or a mortal illness, is thought to be unnatural and therefore caused by some malignant agency. Since there is no obvious evidence of malicious intent, no signs of poisoning, for example, the murder is assumed to have been committed by magic means.

MAGIC, THE ESSENCE OF NATIVE LIFE

MAGIC, we must remember, pervades the whole of primitive life. Even the simplest everyday tasks are often performed with the aid of magic. Anything which has any sort of uncertainty about it, where the relation between cause and effect is not absolutely obvious and inevitable, has a flavour of magic about it, and magic is used in connection with it.

Owing to his very different kind of knowledge of the physical world, the savage classes things together as cause and effect that we should consider had no sort of relation. The phrase " kind of knowledge " is used advisedly, for although the savage has no conception of the complexities and extent of our Western learning, and would be incapable of grasping much of our scientific knowledge, given his native education (just as a backward European peasant would be incapable of grasping it), nevertheless he possesses refinements of practical knowledge and natural lore such as the normal European never dreams of. (One African tribe, for example, cultivates ninety different kinds of millet and has a name for each different kind and its special properties.) His different way of reasoning out the relations between things, however, leads him to put two and two together and make five, or so it seems to the civilised mind. Actually the two and two that he puts together will be things that we are not accustomed to put in the same category at all, and therefore the result seems very ludicrous.

If, for example, a man were sick of a poisoned wound, then the medicine man might make a similar wound in a nearby tree, and apply a piece of the bark to the man's nose and to the infected part, and then wait confidently for the cure. His method of treatment was to transfer the illness from the patient to the tree, sickness being in his mind in the category of transferable things—a kind of spirit. We find the same type of belief in the ancient Hebrew practices of " casting out " spirits. The whole range of the material world is controlled by non-material power, often called *mana*. This power can be used by those who gain control over it, for good or for evil. It may be used, for instance, in getting rid of an enemy.

Among these peoples, therefore, to whom death is an unnatural phenomenon, the obvious explanation of a death, by accident or from sickness, is that it was caused by magic on the part of some enemy of the dead man. In the case of illness the death may be believed to have been caused by introducing the spirit of the sickness into the victim, or by the murderer having stolen the man's soul. It is well known that when a man dies his soul departs from his body, and this departure is held to be the cause of the death. If, therefore, anyone were to steal the soul the body would inevitably die. Stealing the soul is a very effective and silent method of murder. Another method of getting rid of your enemy is to persuade by magic some wild animal to kill him. Thus what looks like pure accident to the European onlooker may be fairly held by the native opinion to be the result of purposeful and malicious planning.

CRIMINALS DETECTED IN A MAGIC SLEEP

SINCE magic was the cause of death, magic must be used either to detect or to punish the criminal, or both. The sorcerer or medicine man of the village is called in, unless it is suspected that he has been a party to the murder by actually being employed by the murderer to carry out the task, in which case there is probably a rival magician to whom the dead man's family will turn. The sorcerer will then employ his arts to detect the perpetrator of the crime. In the Solomon Islands the detection is made by a diviner in an enchanted sleep. He smears himself with lime on his shoulders and toes, and puts a little bundle of lime under the mat on which he sleeps. Once three hundred porpoise teeth were lost. A diviner undertook to find them, but in his magic sleep he saw the theft being committed by his own granddaughter. He described the method of the theft to the owner, but withheld the name of the culprit. He advised the door of the house to be left open, and later the girl was seen to throw back the teeth.

Once the criminal has been found he must be punished according to the customary manner. He might be punished by magic means through the sorcerer, at the instigation either of the injured family or of the village authority. The sorcerer or medicine man himself may be the chief dispenser of justice. Punishment may be coincident with detection, for the fact of illness, accident, or death overtaking a suspected person may be proof of their guilt. He may, on the other hand, after being detected by magic means be punished by an ordinary physical penalty, such as fire, exile, mutilation, or death. There is often a considerable ritual involved in the carrying out of the penalty, which will constitute an important public cere- mony, much as a big execution did in the old days in England. Or the punishment may be carried out privately or even in great secrecy. Punishment may sometimes be avoided by some form of voluntary expiation, such as the performance of some special rite, probably involving sacrifice. This has the effect of purifying the culprit of the offence. He may then be received back into the community, or he may still be considered to have some taint of uncleanness about him, and be shunned by others for some period of time.

The suspected person may attempt to defend himself by refusing to admit his guilt. Where the detection has taken place by magic means, the accused person may very well be innocent, the victim of a mistake on the part of the magic, or of a grudge on the part of the magician. The witch doctor, so long as he keeps the confidence of the people, is in a very strong position. He has considerable opportunity for private revenge, for if he fixes on the wrong person, the really guilty party is not likely to gainsay him. The chief of an African Bantu tribe once became suspicious of the " smelling out " by the witch doctors. So one night he took the blood of a goat and secretly sprinkled it over the walls and floor of an empty hut. The next day he went into the hut in a casual way and rushed out shouting that there had been murder. He gathered the witch doctors together and commanded them to reveal the murderer. They put their heads together, went through the formal ritual, and then pounced upon the murderer. Whereupon the chief revealed his trick, and all the witch-doctors were executed in vengeance for the number of innocent lives that they had caused to be lost.

The accused, if he protests, may be asked to prove his innocence by some form of ritual ordeal. This method of determining guilt or innocence was, as we know, widely practised in Europe during the Middle Ages. Torture as a method of extracting the " truth " from witnesses is characteristic rather of civilised than of savage peoples, where it is very little known. Although denounced in Rome by Cicero as barbaric and useless, torture was still used for this purpose in Italy and elsewhere right through the Renaissance and into the eighteenth century.

THE LAW OF MINE AND THINE

WE have spoken of homicide at some length, because it throws interesting sidelights on the savage mind. We must not, however, imagine that it is the only, or the main, crime recognised in savage societies. In the primitive, as in the civilised world, crimes against property are all too frequent. This brings us to the consideration of the institution of property among primitive peoples, and the laws and customs connected with it. In all societies there are two main forms of property—individual and collective, and special laws relating to each. Among primitive peoples individual property is that which is gained and utilised by individual efforts. Clothing, ornaments, implements, and weapons—what we should call " personal property "—belong to the individual. Other things such as houses, land, cattle, boats, etc., may be private or public property according to the social system and customs of the particular community.

Very often a thing appears to be collectively owned because a number of people use it, when actually it is the property of one person. A canoe, for example, is used by a group of people for their fishing and transport purposes, and seems to the casual observer to be the joint property of the group. Further investigation, however, usually reveals that the canoe has been built on the initiative of one person, who acts as leader in all its operations and who is regarded as its owner.

A good deal has been written about " primitive communism," but the term should be used with the greatest caution. The word " communism " denotes in the civilised world the aims and policy of a definite political party founded on the philosophy of Karl Marx. Whatever system of collective ownership may hold in a savage community, it has little in common with Marxian communism, which has grown out of and is fashioned for modern civilisation.

In primitive forms of property-holding the emphasis is mainly laid upon the use to which the object is put. Land, for instance, is not usually thought of as valuable in itself as real estate, but only as a medium for utilisation, and it is the utilisation which alone gives it value. This is, of course, ultimately true of land or any other goods in any community, for value attaches only to goods that will be used ; but the point of the primitive economic system is that certain commodities, and in particular land, have no worth until they are utilised—their value as potential wealth is not recognised. Land not under cultivation often is not owned by any one, not even by the community in the sense that the state owns a national park in England, for that implies certain obligations of care and upkeep on the part of the state. As soon as anything is done with the land in a primitive community—that is, as soon as use is made of it, and not before—the question of ownership arises.

THE PROPERTY OWNERS OF THE WILDS

Very often the land becomes the temporary property of different people according to the different uses to which it is put. Some may be set aside as common grazing ground (like the " commons " of our own mediæval land system, except that these were given to the community in perpetuity until they were enclosed, while the savage's " common " is often set aside for a limited period only), and some distributed among the whole village for cultivation. At the end of the season after the harvest the cultivated part will revert to its former status of " no man's land " until the next sowing-time. Some or all of the land, however, may be allotted to individuals to hold in permanence so long as they cultivate it ; it may even be owned absolutely. In the latter case it can be given, bought, and sold, but in the former, transfer of any kind is obviously impossible without the consent of the authorities who originally allotted it. A distinction is always drawn in the native mind and reflected in his language between land that is only leased to individuals, and land that is absolutely owned.

WHERE TRESPASSERS FIND A GRIM RECEPTION

AMONG hunting peoples individual rights over certain hunting grounds are sometimes recognised, but it is more usual for the group to have common rights over the whole territory. If outsiders trespass into the tribal hunting ground they will meet with a very hostile reception ; very likely they will be captured and taken to the tribal headquarters to be taught a severe lesson, from which they will be lucky to escape with their lives. The same sort of system will hold among pastoral peoples ; there will be exclusive rights over pastures held by individuals or by the community, but in either case the stranger and his herd will not be welcomed. Life is a tough struggle—the means of subsistence must be wrung out of Nature with toil and sweat—therefore charity begins, and stays, at home.

Nevertheless, hospitality is often a generous feature of savage communities, where the stranger does not seem to have come to steal the food out of his neighbour's mouth. The savage attitude to the stranger is often a mixed one—he is an object both of dislike and of interest, of fear and of curiosity. He is often credited with superior powers—the curse of a stranger is more potent than the curse of a neighbour. Therefore, a tradition of lavish hospitality towards individuals may grow up, combined with a ferocious hostility to outside tribes as a whole, as we find among many Arabs.

HOLDING CATTLE IN TRUST FOR THE DEAD

ANOTHER very quaint complication in savage property law is the fact that communal property is very often considered to belong not merely to the group, but also, and often chiefly, to the dead members of the group—to the spirits of the ancestors. This attitude is particularly well exemplified in many African cattle-herding tribes. Their main wealth is their cattle, but the cattle are the property not of individuals, but of the clan, and the clan consists as much of the dead as of the living. Every living member of the clan is allotted part of the clan herd, but he may not sell or dispose of it, because he is bound at his death to give back to the clan or to pass on to his heirs, at least as many animals as he was given or has inherited, and it is usually a point of honour to increase the number.

This system greatly strengthens the control of the clan over the individual's private life. When he wishes to marry, for instance, and he has to pay so many cattle as bride-price, he cannot part with the animals without the consent of the clan, to whom they belong, and the clan will not consent unless it approves the marriage. Individuals, however, usually find a way of evading the absolute despotism of the community, and a system of individual property in cattle arises side by side with the system of communal property. Thus, although a man may not diminish the number of clan cattle entrusted to him, any surplus which he may obtain above that number, or above the extra that he wishes to add to it as a matter of honour, belong to him unconditionally to dispose of as he likes.

If he wishes to give a feast, he may slaughter as many of his own animals as he wishes, but he may not slaughter one of the clan cattle. If he has none of his own, but is forced to slaughter for a feast or sacrifice, then he must borrow from some one else, and some one else may only lend on condition that the borrower will repay him with interest, say two calves for one bull, so that the clan herd may not be diminished. These difficulties are avoided by collecting private cattle, and pastoral tribes in Africa are often warlike people largely for this very reason ; the quickest and easiest way of obtaining private property is to plunder it from other people.

"STRICTLY COPYRIGHT" : THE SPELL-OWNER'S PRIVILEGE

PROPERTY in primitive life is not by any means restricted to the ownership of material objects. Songs, dances, stories, and decorative designs are just as much owned by individual or by groups of persons, and the performance or use of such things by others than by their rightful owner is not only resented but often prohibited by customs as severe as our own laws of copyright. Not only such artistic property, but magic too, can belong to people. Spells, incantations, magic formulæ, may be owned by individuals, and woe to him who steals a private spell. The magic cannot be returned as an object can, but compensation may be demanded. If the spell were a very good one, working with a specially potent magic, the compensation claimed might take the form of a very substantial payment.

Damages may be customary to compensate for many kinds of wrong, from physical injury and homicide down to bad words. The compensation may be paid in currency or in kind or in services. It may be demanded either by the injured party alone or jointly by him and his relatives or his clan. An injury is often not considered an individual matter at all, but an insult to the whole family or clan. Equally the guilt attaches not merely to the actual culprit but to all his group. Compensation for a single act, therefore, may be exacted not only from the perpetrator but from a number of otherwise innocent people related to him.

THE COURTS OF JUSTICE : THE WITCH-DOCTOR DETECTIVE

WHERE there is a detailed system of compensatory payments, it is usually regulated by some sort of official judicial procedure rather than by individual action. Courts of justice are to be found in most communities where there is a strongly organised administrative authority. The composition of such courts will vary greatly. They may consist of the whole of one age grade of the community—for instance, the warriors or more likely the elders. Or the court may be just a selected few—the same group of elders as that which forms the general council of the tribe for all administrative affairs, or a specially chosen group. Most usual is the court consisting of one supreme judge, usually the king or chief. Solomon was such a judge, and the wisdom of his judgments is still renowned.

The authority of the courts grows only by degrees. At first the judge will be merely an arbitrator who makes suggestions for a settlement, which the disputants may take or leave as they will. Very often he leaves the decision on the rights and wrongs of the case to supernatural powers who manifest their verdict by means of the ordeal. Ordeals may be one-sided or double ; the plaintiff as well as the defendant may be forced to submit to the ordeal, or it may be the defendant, or the accused alone. Where the former is customary, it would seem likely to act as an efficient check on unnecessary litigation.

Probably only certain types of disputes or of criminal procedure will be decided by the court, and others will be left to the individuals or the clan to fight out between themselves. Thus in Europe right up to modern times, and indeed the custom still lingers on in parts, certain kinds of injuries were considered to be affairs of honour, and were regulated by private duels. An original kind of duel is common among the Australian natives, where the two disputants, armed with heavy clubs, stand facing each other, and each in turn puts down his head and allows the other to give it as heavy a whack with his club as he pleases. So they go on (they have very thick skulls) until they tire, by which time they are usually friends again.

Another method of settling disputes or injuries in Australia is by a kind of ordeal by which the accused party voluntarily exposes himself to the spears of his prosecutors. Armed with a shield he stands at a prescribed distance from the accuser and his friends who hurl as many spears or throwing clubs at him as they feel inclined. If the accused man comes out of the ordeal uninjured, either through his own dexterity or the bad aim of his opponents, then the affair is considered settled and he is not open to further prosecution. If he is injured or killed, then the affair is equally settled, but less happily for the accused.

THE LAW-GIVERS OF PLAIN AND FOREST

IN communities where there is a strong centralised authority, matters of dispute and law-breaking tend to be settled more and more by the official court. For one thing judicial proceedings are a good way of raising revenue. The king or judge soon gets in the way of charging court fees for litigation, and punishment by way of fines will be made to enrich the treasury. In a despotic monarchy the money thus raised will all flow into the kingly coffers, while in a more democratic community, particularly where the court is composed of

32. ONE SHREWD BLOW DESERVES (AND GETS) ANOTHER

A duel between Australian natives is fought with clubs. Each in turn allows the other to hit him on the head until both are tired, when the duel is over.

several judges, the funds will be used for communal purposes. As the community grows larger and more organised, so the courts will extend and become specialised according to function into criminal, civil, martial courts, etc., until we get to the complicated system of our own day, presided over by a special corps of very highly trained judges. The authority of the primitive court will depend on the authority of the king or chief who presides over it.

Rulers in any real sense are uncommon among very simple peoples. Chieftainship implies a certain level of organisation not to be found among the lowest cultures. Very often the European who is making contact with a native people imagines a chief where there is none He wants to have some one who will act as a go-between between himself and the tribe, and when he finds some one who seems to have authority to speak for the tribe he immediately dubs him " chief," whereas the man is actually only an intermediary between white man and native. Where, too, the natives have come under European rule or protection, it is customary, for administrative purposes, to select certain individuals to act as heads of the tribe. These European-created chiefs should not be regarded, from the anthropological standpoint, on the same footing as real native rulers. The term " chief " should be reserved for these individuals who are regarded by the natives themselves in their undisturbed organised life as their rightful leaders and rulers.

In very simple unorganised societies, such as the Andamanese, social activities will be directed by one or two influential people of outstanding skill and personality, who will act as leaders for particular pursuits. There will be no one authority for the whole community. In other societies there may be several chiefs for different purposes, a war chief, a hunting chief, a ceremonial leader, and so on. In a more highly organised people there will be a supreme ruler who delegates his powers to officials for the different departments of administration. Such officials often receive titles such as " Right Son of the King," or " Eye of the Chief."

Kings, although in the highest position of authority, are often subject to the direst restrictions, and do not enjoy one-tenth of the freedom of their lowest subjects. Their lives are hedged about with taboos, and the most intricate details regulated by a hundred restrictions. This is because they are such important, and often sacred persons, that every precaution must be taken to assure that they shall do nothing to injure the office that they hold. Their lives are considered intimately bound up with the welfare of their people. Consequently, their every action may have effect upon the well-being of the community. The magic connection between the life of the ruler and the life of the community explains many seemingly barbarous customs. Kings, for instance, are sometimes never allowed to grow old, but are killed as soon as certain signs of age become apparent. They may be deposed or killed after any great catastrophe for the same reason.

WHO SHALL BE THE KING'S HEIR ?

AFTER the death of a king or chief (we use the word " king " only in cases where the character of the ruling authority corresponds more or less with the European conception of monarchy), his heir will be chosen according to different customs. Among some peoples the office is hereditary ; if so, it may be passed on either through the mother or through the father. It may descend not to the eldest, but to the youngest son, or it may pass first to the late king's brothers. Alternatively, the new king may be chosen by a council of elders, or by the chief priest, or elected by some rough plebiscite of the whole community.

There will be different customs, too, regarding the disposal of the dead king's wives and property. In some cases, the widow, or widows will pass to one of his heirs, where such a custom as the levirate exists. In others the dowager queen will be given a house and maintained in greater or lesser state until her death. Or again, she may return to her own people. A more gruesome custom of disposal, which was widespread in ancient times, is the immolation on his grave of the dead king's property, including his wives and slaves, in order that his spirit may not go comfortless and unattended into the next world. In Ancient Babylon persons of the ruling house were interred in huge sepulchres along with their chariots and oxen, their worldly goods and their train of slaves, and all the beautiful women of their household.

THE CREATIVE SPIRIT IN PRIMITIVE MAN

> " ' The time has come,' the walrus said,
> ' To talk of many things :
> Of shoes—and—ships and sealing-wax—
> Of cabbages—and kings.' "

WE have talked of kings already, and any one who wishes to read more of the many strange customs attendant on kingship should dip into Frazer's *The Golden Bough*, which is full of fascinating stories of savage kings. We will reverse the Walrus' order, and turn our attention next to the ships and the sealing-wax, and how they are made among primitive people—to arts and crafts and all the anthropologist knows as material culture.

In the history of man, crafts have grown more slowly than the arts. We have already noticed the beautiful cave paintings of early man, which in feeling and execution rival any other animal studies in the world. When we consider how rough must have been the artist's implements—lumps of native ochres and charcoal for colours, palettes of bone, and only the crudest of lighting facilities—their achievement is all the more wonderful. Not only did they paint in the grand style, but they also made little ornaments for their homes and decorated their everyday tools. Little statuettes have been found, and carved weapons and implements. They were made in the Old Stone Age, thousands of years before the invention of pottery even, and thousands of years again before the discovery of metal opened men's eyes to an entirely new life in material things. Infinitely slowly did man develop the different techniques of making tools and utensils and all the paraphernalia of daily life. For untold ages he made all his sharp implements of stone, chipping away patiently at lumps of flint to fashion his knives and arrows and household tools.

He evolved a very brilliant technique in flint work, and learned to make most delicate implements of perfect shape and astonishing sharpness. In Julian Huxley's fascinating book, *Africa View*, there is a photograph of a lady cutting dainty slices of thin bread and butter from a new loaf with a prehistoric stone knife. Any one who is inclined to doubt the possibilities of flint and obsidian as substitutes for steel, should pay a visit to a museum where there is a collection of Stone Age implements, or, better still, to the magnificent collections in the British Museum. There he will be able to see with his own eyes how precise and finely fashioned instruments of such material can be.

THE ARCHÆOLOGIST HELPS THE STUDENT OF MAN

THE stone tools and weapons were hafted on to wood and securely bound, and they formed implements efficient enough for the rough savage life of our earliest ancestors. Indeed, in some parts of the world, notably Australia and the Andaman Islands, metal is unknown, or was so until the coming of the European, and stone and bone are still the materials for all sharp instruments. In the Andaman Islands shell is largely used instead of stone, as a suitable kind of hard flakeable shell is to be found in abundance on the shores.

In this way anthropology and archæology help each other forward. In piecing together the early history of mankind from what traces our prehistoric forefathers have left behind them, archæology turns to her twin sister, anthropology, to ask her about the life of very primitive peoples who still exist. In her turn anthropology, trying to elucidate the laws and working of society in all its aspects, will seek new light on problems from historic, and prehistoric, parallels.

After the two long Stone Ages, the Old and the New, somehow, somewhere, came the great discovery which heralded the New Age—the discovery of the use of metal. Copper is found native in many parts, and at first was probably just beaten, in its raw state, into rough shapes. The real Metal Age does not begin until some one stumbled on the revolutionary invention of bronze. Bronze is an alloy of copper and tin ; both metals occur mainly in deposits of ore. Think what this means : both the copper and the tin must be mined, extracted from the ore by smelting, and mixed together. Then the raw metal has to be cast, beaten, and polished before the manufacture is finally finished. For all this a certain amount of apparatus is necessary, furnaces and fuel and moulds and casting instruments. But above all, such a process presupposes a knowledge, however rough and ready, of the nature of the metals concerned. Metallurgy, from this point of view, was the first beginning of chemistry.

PREHISTORIC MAN'S " TRADE UNIONS "

IN addition, for the successful manufacture of bronze, a high degree of skill was also necessary. Doubtless this was not achieved all at once. Indeed, we sometimes find broken Bronze Age moulds with the metal still inside, showing that something had gone wrong and the attempt had been thrown away. Probably the art was jealously guarded as a secret by closed guilds of smiths. We find exclusive guilds of craftsmen in many parts of the world to-day ; in India, for example, where the crafts groups are closely connected with the rigidity of the caste system. The closed nature of the organisation was specially characteristic of the mediæval craft guilds, and it even survived into the early days of Trade Unionism in the last century.

In the prehistoric smiths' guilds the exclusiveness was probably maintained not only through the high level of skill required, but also by the introduction of magic into the process of manufacture. Magic, as we have seen, pervades the whole of the savage's life. It is present in everyday occurrences as much as in sacred ceremonies. Life is uncertain even in its small details, and the savage uses magic to increase the likelihood of success in all undertakings of whose successful outcome he is not absolutely sure. When he is making things, therefore, he often employs a customary ritual, the proper performance of which is as important in his eyes as the actual technical process itself. Technical skill touches only the outward form of a thing ; in order to gain complete mastery one must obtain the goodwill of the *mana* and spirit power which controls the object.

Different kinds of creative operations will have different rituals peculiar to each ; the more important the operation the more necessary and complicated the ritual. Unimportant, everyday matters, about which there is little uncertainty, may be done without invoking aid from magic. Ordinary huts for private individuals may be built without an appeal to spirit powers, while in the same community the erection of an important building of social significance, like a " man's house" (a communal house for the men of the village) or a ceremonial building, will be attended with the most careful ritual.

The spells and incantations and magic gestures of the ritual are designed to ensure the co-operation of the spirit elements in two different ways : partly by propitiation and partly by coercion. All magic practices can be roughly divided into these categories. Very powerful and terrible forces have to be approached respectfully with every precaution taken to propitiate and please them. Other forces are of a less awesome and mysterious kind, and mastery can be gained over them by the use of the proper spells which then deliver their powers into the control of the wielder of the spell. Thus in making things there will be two sets of powers or spirits to be dealt with by magic—the one to be entreated, the other to be mastered. In making a canoe the spirits of the water and of fishing will probably be propitiated with gifts or ritual dances or the observance of taboos, while the powers inherent in, say, bark, or resin, or cords will be coerced into co-operation by incantation and spell.

PROPITIATING THE TREE SPIRIT WITH AN EGG

THE African Ashanti people, who are very fine wood-carvers, perform two rituals when they are making a stool. The first is to propitiate the spirit of the tree they are cutting down for wood. The spirit of the particular timber they use for making stools is of a potentially vindictive character, so just before the woodcutter lays his axe on the tree, he breaks an egg on the trunk, saying : " Tree, receive this egg and eat; do not permit the knife to cut me." Similarly, the tools to be used in carving have a rite performed over them before any big job is undertaken, and even again during the course of the work if it is not progressing favourably. Wine and the blood of a fowl are poured over them, while a prayer is made for assistance and freedom from accidents. When the stool is finished another rite induces the now homeless spirit of the cut tree to re-enter the wood in the stool.

The magic may not be so explicitly specific as this either

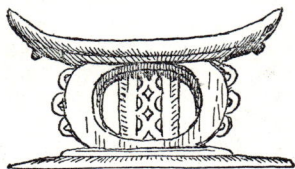

Circular Rainbow
Stool

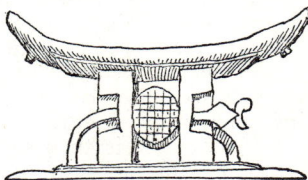

Crocodile Stool
(for Gods to rest upon)

Elephant Stool
(used only by King of Ashanti)

Akyem Stool
(used by Chiefs and Priests)

33. WOODEN STOOLS WHERE SPIRITS DWELL

These stools, carved with considerable skill by the Ashanti people of Africa, all contain a spirit from the parent tree, induced to take up its new home by suitable rites and offerings.

in the form of the ritual or in the minds of the performers. The craftsmen, perhaps, cannot even tell you the meaning of the ritual. It may, indeed, have lost its meaning and be merely a survival of the outward form of a forgotten belief.

Not merely utility but beauty is also considered in primitive crafts. " Primitive crafts " should be read in the sense of the crafts of primitive peoples, for the workmanship is often very finely developed, expecially when the crudeness of their materials is taken into consideration. Prehistoric metal-work of the Bronze Age peoples leaves in its developed stages little to be desired. Axes and daggers and spear-heads, as well as household utensils, such as cups and bowls and knives, are well made and beautifully finished. Æsthetically they please the eye by their form and symmetry as well as by the beautiful designs with which they are frequently decorated.

THE BEAUTY SPECIALISTS OF THE JUNGLES

THE desire to decorate seems to be a universal trait of mankind. Wherever there is a blank surface there seems to be an irresistible urge to cover it with decorative design. So we see children chalking on the covers of their copy-books or scribbling on the shiny expanse of their desk-tops. One type of plain surface which offers considerable scope to many savages is their own skin. Personal decoration by means of paint, tattooing, or scars is to be found in most parts of the world. There will be people who specialise in these forms of artistry, just as there are hairdressers and beauty specialists in our corner of society. Tattooing especially is a real art demanding specialised skill. Very intricate and beautiful patterns that take days to do are often used. The subject will be patiently quiet for hours on end while the colours are being pricked under the tenderest portions of his skin. The savage is said to be more sensitive to touch and less sensitive to pain than the civilised person. Whether this is so or not, and it has not been very well authenticated, the prevalence of tattooing and many forms of superficial mutila-tion as means of personal enhancement demonstrates that the savage is as willing as any civilised lady of leisure to undergo considerable pain and discomfort in quest of personal beauty.

BEAUTIFYING THE INSTRUMENTS OF DEATH

MORE attractive to Western eyes from the æsthetic point of view are the decorations on all kinds of material objects. Weapons, in so far as they are permanent, and not, like arrows, constantly being renewed, are usually decorated in some way. The business ends are mostly left plain, but the handles and other parts are frequently richly carved or painted. The wooden clubs of the Pacific are often covered with carved designs—numberless variations of the zigzag and combinations of triangles, circles, and curved lines. In the development of decorative design geometric patterns seem to come before designs derived from plants or animals. This is surprising, for one would have thought that a geometric design, being an abstract form, would have appeared at a later stage of the development of æsthetic sense than the imitation of concrete sights of everyday life like plants.

There is no hard and fast rule, however; both kinds of design are found together. For example, the Australian aborigines, in many ways the most primitive of all savages, decorate the handles of their spear-throwers (a kind of long-grooved board used to increase the projectile force of spear-throwing, forms of which are common in many parts of the world) with crude geometric patterns in paint, while the end is carved into the rough likeness of a bird's head or beak.

Perhaps the most artistic of all geometric decoration is to be found in the beautiful carvings of the Maori peoples of New Zealand and Oceania. Their long graceful canoes have elegantly-carved prows, while the door-posts of their houses, and the two great cross-beams on the front of the roof are covered with beautiful patterns of sweeping curves and intricate detail. The African negro is fond of carving wood into figures from life, and he makes numbers of carved and painted figures of humans and animals, some very crude and some most finely executed.

These carvings are often of a symbolic religious nature, just as are the designs on a Maori house-beam or a New Guinea club. " Art for art's sake " is rare in primitive society in the sense that form is rarely beautiful merely for its own sake, but usually has a symbolic meaning. As time goes on the original symbolism may become lost, and the forms persist as conventional designs. In Africa and elsewhere carvings are often made to represent the totem animal. The totem-pole is common among the Red Indians and in the Pacific. This is a tall pole, sometimes twelve, fifteen, or twenty feet high, carved all down with symbolic forms and faces connected with the clan totem and with fertility and long life and good fortune. The faces on these totem-poles, painted in crude, bright, semi-realistic colours, are often quite terrifying to behold in their fierce barbaric fantasy.[1] When, as often, they are crowned with the skulls of ancestors or enemies, they make a gruesome spectacle. So, too, weapons of war and of the hunt are often decorated with representations of the totemic animal in order to enlist the totem's aid.

[1] A fine example of a Red Indian totem-pole may be seen in the portico outside the British Museum.

Geometric designs are often largely influenced by religious or magico-religious beliefs. Many geometrical forms are pregnant with magical or religious content, and the savage uses them in decoration with a definite purpose in his mind beyond purely æsthetic delight. Objects of ritual importance and holy things will be decorated with designs of religious symbolism, whereas other purely utilitarian things may be decorated with magic formulæ, or again with symbols of religious import. Both may be in the form of traditional designs.

MAGIC THE PARENT OF ALL SAVAGE BEAUTY

RELIGION has always found expression in art in all societies, for religious and æsthetic emotion are very intimately linked. Both are the outcome of a common striving towards self-expression in beauty. The art of every society is always strongly influenced by the religion of the community. The simpler the society the less divergence is there between art and religion. In Byzantine Christendom and all through the Middle Ages all forms of the fine arts took almost solely religious subjects. Similarly, in primitive societies, all that cluster of semi-religious and semi-magical beliefs and practices, which we may call primitive religions, is fundamentally a part of artistic expression, as it is a part of all other activities.

The savage makes no distinction between sacred and profane art, and no difference between magic and non-magic art. It is not that he is incapable of appreciating beauty purely and simply for beauty's sake. It is just that he is an intensely practical, at the same time an intensely mystical, person. As far as the unseen powers are concerned, he will leave nothing undone that ought to be done, even in the matter of putting a few finishing magic touches to a home-made pocket-knife. Magic to him is all part of beauty ; it cannot be separated from art any more than it can be separated from religion, or religion from art.

Not only the mystic element, but the strong conservative tendency of society as a whole that we have previously noted, leaves its mark on art and craft. Custom is the great master and teacher in the making of things both to please the eye and to be useful to the hand. The lower the level of culture, the more hide-bound by custom a society will be, and the less scope is there for artistic or technical originality. Even in

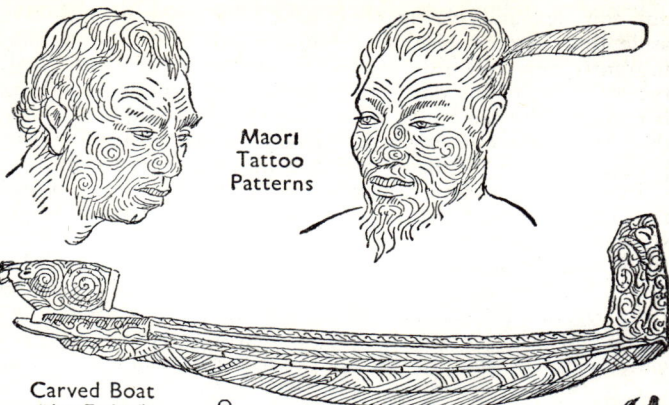

Maori Tattoo Patterns

Carved Boat
(New Zealand)

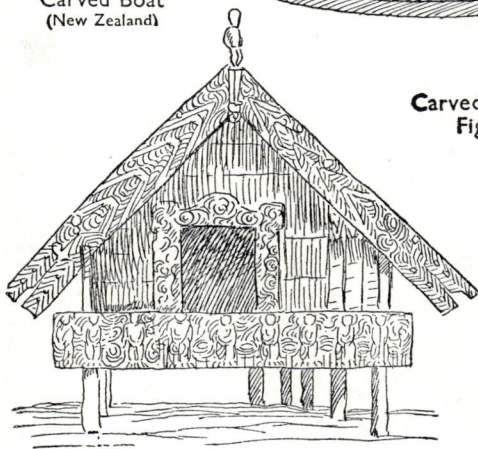

Carved African Figure

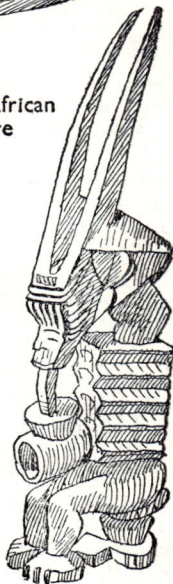

Maori Dwelling
(showing Crossbeam)

34. PRIMITIVE CULTS OF BEAUTY AND ART.

The universal desire for decoration finds expression among the Maori peoples of New Zealand in carvings of great intricacy and beauty. These people tattoo their bodies and even their faces.

our complex and plastic civilisation, the artist who throws aside the customary rules of his art and creates something flagrantly new and different, is scorned and scoffed at by all the orthodox of his day. In primitive life, where everything is regulated by custom, it is unlikely that it would even enter the head of any budding artist to vary the customary forms of his art. Custom regulates both technique and formal beauty.

In primitive societies there is little difference between arts and crafts—savage art is expressed in crafts, there is no separate category of fine art. Custom, which orders how a thing shall be made and with what materials, regulates also how it shall be decorated and with what design. This does not mean that the craftsman has no choice at all in the matter. As far as technique is concerned, that will probably be settled entirely by custom—very likely the native artisan knows only one method of making a thing—the method taught him by his elders, who in turn were taught by their elders, and so on backwards. But in the matter of form and decoration, there will probably be a choice of designs, only the choice will be limited by tradition.

It is the same in our own civilisation. If you travel through a number of European countries you will find in each country that almost all the native objects, like houses and furniture, are made to the same sort of traditional pattern. Cooking is a very good example of the influence of custom. The style of cooking of any one people is much the same wherever you go ; the dishes are similar and the method of cooking the same, and cooking varies little from generation to generation until the whole style of life alters. The English go on and on boiling away their vegetables, even though they know it is a bad method, just because it is the customary way, and the effort to break with custom, with what everybody else is doing and always has done, is too great.

GENIUS EXISTS IN THE SAVAGE WORLD

MAN is essentially imitative in all that he does, and in making things he necessarily copies the models set by custom. All the same, no one should run away with the idea that the savage craftsman is bound hand and foot by tradition, that he never thinks for himself in experimenting in new methods, or lets his imagination create new forms. That the savage is capable of producing innovations is amply demonstrated by the fact that custom itself does change, arts and crafts do evolve and develop, new forms and new techniques do come into being. The development usually arises out of small variations made by many people over a period of time, which lead in the end to new inventions. Sometimes, however, an innovation may be made even in primitive societies by the genius of one man.

Much has been written of the rigid uniformity of savage life, hide-bound by custom. The levelling and unifying force of tradition is indeed one of the most characteristic features of savage society. Nevertheless it is a mistake to infer that individuality is quite unknown either in social intercourse or in material culture. A close study of the creative work of any savage community will reveal numbers of individual variations on the traditional types. No two people ever make the same thing exactly alike. Into anything that a man creates he puts a little of himself, something of his own separate never-to-be-duplicated personality. Moreover, occasionally something quite original will be created. Whether such a creation is accepted by the community and absorbed into the traditional standards will depend on a number of factors—on the prestige of the inventor, on the usefulness and beauty of the invention, on the degree of departure from accepted norms, and on the general social elasticity of the community and its receptiveness to new ideas.

IN THE HOUSEWIFE'S REALM : DOMESTIC CROCKERY

LET us turn back to the story of the development of material culture in the history of mankind as a whole. At the same period as the discovery of bronze, mankind seems to have been impelled forward by some great wave of creative energy. With the epoch-making invention of metallurgy came about the same time a new technique in pottery. Spinning and weaving also probably became common then, for remains of cloth have been found in graves of this period. Agriculture, first introduced by the New Stone Age peoples, was developed and expanded, new varieties of crops were created, and more animals were domesticated. Now that the sharp yet tough bronze was available, the early ploughshare was probably much more effective. Solid houses of stone began to be built instead of the old huts made of wattle daubed with clay. In every department man was beginning to learn that mastery over his environment which was the beginning of civilisation.

Imagine what life would be like without pottery—no plates, no drinking vessels, no pots, no bowls, no jars, nothing to hold food or drink except such vessels as can be made from skins or gourds. (It has been suggested that skull tops upside down were used as bowls.) Pottery-making was first invented by the men (or maybe the women) of the New Stone Age. The Bronze Age people developed new forms and hit on the idea of painting it. The decoration of pottery forms another interesting chapter in the history of primitive art. The first step was the idea of colouring the clay black by the very simple method of smoking the pot while it was being fired. Burnishing and polishing are more advanced processes, as only a fine clay will take polishing, and the coarse pottery of the prehistoric Stone Age world was not suitable. Many backward peoples to-day produce fine polished or burnished ware. Often, too, the surface is varnished with resin, which not only gives a smooth shiny effect but renders the vessel more watertight.

THE FIRST PATTERNS : FINGERS AND TWIGS AS TOOLS

VERY early on somebody thought of making impressions with his finger or a twig in the soft wet clay which would set hard in the baking process and make an incised decoration. At first the designs were crude, sometimes just the imprint of a thumbnail round the rim, but later the patterns became quite intricate, and were made with special instruments and engraved stamps. The Red Indians still use their fingers for indenting the clay, and they also use cords and pieces of cloth to make a number of fine designs. Another method is relief ornament—applying knobs and bands and even figures to the soft pot before it is fired, or modelling out of the body of the pot itself. Then there are the more developed forms of coloured ware, both plain and painted. The finest savage painted pottery is made by the Red Indians, but owing to the disruption of their native life by white civilisation, the art is rapidly decaying.

The invention that enormously widened the scope of pottery-making was the potter's wheel. In most places where pottery is made by hand to-day, the clay rests on some sort of support which can be turned round, so that the potter can get at all sides of his pot without having to move round himself.

This gave somebody the idea of a wheel which, with clay on it, could be constantly rotated by the hands or feet. Later mechanical devices were developed for rotating the wheel so that the hands were left free. The potter's wheel was known in Egypt at least three thousand years before Christ, although it did not reach England until more than two thousand years later, and it is still unknown to many parts of the primitive world. It is an interesting fact that whereas pottery-making is usually the work of women, where the wheel is used it is almost always operated by men.

Pottery making is best developed among settled agricultural peoples, and is usually little practised by nomadic or hunting peoples, since earthenware vessels are too fragile to stand the constant moving about. Such peoples will use vessels made of skins or wood. The Australian aborigines have never made pottery, and it is also unknown among most of the Polynesians. In some places, such as the island of New Guinea, some tribes make pottery while others do not, even though they are in contact with each other. The pots are then traded from one district to another.

Some peoples who have no pottery use vessels made of basket work daubed with clay. It has been credibly suggested that this is the origin of pottery. Some Red Indian tribes used to make their pottery by modelling the clay inside a wicker basket, and then burning away the basket which had not only provided a kind of mould but also left ornamental imprints behind it. Whether or not this was the origin of pottery-making, it is certain that basketwork is much more widespread and more commonly used than pottery. Baskets of some sort are made by all peoples, and were certainly known to man in the New Stone Age. All the chief technical methods used in the world to-day are found in the prehistoric Swiss Lake dwellings. Basketry lends itself particularly well to coloured decoration, and geometrical and natural designs of an immense variety are to be found all over the world. Basket-making, like pottery and weaving, is largely done by women.

Usually in a simple primitive community, except for the division of labour according to sex, all the crafts are practised by all the members. Each household builds its own dwelling and makes what it needs for itself. Objects which are used by groups of people, like canoes, will be made by the groups which are going to utilise them. There will be little specialisation. Nevertheless, certain individuals will be better craftsmen than others, and these people will tend to use their talents on other people's work in return for gifts or services of another kind. This tendency in time develops into specialised division of labour and work for regular payment. In many communities it is not the individual but the family or group that specialises in a certain craft. In India the different castes are allotted by custom each their own pursuits. In parts of Africa particular craftsmen tend to form castes or guilds with a definite status in the social organisation of the community. Some castes are respected and some looked down upon. Sometimes the same craft is despised in one area and privileged in another. Iron workers, for instance, form an outcast class in some parts of Africa, while in others they are accorded a high status and special privileges.

MUSIC, DANCE, AND STORY-TELLING

WE have said that there is no distinction in the primitive creative mind between fine and applied arts. Perhaps this should be modified a little in the case of music and dancing. Dancing is often performed for ritual and cere-monial purposes, but it is also often indulged in simply for pleasure, with no utilitarian motive behind it. Dancing is common to all peoples all over the world. It seems to be the first and most fundamental method of self-expression. Individual dancing is not common among very primitive peoples. The dances are group affairs, performed by bands of dancers before large audiences. Very often dances are actually owned by certain groups, and performance of these dances without permission is a serious offence. The actions and gestures may have a definite symbolic meaning, especially in ritual dancing, or they may be simply rhythmic move-ments with no other significance. Quite likely, however, there will be individual performances of parts of the dance. This happens particularly in ritual dances of a magic and religious character, where various gods or spirits are re-presented by individual performers. This kind of dance is largely mime, and is really bordering on drama since it often represents a story.

It is often a most impressive performance. The dancers are dressed in weird costumes, and often their skins are painted in glaring colours. Heavy ornaments round their necks and on their arms and legs will rattle and clink as they dance in time to the monotonous music. Frequently, the performers' faces will be entirely painted with lines to form a complete mask—usually a very highly conventionalised face, perhaps representing some animal or god. Sometimes a real mask may be used, or, as in Thibet and other parts of Asia, an entire false head of gigantic proportions is worn. Sometimes, too, when powerful spirits are to be represented, the performers will dance on high stilts to give a realistic impression of gigantic size.

THE NATURE BALL : SCENES OF FRENZIED EXCITEMENT

THERE will not be more than five or six individual performers, and the rest will form a kind of chorus, while the spectators will keep time by clapping, or stamping their feet, and singing or shouting at intervals. Everybody, dancers and audience, becomes wildly thrilled, as well they may, for the music and the movement and the costumes deeply impress the sensitive, emotional mind of the savage, and emotional excitement is extremely contagious. The larger the crowd the more excited it gets, and the excitement acts as an extra stimulus to the dancers until sometimes they work themselves into an uncontrolled frenzy, dancing on and on, faster and more furiously, for hours on end, until they fall foaming at the mouth in a sort of fit. Such performances usually take place at night by the light of huge bonfires or hundreds of torches. Very often they will last all night, sometimes for two or three nights in succession. There is an enormous discharge of emotional tension which may lead to acts of violence or to sexual orgies, but, on the other hand, it acts as a safety valve for accumulated passions.

Ceremonial dancing also performs the function of working men up to the necessary pitch, for the undertaking of difficult or dangerous enterprises. Hunting and warfare are often preceded by ritual dances to key up the spirits of the combatants. The " war-dance " has become famous in stories of savages ; for many people, indeed, it seems to form the main feature of their conception of savage life. The war-dance is mimetic in character, the dancers imitating the actions of war in a more or less stylised manner. They may be divided into two groups, representing their own side and the enemy, or the enemy may be represented by a single dancer, or he may be left to the imagination, and imaginary spear-thrusts made into the air. Needless to say the mime represents utter defeat of the enemy, and probably depicts his capture and death in realistic fashion. The performers will be the warriors themselves dressed up in all their war-paint and fully armed. The performance will take place the night before the attack, in order that the stimulant effect may not wear off. Very often women will not be allowed to attend, as they might exert a weakening influence on the men. Red Indian warriors were not allowed to be with their wives for two or three days before setting out on the warpath.

DANCES WHERE WOMEN ARE NOT ALLOWED

THE participation of women in dancing is regulated by very varying customs. Sometimes in very important ritual dances, such as those performed during initiation ceremonies, they will not even be allowed within a certain distance of the dancing ground. Sometimes they may look on from afar or from behind the men. Often, they will take part. It is almost unknown for women to take individual parts in primitive ceremonial dancing ; it is not until we come to the higher cultures of the Orient that women dance in the temples. In non-ceremonial dancing for purposes of pleasure and sociability it is quite usual for women to take part. There are all sorts of ways of combining the sexes in a dance. Sometimes groups of women and groups of men may dance quite separately, sometimes they will combine in figures, sometimes they will break into couples. The women may provide the music while the men dance, and the men may form an orchestra while the women dance.

Savage instrumental music is seldom a *genre* in itself, but is the accompaniment of dancing or songs. It probably originated as simple rhythm beaten out on some kind of drum for dancers to keep time to. Much primitive music is indeed little more than rhythmic percussion on a few notes. There are, however, a large variety of primitive instruments of all types—strings and wind and percussion—ranging from rattles to guitars and rudimentary violins. Africa is par-ticularly rich in instruments of all sorts. Percussion instru-ments include all kinds of drums played with the hand or with sticks, gongs, clappers, and cymbals, instruments that jingle or rattle or rasp. In this group is the primitive xylophone which is found in various parts of Africa. In its simplest form it consists of a single piece of shaped wood giving out one note when struck. The more developed type, consisting of a number of simple wooden bars tuned to different notes and arranged in a scale from high to low, is more common. Though there may be quite a good range of notes, it is difficult to play even a simple nursery tune on an African xylophone, for the intervals are most unexpected, and seem to the European ear to be quite without logic or order.

There is almost as great a variety of wind instruments. One of the most interesting is the bull-roarer. There are several different types of bull-roarer, but the general principle is a number of thin wooden blades attached at one end by a string tied to a stick. The blades are whirled round in the air at the end of the string, and the vibrations cause a loud sound to be emitted varying in pitch as the roarer is whirled faster or more slowly. Bull-roarers are largely used on ceremonial occasions and are often considered sacred instruments. Very simple stringed instruments consist of one string only, that is usually plucked, but sometimes a simple wooden bow is used. In some cases only one note can be sounded, and there will be a series of one-note instruments tuned to different pitches. In this way simple melodies can be produced. Some instruments, on the other hand, are used purely and simply to emit noise. A primitive orchestra, especially when it is becoming excited, can be a very noisy affair. The music may also be punctuated with shouts and yells.

THE NATIVE SINGS OF JOY AND MOURNING

VOCAL music is often largely shouting, or a monotonous intonation with practically no melody. Songs and melody, however, of a kind more attractive to the European ear are not by any means uncommon. Unfortunately, such music is almost impossible to record without a phonograph, as European methods of notation are quite inadequate. Singing may be quite an advanced art, with many voices combined in harmony or unison or alternating the two, with perhaps an individual singer and a chorus. Primitive songs are usually just the records of states of emotion, of love, grief, mourning, hatred, or joy. Often they are very touching in their simple feeling.

The following is a lament composed by a Maori woman

14

for the death of her daughter named Rangi. It is several hundred years old :

> " Oppressed was I with vague and nameless fears
> Perturbing to the mind.
> Who truly are you that thus afflicts me ?
> Causing with warnings vague and formless fear
> This restlessness within me,
> Was it indeed you, O cherished one ?
> Who would have thought that you would go, O Rangi ?
> Wearily inclines my body, as here
> Within Puhirangi I sit and weep.
> Afar the sea-maid surges restlessly,
> But you have gone, borne on ocean stream
> To far Tawhit-nui, to Tawhit-panamoo
> O maid of mine."

Another type is the narrative song, in which sometimes very, very long stories are told, comprising hundreds of verses often of a rather monotonous character. Our own ballads are an example of this kind of folk-song. Much legend and myth are embodied in traditional songs of this type. They will be sung in leisure moments when there is plenty of time to spare. In the evening a group of persons will gather, and one will start one of these epic songs. Presently it will be taken up by another, and then another, and so on, until all join in either together or consecutively. Perhaps one will be specially famous for his voice, and people will come and ask him to sing while they listen and join in the refrain. Such people may even develop into professional singers. Singing may play almost as important a part in social life as dancing. It may, like dancing, form an integral part of magic-religions. It may have an important rôle in social ceremonies, such as weddings and funerals ; it is often used as a stimulant in concerted labour, such as rowing or hauling. The famous Volga boat-song is a song of the latter kind. The Andamanese sing a song while making canoes that runs :

> " Knots are very hard to cut with an adze.
> They blunt the edge of the adze.
> How hard I am working cutting these knots."

Perhaps, instead of the story being sung, it will be told. Literature in primitive society is represented by the spoken word, myth, and legend, and story that is handed down from mouth to mouth, from father to son, from old men to boys. Stories are often the personal property of the teller, who holds a sort of copyright over them. Others are only told at certain times or seasons of the year. Some peoples believe that the recital of certain tales has a good effect on the crops or the cattle. These are usually animal tales, of which a great number exist all over the world. The animals speak and act like human beings. Different sorts of animals have their particular individual characters. A good example is the Brer Rabbit stories which are to be found in different forms all over negro Africa. Some stories have a pointed moral attached, like *Æsop's Fables*, and some are really proverbs or moral sayings put into narrative form. The following is an animal tale told by the natives of southern Rhodesia :

A frog married a beautiful lady. The frog was a player on the *mbila* (a musical instrument). Every evening when he came home from work he would amuse himself by playing on his instrument. One day when the frog was away from home there came the *lurhidi* (a white, harmless snake) and said to the lady :

" Good-day, Mrs. Nobody."

The lady replied :

" I am not Mrs. Nobody, I am Mrs. Frog."

" Thank you, Mrs. Frog, I did not know that. Where is Mr. Frog now ? "

" He is out at work now. Here is his *mbila* which he plays when he comes home," said the lady.

" Will you allow me to play just one tune ? " said the snake.

And the lady said " Yes."

The snake began to play as follows :

> " Some men have spots,
> Some men have lumps,
> I know not whether ladies
> Have eyes to see.
> If they have, why not give me
> A hand in marriage
> I am so fine and smooth."

The lady was greatly touched by the song of the snake. She cooked him nice food, and he ate it up and went away. She then boiled some coarse meal and put it on the shelf for her husband, the frog. She wrapped herself in a blanket and pretended to be ill when her husband came home.

The snake came again soon, and this went on until at last the frog found out. Then he prepared a bow and arrow to shoot the snake. When the snake came again, when the frog was away, and began playing on the *mbila*, the frog came back, and shot him dead. The story is finished.

HISTORY TOLD BY FATHER TO SON

ALL of these are tales pure and simple — they are not believed to be true. There is, however, a large class of stories which are much more important to the anthropologist in throwing light on the psychology of a people, and these are the many legends and myths that are said by the people to be true. These tales embody all the history that an illiterate people can have. Much of it naturally is not literally true, for the stories have been handed on from mouth to mouth for generations, and have picked up a good deal of embellishment on the way. Yet most of these tales embody a core of truth. They are often told about persons or events who were actually historical, although their lives and actions as portrayed in the tales may be fantastically exaggerated. Such traditional accounts of the history of a people are called technically *legends*. *Myths* are sacred tales, but they also often take the place of history, for many myths are concerned with the origins of things. Although in literal fact most myths are quite false, "mythical," as we say, yet they contain certain important truths of a different kind.

Myths arise, half-unconsciously, from the need to *explain* and to *justify* different elements in the social order. In explaining the origin of things they trace them back to supernatural events in the dim past, often tracing a particular custom to the order or wish of a god or spirit, and justifying the social institutions of a people by showing how they arose out of the actions of a higher order of beings. Many myths tell of the creation of man by some great spirit or god. One of the most delightful is an African story.

God, it says, took a handful of clay and created man. Then he took another handful and created woman, and breathed the breath of life into both. Then he took them and set them opposite each other and said to them, " Look ! " They looked at each other for a moment and then both at once burst out laughing.

Unpleasant and evil things are explained by stories of the errors or the wickedness of far-off beings. Pandora's box is such a story—a sort of explanation and reassurance in one. Many myths are concerned with the origin of death, for the primitive mind often will not accept death as natural and inevitable.

An Andamanese myth tells how a woman lived with her two sons, Yaramurud and Toan. One day, as Yaramurud took his knife from the back of his neck to cut some pork, he cut himself. Then his mother knew that he was dead. She said to him :

"You are dead now, you had better go away." She carried him to the jungle and buried him, returning home. Very soon, Yaramurud returned and said :

"Mother, I did not die ; why did you bury me ? " But she knew he was dead, so she took him and buried him again. He came back again. This happened three times.

Then Kalwadi took him into the jungle to a big tree in which there was a big hole. She kicked the tree with her foot and said :

"You go in there."

Yaramurud went inside.

"Well, have you gone ? " his mother asked.

He answered "Yes."

"Tell me how the spirits talk ? "

"*Tokit*," he replied. (*Tokit* means nothing—it is just the way the spirits talk.)

Then his mother knew that he was with the spirits, and said :

"Oh, my child, you are finished now. You will never come back again."

After a few days, Yaramurud came back as a spirit and killed his brother. Before this there had been no death. His mother told the people, saying :

"You see what has happened. Well, we shall all of us die like this, like these two have done."

Stories of the loss of immortality or the passing of the Golden Age, or of the expulsion of mankind from Paradise are to be found in different forms all over the world. Tales and myths from opposite corners of the earth are strangely apt to resemble each other, both in the general trend of their story and sometimes even in details. Some stories seem to be known all over the world in somewhat different dressings.

The story of the bride who is not allowed to see her husband, and one night lights a lamp and looks at him with disastrous consequences, is one of them. Others again are common to large areas. Stories of the flood, for instance, are to be found all over the Near East, Greece and Eastern Europe.

WHERE ARE THE LEGENDS BORN ?

UNIVERSAL legends and myths of this kind can be explained in either of two ways, according to your theory of the evolution of culture. Either they spread over the world from a common source along with all the knowledge common to mankind ; or they represent psychological elements common to all human nature, and so have developed separately and spontaneously. Certainly there is evidence that some tales have travelled a long way, for we find details that are characteristic of the lives of some people far distant from that area in which the tale is current. On the other hand, it is difficult to account for the connection between the story of Jacob wrestling with the angel and similar stories among the Red Indians. It would be extremely interesting to make a study of myths and legends from all parts of the world, classifying them according to subject and distribution, for they form the great bulk of the literature of the world outside Europe and America.

FROM SAVAGE TO CIVILISED MAN

IN examining society piecemeal as we have been doing, looking as it were at a number of cross-sections at different angles, we tend to forget that in actual living fact no one aspect is ever isolated from the rest, but that every side of social life is inter-related with every other. Every kind of social activity influences and is influenced by every other activity, and environment influences them all. It should be borne in mind also, that society, being a living thing, is always changing. Even the very backward peoples cut off from the outer world for hundreds, perhaps for thousands, of years, who seem, like the Australian Aborigines, never to make any progress at all (for they still live in the Stone Age), nevertheless do change very, very slowly, bit by bit. The old men will nearly always have stories of times when customs and methods were different. Even though the stories may not be very accurate in their facts, they indicate an awareness of the essential truth that institutions do alter in time. Even in the most conservative and custom-ridden society, change from within will gradually take place.

Where a community is not isolated but is open to contacts through trade or warfare with alien peoples, society is much more plastic and ready for new ideas. There are, however, wide variations in the ease with which one community will assimilate the customs of another. There are a number of psychological factors involved, such as the prestige of the persons who are introducing the new ideas, the attitude of the community towards the people from whom the ideas are borrowed, the strength of the conservative tendency among the borrowers, and so forth. The study of culture contacts and the diffusion of different cultural elements is one of the knotty problems of anthropology over which much heated argument takes place in academic circles.

THE SAVAGE CUT ADRIFT BY THE WEST

BY whatsoever precise means they come about, changes do undoubtedly follow prolonged intercourse with foreign peoples. When these peoples are much stronger, and penetrate the native area with a totally alien civilisation, then the change is likely to be sudden, radical, and disastrous. Thus at the present time we are witnessing the disruption and decay of many savage peoples and the disappearance of much that was interesting, much that was admirable, in their social life. By the introduction of alien ways and civilised products, such as alcohol, firearms, factories, and clothing, traditional institutions are shattered, tribal authority shaken, and the whole structure of society undermined. It collapses, and the people lose their bearings and drift apart, villages fall into decay, and the population steadily declines. Thus we see the Red Indian, the African Bushman, the Andaman Islander dying out under our eyes, while the native culture of almost every savage people is being rapidly and radically undermined.

So we come to the end of our rapid survey of the workings of primitive society. What bearing has it all on our lives over here in London or New York ? Human society has often been likened to a living organism, so subtly are the different branches related. There is a connection between the life of the far-away savage and our own life. Savage habits and customs are not without parallels in modern civilisation—we attend mass meetings instead of war-dances, we cure our ills with bottles of coloured water instead of with amulets, with couéism instead of with charms, and we destroy each other much more effectively with machine-guns than with poisoned arrows from blow-pipes. Our complex civilisation did not hatch out of an egg ready-made—we have achieved it through the course of many different phases. It is sometimes worth while to pause and look back over the way we have come. History will recount to us the actual story of facts and events. Anthropology can tell us something of the development of the art of living.

Yet, in using anthropology to illuminate our own past, we must walk very warily. To make a thorough study of a primitive community is one thing, but to apply the results of that study to the primitive past of another society needs great caution and discrimination. We know that our civilisation has grown out of a past of savagery, and we know that savagery can be studied to-day in different parts of the globe. But in putting the two together there is room for endless error. For when we come to analyse primitive life we find that there are innumerable varieties of savagery—different ways of doing things, different ways of making things, different customs, laws, and beliefs. A certain classification is possible ; certain societies have a sufficient number of traits in common to justify their being classified into types —hunting types, pastoral nomad types, agricultural types, and so on. Yet it must be emphasised that there is no one " primitive type " of society. Consequently it is very dangerous to deduce the customs of our own prehistoric past from the existing customs of any particular savage society.

CLUES OF THE PAST TO THE CUSTOMS OF TO-DAY

WHAT we can do, however, is to take what clues archæology can give and to follow these out among the existing primitive conditions where we find corresponding clues. Archæology provides us with a collection of prehistoric stone axes, but only the axe-heads—it cannot tell us how they were hafted on to handles. As anthropologists, however, we know that the Australians haft their axes by lashing them with thongs on to a wooden handle. Now, wood decays quickly, and all the wooden objects used by our Stone Age forefathers have long since crumbled to dust. Nevertheless, we assume that they did use wood since every other known people does so, and therefore, given the existing methods of hafting stone axes which are similar in shape to the pre-historic ones, we can fairly safely assume that the Stone Age peoples hafted their weapons on to sticks in much the same way.

When we come to intangible things—social customs and beliefs—our reconstructions are inevitably more tentative and hypothetical. About the social life of early man in the Old Stone Age we can say very little indeed. One or two skeletons have been found with signs of deliberate and careful burial. We deduce from this that the Stone Age people had some sort of belief in an after-life. We know from their paintings that they had a feeling for art and beauty, and we deduce from various pieces of evidence that these were connected with magic. We know of magic hunting-rites among modern savages, and so we connect the two, but at best it is only a hypothesis which fits the facts—and unfortunately the facts that we have to go upon are very meagre. For later times we have much more reliable archæological data, and at length we come to the first written records in Egypt and Babylonia. Evidence from these sources can often be correlated with existing data to give us an approximate picture of the social customs of the past.

The present is never completely severed from the past. Indeed, in one sense there is no real distinction between the two. The past is never dead and buried but lives on in a different dress in the present. Very few of our laws and customs appear new and ready-made—they evolve out of history, and we can trace their descent. Sometimes, especially in post-war years, we have created laws and usages that seem to be a complete break with tradition ; yet, on looking closer, we find that these innovations are the outcome of past experience and so maintain an unbroken link with the past. Ultimately there is, indeed, nothing new under the sun. The past is always operating on the present directly and indirectly. Often it works with a dead hand, obstructing progress with its tradition and prejudices, cluttering the way with outworn obstacles.

BARBARITY AND SUPERSTITION IN WESTERN CIVILISATION

MANY barbarous customs still exist in our midst, and we find the remnants of many more. We are still in many ways crude and cruel in the settling of our differences and in the treatment of the unsuccessful and nonconforming members of society. We still cling with the tenacity of drowning men to old customs and traditions that no longer fit modern conditions. We are still in our private lives largely the slaves of conventional usage. To appreciate how incredibly unhygienic we remain one has only to inquire into the conditions in which much of the working-class, which forms the majority of the population, are compelled to live and work.

A number of past beliefs and customs live on in the outward forms and ceremonies of everyday life. Others survive as superstitions. The prevalence of superstition among Western nations would make an interesting study. One is too readily inclined to consider serious superstition characteristic only of the uneducated. Yet superstitious beliefs and practices are widely current among all classes of society. They are held lightly, one may say, more as amusing curios than as serious beliefs. Yet how many people will sit down happily thirteen at table ? How many people do not possess talismans of some sort that " bring them luck " ? How large a part, indeed, does luck play in our thoughts as a kind of good or evil fairy ? There are dozens of beliefs setting out that ill luck will follow certain actions, such as spilling the salt, unless averted by certain others, such as throwing the salt over the shoulder. Such customs are the exact counterpart of savage ritual, with the same purpose and the same methods. If the ritual is scamped in any way, if it is not carried out exactly according to the prescribed custom in every detail, then its effects will be nullified. So in the same way the spilt salt must be thrown with the right hand over the left shoulder or the ill luck will not be averted.

QUAINT CUSTOMS IN REMOTE COUNTRY DISTRICTS

SUCH superstitious practices are so well known that they have lost their picturesqueness. Many curious and quaint customs, however, are still to be found in remote country districts, especially among the peasant population of Eastern Europe, where strange survivals of paganism linger on. Even in industrialised Britain, relics of past beliefs in magic and spirits survive in country customs, especially in the remoter parts of the West. The Irish usage of " keening " at a death is the counterpart of many savage customs of ritual wailing over the dead. Belief in fairies and spirits is not yet dead in the heart of the Celtic peasant, although as the machine penetrates farther into the depths of the countryside, and education becomes more advanced, it must inevitably be extinguished.   Even the memory of such things is fading as folk-tales become forgotten under the competition of the printed word and the " talkie."

Ancient customs and beliefs are often preserved in folk-tales and folklore.   There is current in many European countries a tale of how a certain bridge or church or city wall was being built, and no progress could be made as it would fall down as fast as it was set up, until a child was taken and walled up alive in the foundations.   There is one German version of the story, where a little boy is bought from his mother, and given cakes to eat while they build the wall right over him.   At intervals he says, " Mother, I can see you—Mother, I can still see you—Mother, I can see you no more."   Surely this tale is the survival of some barbaric custom of human sacrifice on the foundations of a new building.

FROM PAGAN RITES TO MOTHER GOOSE

FOLK-TALES and folklore are the expression of much of the unconscious conflict arising out of the problems of social existence—they may tell us far more of the psychology of a people than the people themselves could ever tell us. A comparative study of folklore from all over the world would throw a hundred side-lights on the evolution of social custom and the principles, conscious and unconscious, that lie behind them.   Children's games and nursery rhymes, too, are the last home of many ancient customs and pagan rites, as well as being memories of historical events like the " fifth of November."

So we see that we cannot disown our barbaric past, for it is very much with us.   Therefore, when we have to deal with peoples who are still living this barbaric past or something resembling it, we are showing ourselves very ungrateful to our own " rude forefathers " if we merely dub these people " savages " and treat them like wild beasts.   Indeed we sometimes treat them rather worse, for they cannot be hunted like animals, and therefore sometimes less interest is taken in their habits and in their preservation.   However, unlike the wild beast, they can work, and work moreover more intelligently and at much more varied tasks than the domestic animal.

The enslavement of black peoples was not by any means invented by the European slave-trader, for it was a native institution in Africa long before the commencement of the American slave trade. But slavery was exploited and developed by the white man to an unprecedented extent, and it seems to have coloured our whole view of savage peoples with contempt and prejudice.

Now that we take a more enlightened view of our responsibilities towards the native peoples of our colonial territories, it is becoming all the more important to make an effort to understand them. And it is not only the business of the colonial administrator to make this effort, but of every settler and trader.

Public opinion at home, too, can have a great influence on the welfare of the distant native people, and public opinion can be educated to the right views on native questions only by knowledge and understanding of primitive life and primitive ways of thought.

HOW TO STUDY ANTHROPOLOGY

THE science of man, as we have already explained in this section, is such a wide subject that it is a little difficult for the interested layman to know where to begin its study. He sees anthropology spreading out into a number of branches with rather high-sounding names, and he feels perhaps a little chilled by the vastness of the matter and the technicalities of the details. He need not, however, be discouraged. If he beard the giant courageously he will find him an amiable enough fellow, not nearly so academic as he appears, and full of strange tales and interesting truths.

The best approach to the subject is first to obtain a general bird's-eye view such as we have tried to give here. Then the intending student will be more in a position to know what particular branch of the subject is likely to interest him most. Perhaps he will take an interest in mythology or the study of magic, in primitive economics or in technology. Perhaps it will be some particular people like the Andamanese or the Fijians which will most interest him, or it will be the study of race and physical characters. Whatever it is, he will have a conception of its place in the general picture, and the next step will be to read up the subject in one or two reliable books.

Travel books by enterprising globe-trotters or missionaries of the last century are not on the whole reliable sources of information. They were written by untrained observers while anthropology was yet in its infancy, and are full of errors not only in their interpretations of customs, but in the recording of the facts themselves. The authors would make no differentiation between hearsay and records by an eye-witness; moreover, they were, like the rest of us, only too prone to read things into what they saw in order to support preconceived notions. Even trained anthropologists are apt to fall into the same error, which is indeed a common temptation in all scientific research. But the results may be twenty times more erroneous in the case of the layman of the last century, because experience has shown that his assumptions as to the nature of savages were very largely false. Many savages are not " savage," very few ever were cannibals within memory, none of them are " children," and all of them are men of the same species as ourselves.

This is not to say that such travel books are to be thrown contemptuously on the dust-heap. They may make entertaining reading as semi-fiction ; but they should not be read as introductions to anthropology, which is a science. There are exceptions to this category. Nothing, for instance, could make a more delightful introduction to anthropology in Africa than Mary Kingsley's account of her travels in that continent.

Mary Kinlgsey was a woman of exceptional courage, sympathy, wit, and powers of observation. She travelled alone into the remote jungles of West Africa where no white woman had ever been before. She recorded what she saw of native life with intelligence and sympathy, and showed a remarkable understanding of primitive mentality. Her writings are pre-eminently, as people of her time would have said, " entertaining and instructive."

BOOKS TO READ NEXT : GETTING A BALANCED VIEW

AMONG the more standard books that one would recommend to the budding anthropologist stands out first and foremost Sir James Frazer's *The Golden Bough* (Macmillan). There is an excellent abridged edition in one volume. Another interesting book by the same author is *The Devil's Plea : a*

Defence of Superstition.　In reading works on anthropology it is advisable to choose books written by people of opposing theoretical camps; otherwise the reader may find himself imbued with a set of very unfashionable ideas and with no notion that they are not the last word on the subject.　Rivers's *Kinship and Social Organisation* and Malinowski's *Argonauts of the Western Pacific* might make a good combination, though the former is a little stiff and the latter rather long.　Shorter works setting forth Malinowski's " functional " point of view and his social theories are *The Sexual Life of Savages in North-Western Melanesia* (Routledge), and the very short *Crime and Custom in Savage Life* (Kegan Paul).　Books of a general nature to be recommended are *Early Civilisation* (Harrap), by Goldenweiser, and Marett's *Anthropology* in the Home University Library, Thornton Butterworth Limited. For special studies of individual peoples the student should certainly read *The Andaman Islanders* (Cambridge University Press), by A. R. Brown ; H. A. Junod's *The Life of a South African Tribe* (Macmillan) ; and *Religion and Art among the Ashanti* (Clarendon Press), by Rattray.　Driberg wrote an excellent little pamphlet entitled *The Savage As He Really Is* (Routledge).　In reading anthropology it is as well to master the technical terms, which, once understood, present no difficulty.　Words such as *exogamy*, *classificatory*, *matrilineal*, each of which has been explained in this section, are constantly cropping up.

But anthropology is not to be studied in books alone.　As a science of society it should be studied at its source—in society. It is not necessary to join an expedition to the South Seas in order to become a field worker.　Anthropological observations can quite conveniently be made at home.　Every town, suburb, and village offers a rich field for investigation to the spare-time anthropologist with a quick eye and ear. Look around at the people in the same bus with you, and note all the different types—dark and fair, short and tall, round-headed and long-headed.　Then consult some standard work on physical types such as Haddon's *Races of Man* (Cambridge University Press) which will tell you what are the traits to look for, and you are ready to make a collection of the different racial types of any particular district, to correlate your findings with similar investigations, and to make your own theory about the racial components of the English people.　It is an amusing pastime to observe from the gallery of any public assembly the head forms of the people below. (When judging the shape of the head always look at it from above, not side or full face.) One might even go so far as to obtain a pair of callipers and make exact measurements of the cephalic indices of the skulls of all one's friends.

MODERN CUSTOMS RICH IN CLUES TO THE PAST

PHYSICAL observations are not the only kind of anthropological research that can be carried out in the heart of civilisation. As we have emphasised elsewhere, modern society is full of survivals of a barbaric past. A collection and classification of current superstitions would be of great interest, and of real use to the professional anthropologist. Not only superstitions, but an impartial survey of any of our social institutions, like marriage or education, or in a smaller way, the outward forms of courtesy, would yield much of anthropological interest and value. Another interesting study would be the collection and comparison of proverbs, riddles, nursery rhymes and games, or a comparative study of the folk-tales of Europe with the aid of Grimm and Andrew Lang. Once we know something of life in primitive society, we are constantly being made aware of resemblances in our own social structure. Often we can congratulate our civilisation on its advance over the old primitive ways, but sometimes we must admit that the " savage " orders his affairs better than we do.

THE PRACTICAL USES OF ANTHROPOLOGY

SO much for the amateur anthropologist in everyday life. What now of anthropology as a profession ? It must be admitted at once that as a method of earning a living anthropology is of little use. It has no practical application at present except as incidental to other occupations, such as colonial administration or native teaching or missionary work. There are no posts for anthropologists as such, except in research or academic teaching.

The value of anthropological research is indeed beginning to be recognised by governments. An anthropologist has lately been appointed by the Australian government to investigate the life of the aborigines. Otherwise research is carried on under university auspices. It is possible for a budding anthropologist who can prove his worth to obtain a grant from certain funds for the purpose which will enable him to reside in a particular area for a period and to carry out field investigations. Expeditions of field workers also are organised from time to time, but the science is not yet sufficiently popular for the financing of such enterprises to be an easy matter. To take up field work as a career you must have either exceptional ability or private means.

Academic anthropology presents much the same difficulties. The science is not a normal subject of educational curricula ; the desire to learn it is restricted to people who are going to work in native areas as teachers or administrators or the like, and to the comparatively small, though growing, number of persons who are attracted to the subject for its own sake. Consequently the demand for teachers is not large. There are chairs of anthropology at a very few of the universities, where it has only lately been raised to the status of a degree subject. The Civil Service examination now includes two papers on anthropology. Otherwise, in so far as it is taught at all, it is taught in scraps incidental to other subjects such as geography, early history, anatomy, and so on.

Of late years, however, there has been a decided growth of interest in anthropology, exemplified in the endowment of chairs at the universities, in the great increase of books written by field workers, and the introduction of the subject into the formal training of colonial officials. The science is still young and comparatively unknown, but it certainly has a wide future.

" The proper study of mankind is man." Anthropology is a fascinating subject, full of romance and drama, full of illuminating side-lights on human nature. Man is such an interesting creature, it seems a pity that more time is not spent on studying his diverse habits. Anthropology displays to us all the wonderful variety of man's responses to the social problems with which he is confronted ; but above all it emphasises the underlying unity of mankind.

THE UNSEEN WORLD : HOW MEN HAVE THOUGHT ABOUT GOD

by C. R. NORTH, M.A.(Lond.), Professor of Old Testament Languages and Literature in Handsworth College, Birmingham, Lecturer in Hebrew for the University of Birmingham, Author of " An Outline of Islam."

MAN has been variously defined as a laughing animal, a fire-making animal, a cooking animal, and a tool-using animal. He may with even more propriety be called a religious animal. Something that we can only call a religious sense seems to have been born within him, and no tribe of people, no matter how savage, has yet been discovered without at least some rudiments of it. They may be reticent about it ; they may try to hide it from the notice of curious strangers ; but always, upon closer inquiry, they are found to have some conception of an unseen, supernatural world, and of their own relation to that world.

It is only as men become civilised that they—or perhaps we should rather say that individuals among them—take leave to doubt the existence of some kind of divine being. That, it is sometimes said, is a mark of enlightenment : religion is born of fear, it belongs only to the childhood of the race, and man will put it away as he becomes older and wiser. We are not concerned to argue that point. Our purpose is not apologetic but descriptive. We begin, therefore, with the undoubted fact that wherever and in whatever age mankind is found, he is religious. It is almost certain, too, that he has never, since he first became differentiated from the lower animals, been otherwise than religious.

To the question, " What is Religion ? " various answers have been given. Generalisations are proverbially precarious, and it is not easy to find a definition that will cover all the many manifestations of religion without being culpably vague. Matthew Arnold's " Religion is morality touched with emotion " is often quoted. But what is it—if anything at all—that awakens the emotion ? Besides, though we to-day have no use at all for any religion that does not issue in moral conduct, that is not to say that primitive religion concerned itself very much, or even at all, with morality. Almost certainly it was not, directly at least, concerned with morals. It was concerned with the gods.

What we need, in an historical and descriptive sketch of this kind, is a definition that will cover the main facts about religion all through its history. Suppose we say that religion is the Quest for God ? That, again, may appeal to many in this age who have only a very hazy idea of what God is, and only wish they had more certainty. But religion, in its historical manifestations, has generally preferred to speak of God's revelation to man, rather than of man's quest for and discovery of God. One of its strongest convictions has been that man cannot " by searching find out God."

Perhaps the best preliminary definition of religion is that of Professor W. Adams Brown : " By religion is meant the life of man in his superhuman relations." It may not, perhaps, cover such distinctively modern developments as the proposal to deify " humanity " or " the spirit of the race " as an object of worship. That, however, is probably only a passing phase—men have in recent years come to be very much out of conceit with themselves. In any case our present purpose will be satisfied by a definition that covers the wide range of primitive religion and the great historic faiths of mankind.

In further explanation of his definition Adams Brown goes on to enumerate three main aspects of religion. In the first place, man feels himself to be *dependent* upon a super-human power or powers. Next, he deems himself to be *responsible* to the authority of those powers. And finally, he believes himself capable of *communing* with the unseen. Out of these three aspects have developed the two most characteristic features of religion, namely, worship and conduct.

THE FALLACY OF " TRUE " RELIGION AND " FALSE "

VARIOUS classifications of religions have been proposed. None of them is entirely satisfactory. The division into true and false is not only uncharitable, it is unscientific. The time is gone by when a man could say : " When I speak of religion I mean, of course, the Christian religion ; when I speak of the Christian religion I mean the Protestant religion ; and when I speak of the Protestant religion I mean the religion of the Church of England "—or for that matter any denomination, Christian or non-Christian. God, we are assured by the New Testament, has never " left

Himself without witness," and there are elements of truth in all religions. A man may be convinced that Christianity is the final and perfect religion ; that does not preclude him from recognising truth in faiths other than his own.

In these days we are, perhaps, inclined to be too tolerant, and to speak as though all religions are equally true. Nevertheless, those who are best acquainted with the religion of primitive peoples are usually the first to grant that there is hardly a custom, however barbarous it may appear to the outside spectator, that has not some moral or social value for those who observe it. A fetish may be nothing but a piece of wood according to our standards ; but it is better that a man should believe in its power to injure evil-doers if, by ceasing to believe in it, he should forthwith rob and kill his neighbour with impunity. It follows, therefore, that the study of religions, even of the most primitive type, should be undertaken with sympathy, and the desire to appreciat⸰ what is best in them.

To divide religions into " natural " and " revealed " classes is hardly more satisfactory. Where does the " natural " end and the " revealed " begin ? All religions, even those that have had no sacred books, have believed that God revealed Himself, and who shall say that He has not, in the measure in which men could understand Him ? For this reason the division into religions that have sacred books and those that have none is artificial, and corresponds to no fundamental differences. Moreover, truth and error can be inextricably mingled even within the compass of books that are revered as sacred.

On the whole it seems best to review first of all the " religion of the lower culture," as it is called. This culminated in the great polytheistic (belief in many gods) systems of antiquity. Then we shall survey the more important living religions of the world. These, too, are developments out of primitive religion. They fall into three main groups, according to the countries in which they originated. There is the Middle East, India, the birthplace of Hinduism and its offshoot Buddhism. In the Far East, in China, we find Confucianism and Taoism, together with Shinto in Japan. In the Near East there originated the three great monotheistic (belief in one god) faiths, Judaism, Christianity, and Islam, which stand in a class by themselves.

Something must be said of Zoroastrianism also, since it

offers a solution to the problem of religion which is in some ways unique. Its original home was Persia, and the Persians were closely related to the invaders of India. But it differs fundamentally from Hinduism, having affinities rather with the Semitic monotheistic religions. Also, after the Sanskrit-speaking branch of the Indo-European race parted company with the Persians, the cultural and political relationships of the latter were, on the whole, with the West rather than with India. In this survey we shall therefore deal with Zoroastrianism immediately before the monotheistic religions.

To the three geographical divisions suggested above there correspond, as we should expect, striking differences in the types of religion that originated in them. It is suggestive, too, that in the Far East, Middle East, and Near East we have three distinct types of civilisation, which have, until quite recently, developed for more than three thousand years independently of one another. Finally it may be remarked that, since the rediscovery of the ancient Egyptian and Babylonian civilisations, it has become apparent that what we call Western Civilisation really originated in the Near East.

THE PRIMITIVE PEOPLES IN SEARCH OF TRUTH

THREE things may be remarked at the outset as characteristic of primitive religion :

(1) It is much the same in all parts of the world. It is only in the higher manifestations of religion that one faith comes to have any distinctiveness or originality as compared with others.

(2) Primitive religion consists in the performance of antique rites and ceremonies, not in believing doctrines about God. The savage has no creed. It is not easy for us to appreciate this fact. We believe certain things about God ; belief in God awakens emotions such as reverence and love ; and emotion finds expression in conduct. The religion of the lower culture has not yet reached the stage of articulate thinking about God. Certain ceremonies are performed because, for all that anybody in the community knows, they always have been performed. Later on the question is asked, Why do we do these things ? The answer takes the form of a mythology, or stories about the gods. Mythology, at

a relatively advanced stage in the evolution of religion, occupies much the same place that creeds do in the highest religions of all.

(3) In early religion the individual is of no importance ; he is simply a member of the community into which he happens to have been born. This, of course, is true of all the activities of early man, social as well as religious, if, indeed, the two can be distinguished. The social unit is the clan or tribe, not the individual. No one dreams of " contracting out " of society, or of holding religious opinions of his own. This peculiarity persists until quite a late stage in the development of religion.

HOW DID RELIGION BEGIN ?

UNTIL comparatively recently it was generally assumed that the earliest religion was monotheistic, *i.e.* that it started with a belief in one God. On this view the religion of the lower culture could only be a degeneration from an originally pure faith. From all that we know of primitive man he was quite incapable of believing in one only God by the aid of his own reason. If God was conceived of as One it could only be because He had revealed Himself as such in the beginning. This, it was believed—on the supposed authority of the Bible—He had done. Modern study of the Bible does not, however, demand it, nor even recommend it as likely.

There is every reason to believe that a good deal in so-called " primitive " religion is degenerate rather than primitive. It is also true that many quite savage peoples have a vague conception of one Supreme Being. But they are not greatly concerned about Him. It is with the lesser gods who are near at hand that they have mainly to do. While, therefore, it is perhaps just possible that this vague intuition of one God above all is reminiscent of an original monotheism, in the present state of our knowledge it does not seem probable, and we are not in a position to assume it.

We have to picture early man as engaged in a ceaseless struggle against wild beasts and natural forces that are obviously immeasurably stronger than himself. He has two continuously pressing needs, food and shelter. He has a rudimentary sense of wonder. The sun rises and sets with unfailing regularity ; the seasons come and go ; but although he must early have learned to calculate the chances of some things fairly accurately, there were other forces, such as earthquake, storm, and flood, which were quite incalculable in their operations. He had no conception of natural law as we understand it ; or, in so far as he had any, there were multitudes of exceptions to it. The same object might bring him blessing one day, and bane the next. The things that most impressed his mind were those that had movement, especially if they had the power to contribute to his welfare or hurt—the cooling spring, the shady tree swaying in the wind, the lightning-shaft, the mysterious denizens of the jungle. All things that moved, he would conclude, were doubtless endowed with life similar to his own.

At first the moving objects themselves were thought of as alive ; the stream moved itself, just as man moves himself. In this there was nothing supernatural. Further reflection suggested that the stream moved not of its own will, but because it was animated by a spirit (Latin *anima*). This is to assume a supernatural agent, and to this general class of ideas the name *animism* has been given. It is probable that all religions have passed through the animistic stage. As a rule, the objects which called for remark were not the far-off heavenly bodies, whose motions were fairly constant, and which, besides, had not so obviously intimate a control over human destiny. They were rather those that were in the near neighbourhood, trees, rivers, and springs, conspicuous rocks and mountains.

Animism is often popularly confused with polytheism—belief in many gods. Animism, it is true, takes for granted the existence of many supernatural beings, but the two are quite distinct from one another. Polytheism, strange though it may seem, belongs to a relatively high stage of religious reflection. It is associated with mythology, and its gods are distinctly personalised : by this is meant that each god has a definite individuality, or character, or personality of his own. Its conception of the gods is anthropomorphic, *i.e.* the gods are thought of as having a human form, and the mental and moral characteristics of human beings. Representations are made of them in the shape of idols.

Crude animism, on the other hand, has only a vague idea of the personality of the spirits or gods that it worships. It does not attribute to them human form, and it makes no idols. The tree, the spring, or the rock is itself the idol, or dwelling-place of the god. The rock itself is the Beth-el, the " house of god," and on it oil is poured, or, in earlier days still, the fat of the sacrifice was smeared. An alternative term for animism is " polydæmonism," or belief in many demons, using the word " demon " in its original sense, which conveyed no suggestion of evil.

PEOPLES WHO DEIFIED THEIR ANCESTORS

ANOTHER class of spirits worshipped by early man was that of his deceased ancestors and relatives. He did not for a moment doubt that they still existed. He frequently met and conversed with them in his dreams, and to his simple mind dreams had all the reality of waking sense-experience. Not that the dead were thought of as actually immortal ; the conception of immortality is too abstract for primitive minds to grasp. But they were still existent, and not very far away. Being unseen, there was no certainty what they might do to the living ; they were endowed with added powers both for good and evil over those with whom they had lately associated. Yet to suppose, as is frequently done, that the dead were always and only objects of fear, is a mistake. Offerings were made to them, and the forms that these took suggest that the dead were not only remembered with affection, but that they were supposed to be still interested in the welfare of the living.

It is improbable that at first the spirits of deceased ancestors were included in the class of the most powerful supernatural beings. The offerings of food and drink which were made to them suggest rather that they were believed to be in large measure dependent for their continued existence upon the charity of the living. The spirits of the dead, on the other hand, were not essentially different from other spirits, and in some communities examples are found of powerful gods who were in the first instance deified ancestors. For example, another name of the patriarch Esau was Edom (Genesis xxxvi. 1). Edom was also the name of a god ; the name Obed-edom (2 Samuel vi. 10) means " worshipper of Edom." The name " Gad," also, the father of one of the Hebrew tribes, means " luck " or " fortune," and even in quite late times (perhaps even to-day !) he is an object of worship (see Isaiah lxv. 11—Revised Version and Margin).

The story of the witch at En-dor shows that necromancy —calling up the spirits of the dead—was practised in ancient

Israel (1 Samuel xxviii. 13–14) and note that the woman sees "a god coming up out of the earth." This does not mean that ancestor worship is a recognised element in Old Testament religion. Wherever it is mentioned it is denounced in the strongest possible terms (*e.g.* Isaiah viii. 19 ; xxix. 4).

Perhaps this is the most convenient place in which to speak of the primitive conception of the nature of the soul. In very many languages the word " soul " meant originally " wind " or " breath." Again we may illustrate from the Old Testament. When Elijah would restore the widow's son to life it is said that " he stretched himself upon the child three times," and " the soul of the child came into him again, and he revived " (1 Kings xvii. 21–22). A similar story about Elisha tells that the prophet " lay upon the child, and put his mouth upon his mouth " (2 Kings iv. 34). Obviously the soul and the breath are thought of as much the same. This conception of the " breath-soul " is well-nigh universal, and many are the means that have been employed to prevent the soul from leaving the body, or, if it has already departed, to coax it back again.

Similar to it is that of the " blood-soul," in which the life or soul is thought to reside in the blood (cf. Genesis ix. 4). This was doubtless a conclusion from the observed fact that when a man is mortally wounded his life ebbs away as the blood flows from him. The idea of the semi-physical nature of the soul may explain the ease with which early man was able to place his deceased ancestors within the category of the nature spirits with which he was everywhere surrounded.

HOW CERTAIN ANIMALS GET EVIL REPUTATIONS

"HOLINESS " and " uncleanness " are related in primitive religions in that both are taboo, and thus have much the same effect upon those who contract them. Long after the Bible was written the Jews continued to speak of it as " defiling the hands," because the hands needed to be washed after handling the sacred volume. The close connection between the holy and the unclean is further evident from the fact that an animal sacred to one god will probably be unclean to the worshipper of another. The primary reason why the pig was an unclean animal to the Jew was, in all probability, not because it is a dirty animal, but because it figured in heathen cults, in which it would, of course, be holy, perhaps originally a totem (cf. Isaiah lxv. 3–4). The original reason why we do not eat horse-flesh is not that it is tough ; it is that the horse was sacred to Odin, the father of the Scandinavian gods, and when our Saxon ancestors became Christian their bishops forbade them to eat it because of its heathenish associations. Many of the early Christians regarded the flesh of certain animals as unclean because they had been offered in sacrifice to idols (cf. 1 Corinthians viii. 4–13 ; x. 23–28).

It follows, since holiness and uncleanness are closely related semi-physical characteristics, that both are contagious. The Ark of Jehovah is holy, and if Uzzah touches it (2 Samuel vi. 7) it will deal death to him as surely as if he had touched an electric wire. The real reason is not that Jehovah loses his temper, but that the Ark is a holy object, and must only be handled in the prescribed way. That Uzzah died we need not doubt. Similar cases are on record where men have died of fright when they have unwittingly touched a tabooed object. Consequently if a thing or a person has contracted either holiness or uncleanness, it will communicate the quality to everything it touches. It must therefore be insulated, or put into quarantine, until it is " cleansed." Thus among the Jews in quite late times the flesh of " sin-offerings " was " most holy," and as such might be eaten only by males of the priestly families, and by them only within the sanctuary precincts (Leviticus vi. 16–18).

If the flesh of a sin-offering was boiled in a metal pot the vessel had afterwards to be scoured and rinsed in water. But if it was boiled in an earthenware pot, the pot had to be broken after use, because the holiness inherent in the sin-offering was supposed to penetrate into the porous vessel so that it could not be washed out (Leviticus vi. 28). In India, to this day, at functions which are attended by members of different castes, refreshments are served on plates of brittle red clay, and guests will finish their repast by breaking their plates so that there is no possibility of their being used again.

It must be emphasised that illustrations are taken from the Old Testament for the sake of convenience. It must not be supposed that the Old Testament contains no higher conception of holiness than that outlined above. It is quite common for primitive ideas to persist for a long time side by side with higher conceptions ; for example, there are still Christian people who are distressed if they happen to espy the new moon through a closed window. The story of the way in which the conception of holiness, out of such unpromising beginnings, came to be moralised, is one of the most fascinating in the long and chequered history of religion.

HOW MEN APPROACHED THE GODS : THE RITUAL OF SACRIFICE

THERE have been several theories as to how sacrifice originated. Some writers have tried to show that at first there was only one purpose underlying it. But, even apart from the complicated sacrificial systems that are found in some of the higher religions, there appear to be sacrifices of three kinds, all of which may be equally primitive. Whether they are so or not we need not attempt to decide. It is sufficient for our purpose that they are all found in the religion of the lower culture.

There is first the type of sacrifice that may be described as " eating the god." This is associated with totemism. The god is supposed to be incarnate in the totem species, and it follows that those who eat the flesh of the totem animal partake of the divine nature. Ordinarily the totemist, whatever else he may eat, does not eat the flesh of his totem. Instead he protects it, and to kill it is an act of sacrilege. But on rare and specially solemn occasions he holds a sacrificial feast, and in the act of " eating the god " he believes that he attains to mystical union with the divine. Every scrap of the slaughtered animal is devoured, sometimes raw, and while the life-principle is still warm within it.

This idea of the " dying god " is very widespread, and there is something impressive about it, even in its crudest forms. The parallel between it and the Christian conception of the death of Christ and the associated rite in which the believer is bidden to " Take, eat: this is My body," is very striking. At the same time it is certain that there is no *historical* link between totemism and the Christian sacrament. It is not even certain whether the early religion of the Hebrews contained any remains of totemism ; it *is* certain that totemism was not even a memory with the Jews in later Old Testament times. If there is any suggestiveness in the parallel, therefore, it can only be on the principle that even the crudest forms of religion contain some adumbrations or foreshadowings of eternal truth.

Another early type of sacrifice is based upon the conception of the god and his worshippers as together forming one community. Hence the communal meal, in which the god has his share, and by means of which the bond uniting him to his people is renewed or strengthened. The portion of the sacrifice that falls to the god consists, usually, of the blood —in which, as we have seen, the life is supposed to reside— and certain intestinal fats. At first the blood was poured, and the fat smeared, upon the natural rock-altar. Later, as the conception of God became more refined, altars of stone were built, and the fat was conveyed to the god in the form of sacrificial smoke. The larger part of the flesh is eaten by the offerer and his friends. All slaughter of domestic animals is a sacrificial act, and the eating of their flesh a treat reserved for high days and holy days.

A less complicated type of sacrifice than the two preceding is that of a gift to the god. Such were the " offerings " of Cain and Abel (Genesis iv.). Here we have a spontaneous act of homage to the god, an attempt to secure his favour, or an expression of thanksgiving for benefits received or anticipated. What has been said above concerning the way in which the offering was conveyed to the god applies here also.

HOW MAN CAME TO VISUALISE GOD

THE stages by which man came to think of the gods as personal were no doubt gradual, and are often obscure. In some communities the process was more rapid than in others. The character of the gods was coloured by human conceptions, and by the forms of human society. This was inevitable. For, if man was left to discover the nature of God for himself he had perforce to base his conception of divine personality upon what he observed of his own. Or if, on the other hand, God would reveal Himself to man, He must do so in terms that man can understand. To object that " in the beginning God created man in His own image (Genesis i. 27), and that ever since man has been returning the compliment " is witty, but religion is not to be discredited by such facetiousness. A measure of anthropomorphism was inevitable, and if the Christian doctrine of the God-Man is true it was even justifiable.

When we come to historic times we find a conception of God as personal that is in some respects similar to mono-theism. A people may restrict itself to the worship of one god, without, however, denying that other gods exist for other peoples. This form of religion is known as "monolatry" (from two Greek words, *monos*—alone, and *latreuein*—to serve). The word itself differs from monotheism (from *monos*, and *theos*, God) in that its emphasis, as befits religion at a comparatively early stage of development, is upon the service or worship of the god rather than upon the nature of his being as one. By some writers the term "henotheism" (from *henos*, a form of the numeral "one," and *theos*) is used in the sense here applied to monolatry; but the word is ambiguous and is better employed for something rather different.

The classical examples of monolatry are to be found in the religion of the early Hebrews, and among such of their near neighbours as the Moabites and Ammonites. The Hebrews called their god Yahweh.[1] They did not doubt the existence of the Moabite god Chemosh, nor of the Ammonite god Milcom, nor that it was perfectly proper for those peoples to worship their respective gods. But the only god who had any claim upon their loyalty, or whom they ought to worship, was Yahweh. Jephthah asks the Moabites, "Wilt thou not possess that which Chemosh thy god giveth thee to possess? So whomsoever Yahweh our god hath dispossessed from before us, them will we possess" (Judges xi. 24). The first commandment in the Hebrew decalogue is literally, "Thou shalt have no other gods in my presence" (Exodus xx. 3). This assumes the real existence of other gods, but denies that they are entitled to worship from Israelites.

Each god is supposed to have jurisdiction within the territory inhabited by his own people, but not outside it. If, therefore, a man is banished, or goes to reside in another country, it is natural, indeed inevitable, that he should change his religion. Ruth, when she leaves her native land, says to her mother-in-law, "Thy people shall be my people, and thy god my god" (Ruth i. 16). The exiled David complains to Saul, "They have driven me out this day that I should have no share in the inheritance of Yahweh, saying, Go, serve other gods" (1 Samuel xxvi. 19). Naaman, when he has been cleansed of his leprosy, is so filled with gratitude and a sense of the power of Elisha's god that he would fain

[1] For the meaning and significance of the name, sometimes spelt Jehovah, see pp. 481-2.

worship him. Accordingly he makes request for "two mules' burden of earth" from the soil of Yahweh's land, wherewith to set up an altar to Yahweh in Damascus (2 Kings v. 17). Only so, according to the popular idea, could the writ of one god run in the territory of another. Naaman's altar would be a small enclave of Yahweh's land within the kingdom of Damascus, much as the British embassy in a foreign capital is legally British territory.

Monolatry is not monotheism, but in the peculiar form that it came to have in ancient Israel it was the soil in which monotheism grew. It is, therefore, historically of the highest importance. It was, since it insisted that men must not dissipate their devotion in the service of many gods, a training for something better. In this way we can see some justification for the much-abused doctrine of the "jealousy" of Yahweh.

PEOPLES WHO WORSHIP MANY GODS

POLYTHEISM, at least in its more elaborate forms, is hardly a religion of the lower culture. The Babylonians, the Egyptians, the Greeks, and the Romans were highly civilised peoples ; yet their religions were polytheisms. On the other hand, there is no cultured people in the world to-day professing an unmodified polytheism of the well-recognised types that prevailed in antiquity. There are still many polytheists in the world—there are many animists, too, for that matter ; but polytheism, as the civilised nations of antiquity knew it, is dead. We may, therefore, before going on to describe the living religions of the world, say something of polytheism, relating it to the religion of the lower culture, out of which it grew, and of which it was the highest expression.

It was hinted at the beginning of the preceding section that the conception of the gods has been considerably influenced by the forms of human society. Suppose an amalgamation of clans into a tribe. Each clan has its divine patron, to whom, in monolatrous fashion, it has hitherto given exclusive worship. What is to be done with the two gods in the amalgamated society ? Neither of them can be ignored, since, in the solemn act of covenant entered into by the clans, each of them acts on behalf of his clients. There is nothing for it but to recognise them both.

If one of the contracting parties is larger or more powerful than the other, its god will become the senior god in what is now the beginnings of a polytheistic system. Or the case may be one of a number of cities uniting into one confederacy. The resultant confederation of gods will be more elaborate than in the preceding example. Usually, in such a case, the confederation is not one voluntarily entered into by the several parties concerned—primitive communities are jealous of their independence—it is forced upon them by one of their number that has become more powerful than the rest. The god of the conqueror becomes the chief god in the pantheon. In a word, full-blooded polytheism is character-istic of the " empire " stage of social and political evolution.

GODS WHO REPRESENT THE ELEMENTS

A SOMEWHAT different type of polytheism is found where a number of gods which were originally personifications of natural forces are grouped together. They will then form a society on the basis of a differentiation of their functions as sky-gods, storm-gods, gods of the ocean or the underworld, and so on. The difference between this type and that already described is not always clearly marked, since the gods in what we have called political polytheisms were, in most cases, originally nature gods. Nevertheless it is possible for quite elaborate polytheistic systems to be built up independ-ently of the pursuit of empire. In that case the several gods are more likely to retain their resemblance to the special forces or objects they personify than if they have passed through the stage of being " general practitioner " gods to monolatrous communities.

This distinction between " political " and " nature " polytheisms need not be over-stressed. Provided the reader grasps what the distinction is—the reason for making it will appear a little further on—it may perhaps be allowed that most polytheisms embrace the two types, of course in different proportions.

If there are many gods it is natural to suppose that they are related to one another in much the same way as men are. The gods, like men, therefore, will have their wives and children. If men have kings, so also will the gods have a king, and the king of the gods will naturally be the one that was originally the god of some such conquering city as Babylon. Stories, or myths, are then told to explain the relationships of the gods to, and their dealings with, one another. Usually the earthly king is supposed to be divine, a " son " or in some other fashion a representative or incarnation of the king of the gods. On occasions when the myth is " performed " in the state ritual the part of the king of the gods will be played by the king, his earthly counterpart. In nature polytheisms the relations of the gods to one another will be determined on the basis of their functions. Thus the sky-god will be the male principle, impregnating the earth, the female principle, by rain to make it fruitful ; " Dawn " will be a beautiful maiden pursued by the Rising Sun ; and so on.

To the scientifically trained mind there is something almost childish about polytheism. If there is a God at all, He can only be One. Yet what is obvious to us was by no means so to the ancient world. Greek philosophers and Hebrew prophets, from their different points of view, might ridicule polytheism and its attendant idolatry. But for most people these things were part of the world into which they had been born, and at this distance of time we can see that polytheism had its historical antecedents, and that these are sufficient apology for it at the particular stage in human progress in which we find it.

Nevertheless all polytheisms are inherently unstable. Take any variety of political polytheism : it is liable to be battered to pieces as one empire falls before another. Logically the next stage in religious development ought to be monotheism. This might conceivably be accomplished in two ways. The chief god might become so exclusively the object of worship as to render all the others unnecessary. Yet he never does. The Assyrian god Asshur came near to ousting all others, until there befell the empire the fate that it richly deserved. Or it may happen, as was the tendency in early Hinduism—perhaps the best example of a nature polytheism—that the gods become confused with one another, each being thought of in turn as possessing the attributes of all the rest. This is the phase of religion that should be properly described as " henotheism." Another term for it is " kathenotheism " (literally " one god at a time "). This also, one might expect, should lead to monotheism. Yet it does not. In India it led to pantheism, the belief that all (Greek *pan*) is God, each god being thought of as a phase of, or emanation from, one infinite principle or Reality.

MAN ASKS SOMETHING BETTER OF HIS GODS

POLYTHEISM had reached the acme of its development by the sixth century B.C. In that century, too, it began to give place to the higher religions that we know to-day. The sixth century or thereabouts before Christ is, next to the century in which Christ was born, the most important era in the history of religion. In China it saw the birth of Confucius and of Lao-tse; in India, the birth of the Buddha and the rise of the *Upanishad* philosophy.[1] Zoroaster was born, according to many scholars, about 660 B.C. Socrates was born about 470 B.C., and for a century or two before him philosophers had been busy. The eighth century saw the rise of a new type of prophecy in Israel, and by the middle of the sixth the doctrine of the existence of only one God is clearly stated. Whether there is any real connection between these facts, or whether they are only coincidences, it is impossible to say. It may only be that everywhere the old faiths had outlived their usefulness, and that the time was ripe for something better.

HINDUISM : THE RELIGION WITHOUT A CREED

INDIA is a country of many languages, and its people are a mixture of several distinct racial types. Its art is in the highest degree ornate, and any one who has seen a Hindu idol, with, perhaps, a profusion of heads and arms, will not be surprised to find that Hinduism is exuberant and complex beyond anything of the kind with which we in the West are familiar. There is about it a tropical luxuriance, a fertility of imagination that is nothing short of bewildering.

Hinduism is in no sense a missionary religion. It is not in the least concerned to make converts outside India, and there are even some sixty millions of " untouchables " in the country who are excluded from its temples. For more than two thousand years they have been outside the pale of Hinduism. Mr. Gandhi's campaign on their behalf is something new, and if it succeeds some fundamental presuppositions of Hinduism will have to be modified, if not abandoned.

Hinduism knows no authoritative creeds. It is possible

[1] See pp. 452 and 460.

to believe that there is one God, or that there are many gods, or that all is God, or even that there is no God at all, and still be a Hindu.   Nor are there any prescribed standards of conduct.   Hinduism may be described as a social system based upon certain semi-religious principles, rather than a religion as the West understands it.   Those underlying principles are broadly two, viz. *Karma* and Transmigration, and are closely related to one another.   The word *Karma* means " action " or " deed," and the doctrine it embodies is the Hindu way of expressing the truth that " whatsoever a man soweth that shall he also reap."

Most higher religions have a doctrine of retribution.   They differ in their conceptions of the manner in which, and also of the place where, the retribution will be effected.   In the Old Testament, for the most part, judgment overtakes men upon this earth and within the compass of this present life. In Christianity and Islam final judgment is deferred to another life beyond this world.   In Hinduism it is effected in a series of lives upon this planet, and the passage from one life to another is known as Transmigration.   It is believed that all men have lived many times before this present life, and that normally they will live many times more.   Their present status, or " caste," is the result of their behaviour in previous lives, and the cumulative effect of all their lives up to this present will determine the character of their next rebirth. So long as a man was born into a caste, and does not break caste by (say) receiving food from a member of an inferior caste, he is a Hindu.   His private religious beliefs are a matter of secondary importance.

" GODS MANY AND LORDS MANY "

To say that no particular belief in God is binding upon Hindus is not to assert that there are no gods.   On the contrary, there are " gods many and lords many," and it would perhaps be difficult to find a Hindu whose religion consisted simply in the acceptance of the ideas of Karma and Transmigration without relation to a divine being or beings.   Hinduism has a history going back more than three thousand years.   The difficulty in understanding it is due to the fact that from time to time one system of beliefs has been superimposed upon another with which, perhaps, it had no obvious affinity.   One system has not abrogated another, and attempts to co-ordinate them all into one

15

comprehensive whole have been extraordinarily difficult. Nor is it easy to see how polytheism, pantheism, and monotheism can be combined into one great synthesis. For this reason it seems best to give a brief historical review of the various stages in the development of the religion.

The earliest Hindu sacred book, the *Rig-veda*, dates from about 1500 to 800 B.C. Its authors were the Sanskrit-speaking branch of the Indo-European family, who invaded India through the north-western passes in the second millennium B.C. When the *Rig-veda* was composed they had not yet advanced beyond the Indus valley to that of the Ganges. The book consists of just over a thousand hymns in praise (*Rig* means " praise " and *Veda* " knowledge ") of the gods, chanted by the officiating priests at the offering of sacrifices. The divinities addressed are some seventy or eighty in number, and it is obvious, both from the names they bear and the characters assigned to them, that they were originally personifications of natural forces.

They were early divided into three groups, according to the spheres in which they operated. Of gods of the Bright Heaven the chief are Dyaus-Pitar and Varuna. Dyaus-Pitar (literally " Sky-Father ") is the equivalent of the Greek Zeus Pater and the Roman Jupiter, and it is therefore to be presumed that the worship of him goes back to very early times. In India by the time of the *Rig-veda* he was already ceasing to be important. The same is true of Varuna (" Heaven "), the most strikingly ethical deity in the Vedic pantheon ; in later Hinduism he becomes an unimportant water-god, reminiscent of his function as rain-giver. On the other hand, Vishnu, a sun-god of little importance in the *Rig-veda*, in later times attained to a position of the highest prominence.

In the second division, gods of the air, we find Indra, a warrior god who with his thunderbolts overcomes the demon that would withhold the monsoon rain. Of all the Vedic deities he is the most prominent. Another atmospheric god is Rudra, a fierce storm-god who, though of little account in the *Rig-veda*, is of the highest importance in the long history of Hinduism because, under the euphemistic name Siva (" the propitious one "), he became, with Vishnu, one of the chief objects of later devotion. The third class, gods of the earth, includes Agni (cf. Latin *ignis*), fire, and Soma, an intoxicating drink invigorating alike to men and gods.

In only one hymn of the *Rig-veda*, and that one of the latest in the collection, is there any reference to caste. There is as yet no repugnance to eating beef. Nor is there any doctrine of the transmigration of souls. Life is good, and when it is over men hope to dwell for ever in a heaven of peace and happiness.

FROM MANY GODS TO ONE GOD

MOST people have at some time or another seen that freakish thing, a composite photograph. It is not featureless, but it is quite expressionless, a kind of abstract man. We have seen that one of the characteristic tendencies of polytheism is for the distinctions between the various gods to become blurred. Each separate deity comes in turn to be thought of as possessing the attributes of all the rest. This tendency is the more likely to manifest itself if the several gods are still transparently like the natural forces they personify. This they were in *Rig-vedic* Hinduism, and the next great stage in the development of the religion was the attempt to discover the underlying principle behind all phenomena or appearances.

After several tentative efforts of thought, the word *Brahman* came to be used for this one Supreme Being or Reality. The word is found in the *Vedas*, where it appears to mean " prayer." Such is the power of prayer—originally in the sense of magical incantation—that it can even coerce and compel the gods. It thus becomes superior to the gods, until in the subsequent development " Brahman " is elevated into the universal principle from which all things, including the gods, are derived. In the age following that of the *Rig-veda* it was widely believed, too, that the gods were so dependent upon the sacrifices offered to them that the Brāhman who manipulated the sacrifice and could recite the appropriate prayers was their equal or even their superior. (Brāhman and Brahman should be carefully distinguished : a Brāhman is a member of the highest, or priestly, caste ; Brahman is the Divine Principle of all things, infinite and incomprehensible, and is of neuter gender.)

Closely related to the conception of Brahman is that of the *Ātman*, or " soul " of the universe. In due course the obvious equation was made, and Brahman and Ātman were identified with one another. Further, man is possessed of a soul. In his innermost being he is superior to the body that imprisons him, and to the forces of nature that are everywhere about him. If by means of rigorous self-discipline, together with meditation upon the unchangeable Brahman-Ātman, man could rise superior to his earthly passions and desires, he would attain to the knowledge that his real self is none other than the Ātman or soul of the universe. He would be able to say, " Thou art That " ! The entail of Karma would be cut off ; there would be an end to the weary round of rebirth after rebirth, and the liberated soul would be at peace.

THE SEANCES OF 800 B.C.

SUCH is the doctrine of the *Upanishads* (literally " seances "), which are to be dated from about 800 to 600 B.C. By this time the caste system was in operation in substantially the form that it has to-day. The four main caste divisions, in their order of precedence were (1) *Brāhmans*, or priests ; (2) *Kshatriyas*, warriors and rulers ; (3) *Vaisyas*, traders and agriculturalists ; and (4) *Sudras*, servants. The Sanscrit word for caste means " colour," and it appears that the fair-skinned invaders of India hit upon this means of preserving their racial purity as distinct from the dark-skinned Dravidian peoples whom they found in the land. Then the system was given a religious sanction, and by means of it, coupled with the doctrines of Karma and Transmigration, an explanation was offered of the social and moral inequalities of life.

The prospect of an endless series of lives upon this planet is anything but an inviting one, and it is practically certain that the fundamental pessimism of the *Upanishads*, as compared with *Rig-vedic* religion, is due in great measure to the enervating influence of several centuries of Indian climate upon the hardy invaders from the North. The belief grew up that everything except Brahman is illusion (*māyā*). On the other hand, Brahman is passionless and impersonal, and the man who would be free from the cycle of rebirths is left to his unaided human resources. Nor is help to be looked for from any god, since the gods themselves are also involved in the karmic process. Those who live ill must expect to be reborn into an inferior caste—they may even degenerate into animals—until, perhaps, after many ages of time, they may be able to extricate themselves. Those who live well will, after enjoying the reward of their good deeds, have a happy rebirth as a Brāhman or Kshatriya. Only those who have experienced union with Brahman will return to earth no more.

The Upanishad philosophy has left a deep mark upon all subsequent developments of Hinduism. But obviously it was not, as it stands, a gospel for the masses. Man cannot be saved by a passionless It, in which, and for which, all moral distinctions are meaningless and void ; and if ever a people has yearned for deliverance it is the Indian. Hence the paradox, an Abstract Infinite unlike anything that man can conceive on the one hand, and a land full of idols, many of them grotesque idols, on the other. It is as though man must have as an object of worship something, Someone, that can awaken his passionate devotion.

This more popular expression of Hinduism centred round the figures of Rāma and Krishna, the heroes of two great epic poems, the *Rāmāyana* and the *Mahābhārata* respectively. These poems are probably composite, the originals dating from about 500 to 400 B.C., with later additions down to the beginning of the Christian era. It is impossible to give here even a summary of their contents, and the reader is referred to the abridged translations of them in " Everyman's Library." In the earlier portions Rāma and Krishna are no more than earthly heroes, and there is no reason to doubt that behind the legends concerning them there is a nucleus of historical fact. Rāma is the beau-ideal of Indian manhood, and his wife Sita the pattern of wifely devotion. In the later portions of the epics Rāma and, still more, Krishna are believed to be incarnations, or it would be better perhaps to say " descents " to earth, of the god Vishnu.

Of great importance is one of the later additions to the *Mahābhārata*, the so-called *Bhagavadgītā*, or " Song of the Beloved," which occupies much the same place in the estimation of Hindus as the Gospel according to St. John does in Christian devotion. The story goes that a warrior named Arjuna had conscientious scruples about fighting, whereupon his charioteer took it upon himself to bid his master lay aside his hesitation, since there is no slaying the soul, which is as much at home in one body as in another. The charioteer then reveals himself as none other than the divine Krishna, and he declares that whenever lawlessness arises he brings himself to bodied birth for the purpose of protecting the righteous, of destroying evil-doers, and re-establishing the law. Those who truly know him do not return to earth after they have left the body. He is none other than Brahmā, and those who turn to him with true devotion (*bhakti*) shall find salvation.

THE TRAGEDY OF AN UNSCRUPULOUS DEITY

THE idea of incarnation associated with Krishna differs in some important respects from the corresponding doctrine in Christianity. As already indicated, we should speak of temporary "descent" (*avatar*) rather than incarnation proper. There is no idea of a true union between the divine and human natures in one person. Further, there is no reason to believe that the "descents" of the divine Krishna are historical. Nor is there any indication that the Krishna of the original epic, still less the obscure Krishna of history, was thought of as divine. The conception, even such as it is, was a creation of the human imagination. It shows a yearning in the human heart for a God incarnate, but it does not in the least prove that God ever was incarnate. Lastly—and this has been described as the tragedy of Hinduism—many stories told of Krishna in other books than the *Bhagavadgītā* represent him as unscrupulous and lascivious, so that in popular thought the good and bad traits in his character have been confused together.

We have seen that the Hindu conception of Brahman was impersonal—"It" rather than "He." Yet many Hindus would deny that they are pantheists, if by pantheism is meant that all is God. They would prefer to say that all is *in* God, in Brahman. To the Western mind that may be a subtle distinction. Nevertheless it does explain how the Hindu could then proceed to a further analysis, and think of emanations from the one Supreme Reality. Only so could there be a religion capable of awakening the emotions ; and religion without emotion is impossible for great multitudes of people and over long periods of time. Hence, though Brahman is the ultimate Unity, it manifests itself in a threefold form as Brahmā the Creator (this word is now of masculine gender), Vishnu the Preserver, and Siva the Destroyer.

Normally the worshipper devotes himself to one only of these three manifestations. There has even been a good deal of sectarian rivalry, each sect claiming that its own divinity was supreme. Hence we find something approaching monotheism in Hindu thought, though monolatry would perhaps be a more correct term to use. The worship of

Brahmā has never been very popular, no doubt because the name, and consequently the ideas connected with it, might lead to too close association with the passionless Brahman. The two great cults are therefore those of Vishnu and Siva.

The conception of devotion to Vishnu-Krishna has already been illustrated, and it must suffice to say something of the

35. FOUR-ARMED SIVA, THE DESTROYER

Hinduism consists mainly of the cult of three gods : Brahmā the Creator, Vishnu the Preserver, and Siva the Destroyer. Siva is here shown in a characteristic dancing attitude.

cult of Siva. Siva was originally the Rudra of the *Rig-veda*, and was hopefully called Siva (" propitious ") with the object of warding off his terrors, much as the Greeks called the Furies the Eumenides (" gracious ones "). His home was believed to be in the inaccessible and storm-swept Himalayas. No incarnations are related of him, as of Vishnu ; only temporary theophanies or manifestations. There is about him, and his bloodthirsty consort, Kali, much that is utterly repellent, and Benares, the most sacred city in India, is full of phallic emblems of him. And yet there has gathered round him much intense, and often pure, emotion. This may have been originally suggested by the snow-white purity of his mountain home, However that may be, Siva has been conceived as the great ascetic, benign and merciful toward his devotees. Hinduism is full of paradoxes, and nowhere is the paradox more striking than here.

THE THREE ROUTES TO HINDU SALVATION

GREAT Hindu teachers have tried to reconcile the obvious contradictions between one part and another of their complex religion by saying that for the highest minds salvation is to be found in the Upanishad philosophy, while for the unenlightened masses the grosser forms of polytheism and idolatry are true in their measure. By this means sanction is found for everything. A few try to find deliverance by the way of knowledge (*jnana*) of the true Brahman ; more seek it by the way of devotion (*bhakti*) to a god ; the great majority seek it by the way of works (*karma*), pilgrimages to sacred shrines, and the like, not expecting to travel more than a short stage toward the far-off goal of their desires.

The religion of millions is hardly different from a crude animism, the placation of small-pox, cholera, and other malignant demons. Each man must work out his own salvation : he has brought himself to the pass he is in, and he must get himself out of it as best he can. Redemption is sought, but there is no redeemer. Family ties are strong in India, stronger indeed than they are in the West ; but in the wider sense of the term there is no social conscience, except in so far as it is now being learned from the West. Nor has Hinduism any conception of a meaning or divine purpose in history. The fervent nationalism of the past two decades is an importation from the West, and from the point of view of the highest Hindu thought it is no matter who rules the country, since all phenomenal things are illusory and unreal.

There is, however, no doubt that the newly-awakened national consciousness of India has come to stay ; no doubt, too, that the national conscience must refuse to tolerate indefinitely the reproach of having in its midst millions of untouchable outcasts. The problem that Hinduism will then have to face will be, how to adjust the conception of Karma to their recognised status in the community.

BUDDHISM: THE RELIGION OF THE SCEPTICS.

BUDDHISM is remarkable in that it has practically died out in India, the country of its origin—there are only about 2000 Buddhists in India to-day—while it has many millions of adherents in other lands. In the course of its migration to other countries it has largely changed its character. We shall therefore describe first of all the original Buddhism, as nearly as it is possible to discover it, and then say something of later developments.

In its shortest and most primitive form the Buddhist confession is simple : " I take refuge in the Buddha, in his Teaching, and in his Order." This formula is known as the " Three Refuges," and our obvious course is to arrange the materials under those headings. To write a " life " of the Buddha is not easy, for the two reasons that, first, the early Buddhists appear to have been more interested in their master's teaching than in his life ; and, secondly, that in the course of time a great deal of obviously legendary material gathered round his person. For example, he is said to have been supernaturally conceived and born, a late development which may even be due to Christian influence. It should be said, however, that the legendary matter is of great importance for the understanding of later Buddhism, since it shows how the Buddha, from being a man, gradually became worshipped as a god.

" Buddha " was not a personal name. It means " the Enlightened One," and was a title given to the founder of the religion after his attainment of illumination. His family or surname, by which he is often called in books to-day, was Gautama. His personal name, by which he is little known, was Siddharta. He was the eldest son of the ruler of a small principality about a hundred miles north of Benares, and was born about 560 B.C.

Buddhist piety, desiring to emphasise the magnitude of the surrender that he made, has loved to dwell upon the luxury with which the young prince was surrounded in his early years. At the age of nineteen he was married, but it was ten years before a son was born to him. Soon after this he stole away at night, leaving his sleeping wife and babe, and set out to seek salvation.

When we consider the India into which Gautama was born, there is nothing very surprising in the course he took. It was the age of philosophical speculation and the search for union with Brāhman, and it was more often than not those who were leisured and high-born who were afflicted with the current moral pessimism.

Left to himself, Gautama sought first of all to find peace by the then prevalent way of knowledge. He next made determined trial of the way of asceticism, living, it is said, upon one grain of rice a day. Six years were spent in such austerities, and the Buddhist scriptures graphically put it that they were "like time spent in endeavouring to tie the air into knots."

BUDDHA SHARES HIS GREAT SECRET

AT length, when he was thirty-five years old, enlightenment came. He was sitting, absorbed in meditation, under the famous Bo-tree, not far from Benares, when an answer came to the problem that had so long perplexed him. It took the form of the so-called "Four Noble Truths," which will be explained in the next section. Henceforward Gautama was called the Buddha, or "Enlightened One." He himself frequently referred to himself as the Tathagata, "the one who had arrived."

A tradition which may well be true tells how the Buddha debated within himself whether he should pass out of existence with his secret untold, or whether he should share it with others. His conception of the universe, as we shall see, was such that there was no compelling reason, except that of compassion for his fellow-men, why he should trouble to declare it. It would be no loss to him if he remained silent, and, besides, his doctrine was difficult to understand. On the other hand, to spend his life in a ministry of service would be of great gain to others. This he decided to do, and thus it came about that, although its fundamental presuppositions are entirely pessimistic, Buddhism is nevertheless in some sort a gospel of good news. This fact must be appreciated if the later developments of the religion are to be understood, or even if they are to have any meaning and justification.

The rest of the Buddha's long life—he lived to be eighty—

was comparatively uneventful. He was a teacher rather than a man of action. His teaching was from the first better received than that of many great reformers. Many of his disciples were people of wealth and high rank, and the order which he founded was liberally endowed and supported. During the rainy season—our June to September—he would

36. WHERE BUDDHA FOUND THE TRUTH

It was while meditating under the famous Bo-tree at Budh Gaya, not far from Benares, that Buddha received the inspiration upon which his teaching rests.

reside at one or another of the monasteries which were founded by generous converts and patrons. For the rest of the year he travelled over a considerable area preaching his doctrine. He died in 480 B.C. His last words were: "And now, O priests, I take my leave of you; all the constituents of being are transitory; work out your salvation with diligence."

"THE FOUR NOBLE TRUTHS"

WHEN the Buddha bade his followers work out their own salvation he was reflecting the spirit of the age in which he lived. We have seen that the Hindu sages did not look for help from any divine power in their endeavours to attain to union with Reality. In this respect the Buddha was, if that be possible, an even more thoroughgoing sceptic than they. He definitely discouraged theological speculation. His system was agnostic and, to all intents and purposes, even atheistic. He was solely concerned with the practical problem, how to escape from the karmic process. His one fundamental point of agreement with his contemporaries was his acceptance of the doctrine of Karma.

He had found no help from the Upanishad doctrine of salvation by identity with Brahman. He had tried and rejected the method of extreme asceticism. Instead he propounded the doctrine of the "Four Noble Truths." These were (1) that all existence involves suffering, (2) that all suffering is caused by "thirst" or desire, (3) that suffering will cease if desire is suppressed and eliminated, and (4) that the way to eliminate desire is to cultivate right belief, right aspiration, right speech, right conduct, right means of livelihood, right endeavour, right thought, and right meditation: this is the "Noble Eightfold Path," and he who pursues it will attain to Nirvana.

This summary bears out what has already been said, viz. that the original Buddhism was an ethical system rather than a religion, properly speaking. For if religion be, as we have defined it, the life of man in his supernatural relations, Buddhism in its most primitive form hardly comes within the scope of such a definition.

The meaning of the first Noble Truth, that all existence involves suffering, is clear, even though we of the West may feel that it is exaggerated. But the scene lies in North India, one of the most torrid regions in the world, in the sixth century B.C. The second and third Noble Truths, that all suffering is caused by thirst or desire, and that suffering and with it self-conscious existence will cease with the cessation of desire, are also, on the surface, tolerably clear, even though the presuppositions are once more thoroughly Buddhistic. Nevertheless for their complete understanding they require some knowledge of Buddhist psychology, a subject of considerable complexity.

We have seen that the Hindu believes in Transmigration, the passage of the soul from one body to another through succeeding ages. The soul is an entity ultimately identical with Brahman, though the circumstances, and to some extent the character, of the individual, may change with successive rebirths. Now the Buddha denied that the soul is either permanent or real. What men call the " ego " or soul is only a temporary collection of physical and mental states, held together by thirst or desire for existence. Desire is a sort of magnet which attracts the several states together into the semblance of a real personality.

Both ideas, that of a collection of states and also of the temporary nature of the collection, are illustrated from the figure of a chariot. Just as—or so it is maintained—the word " chariot " is only a convenient term for an assemblage of parts, so also the human " ego " is but a bundle of desires and their several expressions. Further—for so again it is maintained—there is properly no such thing as motion, for at any given instant the wheel of the chariot is in one definite and fixed position. We might put it that a line is only a succession of points. What a modern psychologist would call the stream of consciousness is therefore an illusion. There is a succession of thoughts, but no thinker ; deeds, but none to do them. Misery indeed exists, but there is none miserable.

From these premises it would seem obvious to us that death in every case ends all. Not so, said the Buddha ; there is Karma to be reckoned with. Such is the power of Karma that it can reassemble the scattered parts. Hence, while there is, properly speaking, no such thing as Transmigration— since there is no soul to be transmigrated—there is nevertheless Rebirth ; and the resulting concourse of states is similar to that which death has resolved. One candle goes out, but as it does so it lights another. It is only by utterly annihilating desire, even good desire, that the process can cease.

NIRVANA : THE GOING OUT OF THE LAMP

THIS is not to say that good deeds are no more to be commended than bad. The moral ideal of Buddhism, as expressed in the Fourth Noble Truth, with its Noble Eightfold Path, is a very high one. Those who do not expect to arrive at Nirvana at the close of this present life may still, by good works, obtain a good Karma, and so, by improving their status in their next rebirth, make progress toward the ultimate goal.

The inner circle of the Buddha's disciples, however, were confident that this life would be their last. They had passed even beyond good works. Desire, whether good or bad, no longer beset them. Theirs was the peace of *Nirvana*. The word " Nirvana " means literally " a going out," as of a lamp. Whether it involves absolute annihilation is disputed and uncertain, and when the Buddha was asked about it he declined, so it is said, to give any definite answer. It was one of those speculative problems with which he had no concern.

In strict logic, if there is no human soul, there is neither feeling nor self-consciousness for those who arrive at Nirvana. On the other hand, the monk who has completely overcome desire has already, like the Buddha, in a sense arrived at Nirvana. Yet he still lives. It is, however, his last life. When he dies he will enter into the state of *Parinirvana* (" further or complete Nirvana "), described as a condition of passionless peace. There we must leave it, so far as the early Buddhists are concerned. It may be that Tennyson's

> " No life that breathes with human breath
> Has ever truly long'd for death,"

is true even for India in the strange, far-away age of the Buddha. It is certain that later Buddhism, though it might understand by Nirvana complete cessation of existence, has usually postponed indefinitely the realisation of so doubtful a blessing.

The innermost circle of the Buddha's disciples, those who were pledged to seek immediate entrance into Nirvana, were organised into monastic communities. At first only men were admitted. Later on the Buddha, with some misgiving, gave permission for the formation of an order for nuns. All who entered the orders were pledged to celibacy and absolute poverty. The discipline was severe. There was, naturally, nothing that can properly be called worship ; the order existed rather for the purpose of mutual encouragement and self-discipline. Within it no caste distinctions were recognised, and it may be that its refusal to tolerate caste was one of the principal causes why Buddhism died out in India. Outside the order proper were lay associates. These did not expect to reach Nirvana immediately, and were naturally under a less severe discipline, though they were pledged not to kill, steal, commit adultery, lie, nor drink intoxicants.

We have seen that, according to quite early tradition, the Buddha refused to enter selfishly into Nirvana without communicating his secret to others. For nearly half a century he laboured unceasingly to instruct others in the way. But why, if he laboured for so long, should he not have been labouring for very much longer, indeed through many previous ages? This question must early have suggested itself to the faithful. They worshipped no god, and no community can be religious for long without some object of worship. The Buddha himself was obviously more worthy of worship than anything or than anyone they knew.

Moreover, the Buddha, even starting with the belief that he was only human, must, like themselves, have lived many lives before he became born in 560 B.C. What was he doing during those earlier lives? Surely he could not simply have been seeking Nirvana, for such an exalted person as he had come to be in their minds, would never have taken so long to find it. He must have been labouring to deliver men, age after age. Accordingly strange and wondrous tales were told of his previous lives. Or it was said that the gods came to him in heaven, and besought him to be born as the Buddha, that so he might bring deliverance to mankind. In this way Buddhism, from being a religion of redemption without a redeemer, came to have a redeemer. It began by worshipping no god at all, and then came to deify its founder.

THE LESSER BUDDHAS: DEFERRING THE DIVINE STATE

IN course of time many more divine or semi-divine beings became associated with the Buddha as objects of veneration. They are known as Bodhisattvas, or potential Buddhas, and it is supposed that they have purposely deferred the attainment of Buddhahood for themselves in order to assist the less enlightened mass of mankind. The resultant system is a kind of polytheism. Instead of being left to work out his own salvation, as the Buddha had bidden him, the Buddhist trusts in the merits and help of the Bodhisattvas. This naturally involves a considerable change from the ethical ideal of primitive Buddhism. A man should give himself to help others, even though it may mean loss to himself. An extreme case is related in the story of a monk who had been faithful for 42,000 years to a vow of chastity, and then deliberately, for no other motive than charity, forfeited his reward by yielding to the solicitations of a woman.

This new type of Buddhism styled itself the *Mahāyāna*, and stigmatised the earlier type as *Hīnayāna*. The two words mean " Great Vehicle " and " Little Vehicle " respectively. The metaphor seems almost flippant, but since the terms are Buddhist it seems legitimate to employ it : the Mahāyāna is a sort of char-à-banc to carry people to heaven—heaven and hell are very real in the new Buddhism—as contrasted with the Little Vehicle which a man himself must toilsomely push up the long and steep ascent to Nirvana. There is a wider charity about Mahāyāna Buddhism, but it has been accompanied by a loss of the sense of urgency and moral passion. No one expects, or perhaps even desires, to reach Nirvana quickly.

Broadly speaking, Northern Buddhism, that of China and Japan, follows the Great Vehicle tradition ; Southern Buddhism, in Ceylon, Burma, and Siam, the Little Vehicle. Something will be said of Northern Buddhism when we come to deal with the religions of China and Japan. Even Southern Buddhism is much changed from what it was in the days of the Buddha himself. When Buddhism was introduced into Ceylon, Burma, and Siam, the religion of those countries was still to a large extent primitive and animistic. The result was a compromise between Buddhism and a crude spirit or devil worship, and, as has frequently happened in such circumstances, the masses of the people are more concerned to placate the various demons that are everywhere around them than to follow the higher teaching. Yet the higher ideals have acted as a leaven, and, in the opinion of all who know them, the Burmese especially are an attractive people.

BUDDHISM DECLINES : THE CULT OF THE PRAYER WHEEL

THE Buddhist compromise with demon worship is most clearly seen in the Lāmaism of Tibet. The Lāma in Kipling's " Kim " is a most engaging and delightful old man ; but readers of the book must not be deceived into supposing that Tibetan Buddhism is a high type of religion. It is anything but that. A rosary can be a sufficiently mechanical aid to the saying of one's prayers ; it is nothing like so mechanical as prayer-wheels that are set to revolve in the wind. Pictures of Tibetan monks wearing devil-masks are attractive enough in the records of Himalayan explorers. They are, however, eloquent testimony to the way in which Buddhism has degenerated since it came to terms with devil-worship.

At the head of the Lāmaist order is the Dalai Lāma, who has his residence in Lhasa. He is believed to be an incarnation of Avalokita, the principal Bodhisattva worshipped in the country. It is supposed that when he dies the Bodhisattva reincarnates himself in a child born about the time of his decease. Search is then made for a suitable infant, who is taken to Lhasa, and, by successive stages, enthroned and invested with both temporal and spiritual power in the land.

THE RELIGIONS OF CHINA AND JAPAN

OF the " Three Religions of China "—Confucianism, Taoism, and Buddhism—the first two are native to the country. Buddhism, as we have seen, originated in India, and was introduced into China about the beginning of the Christian era. The phrase " The Three Religions of China," needs to be qualified if it is not to be misunderstood. A man does not make choice of one of the three to the exclusion of the other two. Nor is it that each is predominant in some particular area or areas of the country. It is that each has contributed something to one complex whole. The several contributions are in different proportions, alike in the general religious life of the country, and in the life of individual Chinese.

Chinese civilisation may not be the oldest in the world—it does not go so far back as the civilisations of Egypt and Babylonia—but it is the oldest in the sense that it goes back in unbroken continuity to a remoter period than does any other civilisation at present existing. It was already old when Confucius was born in 551 B.C., though we are not to think, even by that time, of an empire as large as China is to-day, controlled by one sovereign ruler. A great deal of the material embodied in the Chinese classics is earlier than Confucius, and from it much may be learned of worship in ancient China.

It has been argued that the religion of early China was monotheistic, even though worship was also paid to inferior spirits. And, indeed, if a case can be made out for the original religion of the race being monotheistic, China is perhaps the likeliest place to turn to for evidence. Two considerations, however, make it doubtful. In the first place, in the earliest period about which there are records, it is plain that sacrifices were offered to other natural forces and objects besides Heaven, the chief deity. Monotheism, if it was such, could not therefore have been very exclusive or intolerant.

In the second place, later Chinese religion has been anything but monotheistic. This may, of course, be due to degeneration, but it is more likely that popular religion contains survivals of early practice. Any appearance there was of monotheism in the state worship of heaven was probably due to the fact that the state, for its own aggrandisement, appropriated to itself ceremonies which it was once the right of any householder to conduct. At least it is significant that in the days of the empire it was high treason for a subject to offer sacrifice to Heaven.

The word for Heaven is *Tien*, and the conception it embodies is impersonal. Closely related to Tien is *Shang-ti*, which is personal, and means Supreme Ruler. The two would seem to be almost identical, since the words are interchangeable in the classics. If anything Heaven is superior to *Shang-ti*. *Shang-ti* is the mouthpiece of Heaven, and in two passages in the Sacred Books he is made to speak as if he were a man. This paucity of anthropomorphic conception is characteristic of native Chinese religion, which is nothing like so profusely mythological as most nature cults. In ancient times sacrifices were offered to " the hills and rivers," almost as if these were themselves objects of worship and the underlying ideas little removed from animism. Much the same may be said of the religion of the masses to-day.

So long as the empire lasted, the most important rite in the state religion was the sacrifice offered by the emperor in person to *Shang-ti*. This was performed at the winter solstice on the altar of Heaven, which was open to the sky, and circular, symbolising the round expanse of heaven. (The great three-terraced altar, of white marble, situated on the south side of the city of Peiping (Peking), is the largest altar ever built, and is a modern erection.) But the sacrifices of ancient times, though on a less grandiose scale, were much the same in purpose and method. At the summer solstice sacrifice was offered to the Earth, this time on an altar north of the city, in shape a square and surrounded by water, fitting symbols of the " four corners " of the earth, and of the sea by which it was supposed to be surrounded.

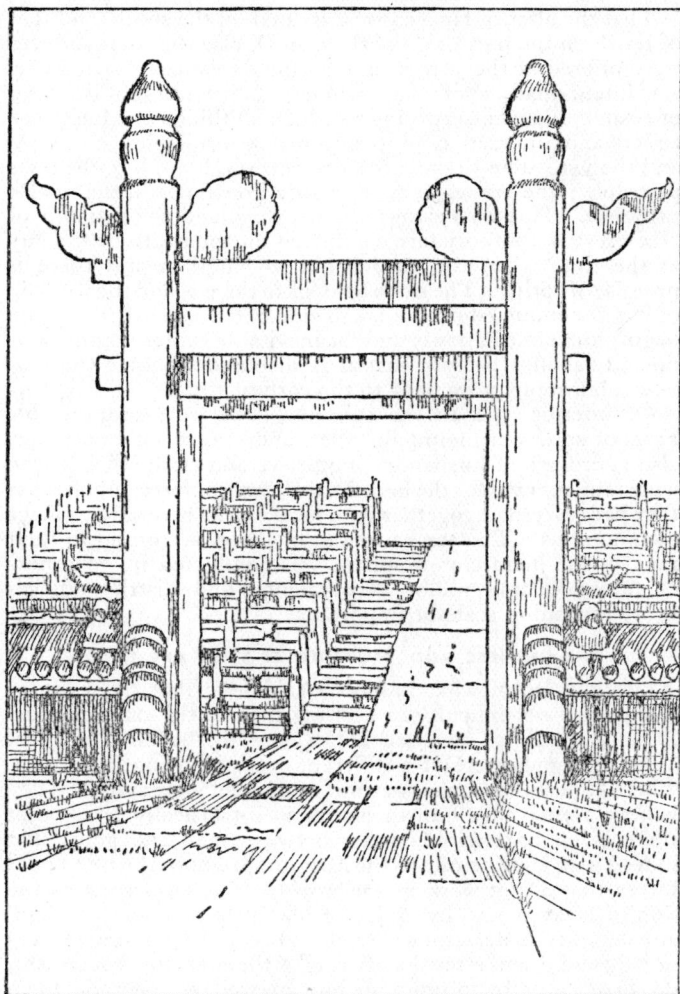

37. THE GATEWAY TO THE ALTAR OF HEAVEN.

Until the fall of the Empire, the Altar of Heaven was the scene
of a sacrifice offered by the Emperor of China at every winter
solstice to Shang-ti, the Supreme Ruler.

That the altar of Heaven was situated on the south, and that of Earth on the north side of the capital, also that the sacrifices were offered at the winter and summer solstices respectively, was intentionally symbolic. Chinese nature worship is a kind of cosmic dualism, according to which all things are due to the action and interaction of two contrary principles, the *yang* and the *yin*. The *yang* represents warmth, light, life, the male principle ; the *yin* epresents cold, darkness, death, the female principle. Heaven belongs to the *yang*, and the worship of Heaven was appropriately conducted on the south of the city at the time when the days begin to lengthen and there is promise of spring. The earth belongs to the *yin*, and the worship of it was conducted on the north side of the city when the sun begins to decline in power and the inevitable winter is approaching. It should be said that it is disputed whether the *yin-yang* philosophy goes back to the earliest times.

Of inferior rank to the supreme gods were innumerable hosts of spirits of mountain, river, and sea, of soil and crops, also guardians of husbandry, ministers and state officials who were remembered for the benefits they had conferred upon those they had governed, together with local spirits revered by village communities. The state worship of these, according to their rank in the hierarchy of spirits, was conducted by governors of provinces and minor departmental and district officials in a descending scale of importance.

THE CHINESE GODS MUST DO AS THEY ARE TOLD

IT follows from what has been said here that the Chinese have had no difficulty in exalting men to the rank of gods. Strictly speaking, men are not exalted to the rank of gods, as though gods were of a different order of being from men. The Chinese have no doctrine of human depravity. They believe rather that human nature is intrinsically good, that there is no impassable barrier between men and gods, that indeed man is by no means the least important of the intelligent forces that are at work in the world. The emperor was the Son of Heaven, and by virtue of his office he could proclaim any deceased benefactor as divine. He could even, if the forces of nature did not, after the offering of the prescribed sacrifices, do their duty by promoting human welfare, degrade them from their rank as gods. We need not, therefore, be surprised that deceased emperors were important gods, who ranked even higher than sun and moon.

The worship of ancestors was part of the earliest Chinese religion In this department also it was natural that the greatest prominence should be given to the worship of ancestors of the imperial house. But if one thing more than another is characteristic of private and family religion in China it is the cult of ancestors. This has resulted in that filial piety which has done so much to give stability to the fabric of Chinese society. It also explains the conservatism which for centuries has held sway in Chinese life. One defect of it is that it leaves scarcely any place for a doctrine of future judgment. If a man knows that when he dies he will take his place among the divine and honoured fathers he may give little heed to how he lives ; any Chinese would be horrified at the suggestion that an ancestor of his might be suffering the pains of hell.

Curiously enough, despite the cult of ancestors, Chinese religion has laid little stress upon a future life. At the same time the moral standards of the religion are high. This is due to the fact that Heaven, the Supreme Ruler, is morally, not mythologically, conceived, and most of all, perhaps, to the influence of Confucius.

The name Confucius is a latinised form of the Chinese Kong-fu-tse, " Kong the philosopher." The sage was born in 551 B.C., in what is now the province of Shantung. He was the youngest of eleven children, and in his boyhood he knew the pinch of poverty. He records that at fifteen his mind was bent on learning. He married when he was nineteen, and it is probable that his married life, like that of Socrates, was not altogether happy. In his early twenties he started a private school, which attracted many pupils. The curriculum was varied, but almost exclusively secular. He was fifty-one years of age when he was appointed a magistrate in his native state. He showed himself a successful administrator, and in due course became a superintendent of public works, and finally chief justice.

CONFUCIUS' EFFORTS TO RESTRAIN THE POLITICIANS

CHINA in the time of Confucius was in a state of political chaos, due to the depredations of feudal barons who were beyond the effective control of the central executive. Confucius strove to restore the tranquillity and firm government of the " good old days." When he found it impossible to influence for good the ruler of the principality in which he was employed, he sorrowfully resigned his office, and spent thirteen years wandering from state to state in a vain endeavour to find a position in which he could give effect to his ideals. More than once his life was endangered, yet he was uncomplainingly cheerful. He finally returned to his native state, and spent the last years of his life in literary labours. Whether he was so extensive an editor of the ancient classics as tradition asserts may be doubted ; but he did much to give them their final form, and some portions of them are genuinely his. He died in 478 B.C., a disappointed, and, except for the esteem in which he was held by his immediate disciples, an apparently unsuccessful man.

Confucius was a man of high character, though he frankly confessed that he was not perfect. His disciples report with engaging candour that his only indulgence was wine, though " he did not allow himself to be confused by it." Their assurance that he had " no foregone conclusions, no arbitrary predeterminations, no obstinacy, no egoism," may perhaps be unreservedly accepted. He was in no sense the founder of a religion, nor did he claim to be. He described himself as "a transmitter, not an originator." He was punctilious in his observance of the externals of religion, and although he once confessed that " it must be a long time since I prayed," there is no need to doubt his genuine piety. " There is Heaven, that knows me," he said.

With speculative and ultimate questions he was unconcerned. When a disciple asked him how he could serve the spirits of the dead, his reply was, " While you are not able to serve men, how can you serve the spirits ? " To the further question, what man could know about death, he answered, " So long as you do not know life, how can you know about death ? " When he was asked what wisdom was, he replied, " To give one's self earnestly to the duties due to men, and, while respecting spiritual beings, to keep aloof from them." It is in line with this attitude that he almost always referred to Heaven as the impersonal *Tien*, not as the personal *Shangti*.

The question will naturally be asked, Why should a religion to which Confucius brought nothing original be called Confucianism ? The answer is that the Chinese do not call it Confucianism ; they call it the " School of the Learned," and they venerate Confucius as the learned and moral man *par excellence*. He is exactly their ideal of what a man should be, and his influence upon all subsequent generations of Chinese has been incalculable.

They are a practical, not a speculative people. Even their nature worship, with its almost entire lack of anthropomorphic mythology, shows that. In the early religion there is no cosmogony, no myth, nor even doctrine, of creation. Heaven and earth are, and presumably they have always been. They themselves are objects of worship, not some ulterior power that made them.

The Chinese worship their ancestors. Yet for all that they show little interest in the whereabouts or state of the dead. They are essentially " this-worldly," not " other-worldly," in their outlook. No doubt the influence of Confucius has done much to make and keep them what they are ; but he is a genuine product of Chinese culture and morals, and his very limitations have made him intelligible and commendable.

HOW CONFUCIUS BECAME A GOD

THAT Confucius has been accorded divine rank in the state religion of China is, in view of the thin partition which in Chinese thought divides the bounds of human and divine, by no means surprising. It is, however, interesting to note the stages through which veneration of him has passed. It was shortly after 200 B.C. that an emperor visited his tomb and sacrificed to him. During the first Christian century it was decreed that sacrifices to him should be regularly offered. In the sixth century temples were built to him at important cities in the empire. In the eleventh he was raised to the rank of Emperor. As late as 1906 he was made co-equal with Heaven and Earth. There is something pathetic about this final apotheosis : it was the year after examinations in the Chinese classics were abolished as the one door of entrance to government office, since when the cult of Confucius has inevitably declined, until now his temples are neglected and deserted.

LAO-TSE AND THE UNKNOWABLE

LAO-TSE, the founder of Taoism, was born in 604 B.C. in Central China. He was thus an elder contemporary of Confucius, and tradition has it that the two sages once met. The tradition goes on to relate that they did not agree. Whether they did meet is by no means certain ; but nothing is more certain than that, if they had done, they would have found little in common. Lao-tse was a mystic ; Confucius was essentially practical. Lao-tse, in true mystic fashion, would have said that Confucius was thoroughly unpractical, fussing about trying to mend men's ways, when the one thing needful was to apprehend the *Tao*.

The word *Tao* means " way," and the metaphor of a way or path is employed by most religions. In Chinese literature it denotes the " way of Heaven," and thence, by a natural process of thought, the moral and physical order of the world as directed from Heaven, also the way of virtue which Heaven itself follows and which it approves in men. Lao-tse went further still. For him the *Tao* is the mystic first principle, the ultimate reality behind and beyond all things. Even Heaven is subordinate to it.

The conception is not unlike the Hindu Brahman, though it is not accompanied by the belief that the phenomenal world is illusion. Yet the *Tao* is essentially unknowable, and can only be defined in negative terms such as the formless, changeless, nameless, inexpressible Something. It is inactive, doing everything without doing anything. In so far as man can know the *Tao* it is not by intellectual effort, nor by moral striving, but by intuition.

WHERE AMBITION IS THE GREATEST SIN

IT follows that the moral ideal of Taoism is one of " not-striving," " not-doing " (*wu-wei*). *Wu-wei* is alone successful, and there is no greater sin than ambition. It has often been remarked that Lao-tse enunciated the Golden Rule centuries before Christ. He said that men were to " recompense injury with kindness." He also said, " To those who are good to me, I am good ; and to those who are not good to me, I am also good ; and so all get to be good." When someone reported these maxims to Confucius, he said, " Recompense injury with justice, and recompense kindness with kindness." This, at its face value, is little better than the law of " an eye for an eye and a tooth for a tooth," and is far inferior to the ethic of Lao-tse. Yet we must not be unjust to Confucius. Lao-tse's doctrine is sublime—with qualifications. It is the logical outcome of his central conception, and in the light of that conception it must be judged. The *Tao* is not in the least actuated by benevolence, neither is the holy man who would order his life after the pattern of the *Tao*. The words of Lao-tse may be the same as those that Jesus used, but he commended no active benevolence. He did not, as Jesus did tell men to love their enemies, and to " do good, never despairing " (Luke vi. 35). It by no means follows that if Lao-tse's precept is followed " all get to be good."

That this is not a harsh judgment will appear from the subsequent history of Taoism. Mysticism of any kind has its dangers, and a mysticism that is the product of philosophical speculation, however emotionally uplifting it may be, contains within itself the seeds of its own corruption. Lao-tse had said that the *Tao* makes its knower " invulnerable, immortal . . . his body undecaying." To teach such doctrine to a prosaic and worldly-minded people like the Chinese was disastrous, and it is questionable whether extremes have ever so met as in Taoism.

Taoist monks led quiet lives, and they sometimes attained to prodigious longevity. " Therefore," said the Chinese, " give us of the elixir that can work such wonders," and the monks were quite ready to make up concoctions—for a consideration. Emperors were poisoned in this way. The *Tao* could do anything, and so adepts busied themselves trying to turn base metals into gold, until mysticism degenerated into a spurious theosophy, and theosophy into quackery and hocus-pocus. Scarcely anyone to-day, whether Chinese or outside observer, has a good word to say, either of the religion —which, from being originally an atheistic pantheism, has deified its founder, and, besides, borrowed a medley of gods from Confucianism and Buddhism—or of the monks who exemplify it.

THE RELIGION OF THE ORDINARY MAN

THE everyday religion of the masses of China is a compound of elements from Confucianism, Taoism, and Buddhism, blended together with the original nature worship and ancestor worship of the country. Reference has been made to the *yin-yang* dualism. Whether or not this is ancient, it has certainly been of great practical importance in more recent times. Granted that there are two contrary principles in nature, the *yang* being propitious, and the *yin* unpropitious, it is obvious to the Chinese that it must be to his advantage to live and carry on his enterprises, and, when death comes, to be buried where the *yang* influences are stronger than the *yin*. *Yin* localities swarm with demons and spectres which must be exorcised if they are not to work harm. For this purpose Taoist priests, who are supposed to be expert exorcists, have been employed. Taoist and Buddhist sacred sites, too, are frequently in delectable surroundings, and this has brought them credit with the populace.

To decide upon suitable places for living, and especially for burial, is the task of the expert diviner, and not uncommonly the people have to pay exorbitantly for the deliberate delay of rascals to whom superstition gives abundant license. It is also of great importance that the balance of nature—in other words the existing preponderance of *yang* over *yin* in any locality—should not be disturbed ; otherwise disaster will follow. It was this that made the Chinese, in the days when the country was being opened up to European influence, so fearful of such enterprises as the making of railways and the sinking of mines.

Buddhism has always suffered under the disability of being a foreign religion in a country that has been inordinately proud of its superiority over all others. No matter how learned a man might be in the Buddhist scriptures he has been accounted illiterate by a people whose education has been almost entirely concerned with the Confucian classics. A further disability under which Buddhism has laboured is that its deepest mysteries are accessible only to monks, and the Chinese are not a monkish people. Yet its concern with the hereafter has commended it to many whose horizon, despite the cult of ancestors, is bounded by this world, and who, when the thought of death presses upon them, are conscious of their lack. In this way Buddhism has brought comfort and hope.

THE WEST UNDERMINING CHINESE RELIGION

THE outlook for the Chinese religions is not promising. When the Manchu dynasty was overthrown in 1911 the first President of the Republic, Yuan Shi Kai, conducted the worship of Heaven on the historic altar in Peking ; but of late years this has been suffered to lapse. Hinduism and Islam, in face of the encroachments of European civilisation and Christian missions, have to a large extent rehabilitated themselves, and are now more self-confident and even ag ressive than they have been for a long time. The same can hardly be said of the Chinese religions. For the time being, at least, they appear to be in process of disintegration, and their place is being taken by secular nationalism. Paradoxical as it may seem, this decay of Chinese religion is, perhaps, assisted by the fact that China is self-governing. Had the country been in the position (say) of India, governed by a European power, it may well be that in self-defence the Chinese would have tried to rehabilitate their religion as part of an endeavour to throw off a foreign yoke.

SHINTO : THE WAY OF THE JAPANESE GODS

THE general religious situation in Japan is closely parallel to that in China. Japanese religion is a complex of elements from three religions, two of which, Confucianism and Buddhism, are also found in China. The native religion is known as Shinto ; Confucianism was, of course, introduced from China ; Buddhism came by way of Korea in the sixth century A.D.

The name *Shinto* is Chinese, and means " the way of the gods," the second element in the word *to* being the same as the Chinese *tao*. Of all the living religions of the world Shinto is perhaps the crudest and most primitive, and if it were not that Japan is now one of the premier powers in the world there would scarcely be need to mention it in an outline account of the religions of mankind. There are not wanting Japanese—and they not Japanese Christians—who doubt whether Shinto is entitled to be called a religion. For many it is little more than a patriotic cult, " a systematised and complicated form of taking off our hats before the emblems of our ancestors and national heroes." At the same time it should be remembered that the religion of the Japanese is not quite the unmodified polytheism of early Shinto. It has been deeply influenced by Confucianism and Buddhism, and, in recent years, by Christianity.

Pure Shinto is well called " the way of the gods." Its doctrines and morals are rudimentary in the extreme, and its mythology is extravagant beyond European imagining. Its scriptures are largely concerned with the births, marriages, begettings, deaths, and burials of the deities, who number as few as eighty myriads according to one book, and as many as eight hundred myriads according to another. Out of the original chaos heaven and earth were formed. Then a succession of divine beings came into existence, apparently without being born, and again passed out of existence.

Such preliminary efforts at god-making are not uncommon in mythology. Thus in Greece there was a reign of Saturn before that of Zeus, and the Babylonians told of the first generations of gods who were born out of the original chaos, gods who were neither refined nor respectable. At length from the union of Izanagi (" the male-who-invites ") and Izanami (" the female-who-invites ") a whole assortment of gods and goddesses was produced, together with the numerous islands of Japan.

The books go on to describe the loves and hates of the deities with sometimes untranslatable frankness. One god behaved himself so badly that the rest of the eight hundred myriads " took counsel together, and cut his beard, and even caused the nails of his fingers and toes to be pulled out." It is often said that no people can be better than its gods ; but a civilised people like the Japanese could hardly help advancing beyond such crude conceptions of the divine.

THE ONE RELIGION WHOSE GOD IS FEMALE

THE divinities themselves are patently personifications of nature forces. Most prominent among them is Amaterasu (" Heaven-Shining-One "), the Sun-goddess, who is popularly regarded as the Supreme Being. It may be remarked that Shinto is unique among the religions of the world in that it represents the Supreme Power as feminine. The cult of Amaterasu is twofold. As the giver of light and fertility, she is the most important agricultural deity. As the (physical) ancestress of the line of Mikados, she is the embodiment of wise rulership. It is this relationship of the Mikado to the Sun-goddess that is the foundation of Shinto as a patriotic cult. Only so, it is probable, could the religion retain the respect of intelligent Japanese.

Many who regard the original pure Shinto as nothing more than a collection of unbelievable fairy-tales are yet prepared to maintain that the devotion to the Emperor which it inculcates serves a useful purpose as a rallying-point of national sentiment and loyalty.

They are quite content that Shinto should be secularised, and feel that whatever a man's private religious beliefs may be—there is complete toleration of religions in Japan—he should take formal part in state ceremonies. This attitude is somewhat similar to that of the Roman Empire in the early Christian centuries ; it was prepared to ask no questions about a man's private beliefs so long as he did not break with the official religion.

THE CREED OF THE ANCIENT PERSIANS

THE religion of the ancient Persians was a nature polytheism similar to that of their cousins, the light-skinned
people who invaded India, and there composed the hymns
of the *Rig-veda*. Many of the gods were common to the two
peoples. Examples are Mithra (Vedic Mitra), Indra, and
Haoma (the Vedic Soma—the Persian *h* is in Sanskrit *s*,
exactly the same mutation of consonants as appears in the
Greek *hex* and the Latin *sex*, six).

At some time between the tenth and the seventh centuries
B.C. there appeared among the Persians a zealous religious
reformer named Zarathushtra, or, as the Greeks called him,
Zoroaster. Little is known of his life, and both the date of
his birth and the exact scene of his ministry are still in dispute.
It may, however, be taken as certain that he lived, and among
the larger canon of Zoroastrian scriptures there is a section
of some length, written in an ancient dialect, and embodying
his authentic teachings. Zoroaster's conception of his calling
and of the divine message was similar to that of the Hebrew
prophets. His teaching was a near approach to monotheism,
and it is significant that, like the Old Testament prophets, he
thought of God as essentially moral. He called Him Ahura
Mazdah, " the Wise Lord." The word *ahura* is the equivalent
of the Sanskrit *asura*, the name given in the *Rig-veda* to a
group of high gods that included Varuna, and possibly
Zoroaster began with the ethical qualities associated with
Varuna, and bestowed them all upon the " Wise Lord."

WHY ZOROASTER WAS INTOLERANT

THERE is about Zoroaster's teaching nothing of the com-
plaisant tolerance that characterises Hinduism. It is not
natural for monotheism to be tolerant. Those who believe
in a one and only God would be untrue to their convictions
if they could readily endure the thought of rivals to Him.
Zoroaster, therefore, was not tolerant, and we have no
right to expect that he should be. He was profoundly convinced that good and evil are antagonistic and irreconcilable.
There is right and wrong, truth and falsehood. There is
blessing and bane, for the conflict between these two opposing
principles runs right through nature. Yet Zoroaster was not
so absolute a monotheist as to deny the existence of the gods

of the popular religion. Even St. Paul, it will be remembered, spoke of " the principalities, . . . the powers, the world rulers of this darkness, . . . the spiritual hosts of wickedness in the heavenly places " (Eph. vi. 12). It is not uncommon for one-time gods to be degraded into demons, and this is what Zoroaster did with them. He said that the *dævas*, or divine beings—the Persian *dæva* and the English *divine* are from the same root—of the popular religion, Indra and the rest, were nothing better than demons. They had chosen the Lie (*druj*), and were the enemies of Ahura Mazdah.

There is one passage in Zoroaster's teaching in which he speaks of " the enemy," or Evil Spirit (*Angra Mainyu*). The fact that there is only one mention of Angra Mainyu shows that the conception of him was not so clearly defined in the mind of the prophet as was that of Ahura Mazdah. It is an exaggeration to say that Zoroaster taught the existence of two gods, one good and the other evil, or even that he had a developed conception of a personal Devil. For him the emphasis is upon the conflict of Ahura Mazdah with the *dævas* and the Lie rather than with Angra Mainyu. At the same time evil was anything but a negative " not-good." It was a positive something that must, on reflection, have seemed of necessity to be embodied in a personal agent or agents. This, almost inevitably, was the conclusion that later Zoroastrianism drew, until Ahura Mazdah—or, as he came to be called, Ormuzd—was confronted by Angra Mainyu—contracted to Ahriman—the creator of all things evil.

THE TENDENCY TO TURN VIRTUES INTO GODS

IN yet another respect the monotheistic teaching of Zoroaster was open to misinterpretation that later compromised its purity. He associated with Ahura Mazdah certain other *ahuras*. Among these were Truth—the opposite of the Lie already mentioned—Good Thought, Dominion, Piety, Welfare, and Immortality. They were called *Amesha Spentas*, or " Immortal Holy Ones." They sound like virtues in a mediæval morality play, and their names show clearly that they were not distinctly personalised. They were rather attributes within the being of Ahura Mazdah. But in later Zoroastrianism the Amesha Spentas became personal beings to whom worship was due.

Zoroaster was an optimist, and never doubted that the cause of Ahura Mazdah would ultimately triumph. His teaching about judgment, heaven, and hell was realistic, and has had considerable influence upon Jewish-Christian, and, especially, upon Muhammadan doctrines of the " last things." He taught that between this world and the next there is a Bridge of Separation. The good will find it wide when they come to cross it. For the wicked it will be finer than a razor's edge, and they will fall headlong into the pit of hell beneath.

A disability under which the religion laboured was that Zoroaster had no worthy successor. When the powerful personality of the founder was withdrawn many of the polytheistic ideas against which he had protested returned. For Zoroaster the *dævas* were demons. Many of them now became angels.

Chief among these re-enthroned divinities was the Sun-god Mithra, whose worship was very ancient, and who was evidently during Zoroaster's life-time an object of widespread popular devotion. Mithra is not named among the *dævas* denounced by the prophet, and it is probable that his cult was so popular that it was impolitic to attack it openly. However that may be, Mithra returned to be associated with Ahura Mazdah as an equal. For the masses he even outshone Ahura Mazdah, no doubt because as a mythical sun-god his character was more clearly defined than that of his more ethical compeer. Mithraism spread westwards until it reached Europe, and was once a rival to Christianity.

PARSEES : THE MODERN ZOROASTRIANS

IN the seventh century of the Christian era Persia was overwhelmed by the armies of Islam. Zoroastrianism continued to be a tolerated religion, but gradually its adherents found themselves, economically and socially, in an impossible position. Many of those who did not become Muslims found a refuge in India, where their descendants are now found, in number about 100,000, mostly in Bombay and its neighbourhood. In Persia there are only a few thousand Zoroastrians left.

The Parsees, as they are now called, are, in proportion to their numbers, the wealthiest and most highly educated community in India. Cut off from their ancestral home, they forgot their sacred language until their scriptures were almost closed books to them. Largely through the labours of sympathetic European scholars they are recovering their interest in what, when the genuine teachings of Zoroaster are disengaged from the additions of later times, is seen to be one of the most fascinating chapters in the history of religion.

THE PEOPLES WHO WORSHIP
ONE GOD

ALTHOUGH it happens that the three great monotheistic religions, Judaism, Christianity, and Islam, are of Semitic origin, the truth of Renan's statement that the Semite had an instinct for monotheism is not particularly obvious. Christian monotheism is derived immediately from Judaism, and in that respect makes no claim to originality. Islam in its turn is based upon the two preceding faiths. The credit, therefore, if any, must be given to the Jew.

The Semitic peoples contemporary with the Hebrews show no disposition toward a monotheistic conception of God. Nor, if we are to judge from the denunciations of the Old Testament prophets, were the great mass of the Hebrews monotheistically inclined. The originality, then, must lie with " the goodly fellowship of the prophets." It may be that the prophets were only giving clear expression to an instinct that was latent in the rest of their fellow-countrymen, an instinct that only waited for leaders in order to become conscious and articulate. It is perhaps true that the Semite is less imaginative, and therefore less likely to develop an exuberant mythology, also more austere, and therefore more likely to stress moral values, than the Indo-European. Yet even this may have something to do with the fact that his original home was the sandy desert, the " howling wilderness " of Arabia.

On the whole, it is more probable that Semitic monotheism is due to the peculiar geographical situation, and, as will appear, historical circumstances of the Jews, than that it is due to an " instinct " that was lacking in other peoples. The Hebrew prophets were emphatic that God " revealed " Himself to them. That, maybe, is not a proposition that ought to be accepted uncritically. But we are dealing with a faith that has an intimate relation to history, and we should be prepared to keep an open mind on the subject. Even the physicist is not the determinist he was a generation ago. And in history the incalculable element of " chance," or " revelation," or whatever we should call it, is much greater than in the physical sciences.

The words Jew and Judaism are, of course, derived from

Judah, the name of the more southerly of the two Hebrew kingdoms, whose inhabitants were deported to Babylon in 586 B.C. To be strictly correct we should speak of " Hebrews " before, and of " Jews " only after, the Exile. On the other hand, the modern Jew thinks of Judaism as beginning with Moses, if not earlier still, and indeed the development of Jewish monotheism cannot be described without taking into account persons and events before the Exile. For this reason, and to avoid the use of an awkward word " Hebraism " side by side with " Judaism," we shall here mean by Judaism the religion throughout the whole course of its development.

THE BEGINNINGS OF CHRISTIANITY

IT has already been noted that the Hebrews were not the only monolatrous people in Old Testament times. Moabites and Ammonites, amongst others, confined their worship to one god. A Moabite inscription dating from the ninth century B.C. gives the impression that, in externals at least, Moabite religion was at exactly the same stage of development as that of the Hebrews. Yet there was an important difference. The Moabites, it would seem, thought of their god Chemosh as their ancestor, no doubt in a physical or quasi-physical sense. They were the " sons and daughters of Chemosh " (Numbers xxi. 29, Jeremiah xlviii. 46; cf. Malachi ii. 11). The more enlightened Hebrews would never speak so of Yahweh. They might call their sons by the name Abijah— meaning " Yahweh is father "—but, even if for some the name implied the physical paternity of Yahweh, there was current in the nation an entirely different account of their relation to Him. All through their history the Jews retained a vivid remembrance of a time when Yahweh was unknown to their forefathers, when, indeed, He *began* to be their God (cf. Exodus vi. 2–3 ; Hosea xi. 1, in the original, implies the same). That was at the Exodus, when He had delivered them from the Egyptians at the Red Sea.

That the Exodus and the incident at the Red Sea—however the latter is to be explained—are historical events, admits of no doubt whatever. No people so proud as the Jews were would invent a story that their national life began with a deliverance from galling slavery. Something happened at the Red Sea, and the Jewish explanation of it was that a God who was new to them had taken compassion upon them and rescued them from their evil plight. For them at least he was not the

16

personification of some natural force, still less was He some
mythical ancestor. They called Him Yahweh. What the
original meaning of the name was is uncertain ; but we know
that by the eighth century at the latest they interpreted it
as meaning " He will be " (Exodus iii. 13–15, adopting, with
most present-day scholars, the third translation in the Revised
Version margin). The Hebrew verb " to be " does not mean
" to be " in the sense of " to exist," but " to fall out," " to
come to pass," " to happen." The emphasis lies not upon the
" self-existence " or " eternity " of Yahweh—such ideas were,
besides, too philosophical for the early Hebrews to appreciate
—but upon His ability and His willingness to be their deliverer,
to do things on their behalf.

On the whole the opinion grows that Yahweh was the God
of the Midianite-Kenite clans among whom Moses found a
home after his flight from Egypt (cf. Exodus iii. 1 ; xviii. 1-12,
and note that in verses 9-12 Jethro speaks not as a new
" convert," but as a lifelong believer, as who would say, " I
told you so ; Yahweh is greater than all gods "). On this
theory, Moses, so to speak, " introduced " Yahweh and the
Hebrews to one another. However that may be, Yahweh was
to all intents and purposes a new God to the Hebrews, and
His adoption of them was associated with the crisis in history
in which they, as a nation, were born. Their relationship to
Him was, therefore, one of " covenant " (so very frequently
in the Old Testament), of choice, not a physical and inevitable
relationship, beginning no one knew when. It is to this fact
that the possibility of a progressively ethical development of
the religion is due.

AMOS : THE PROPHET WHO DENOUNCED CRUELTY

WE hear of prophets in Israel before 1000 B.C. The middle
of the eighth century saw the rise of a new type of
prophecy. It was new not simply because it came to be written
down ; it was written down because there was felt to be
something original and creative about it. Four names call
for particular mention—those of Amos, Isaiah, Jeremiah, and
the so-called " Second Isaiah."

Amos prophesied about 750 B.C. In the first chapter of
the book that bears his name, he delivers a series of indict-
ments against nations who were near neighbours of the
Hebrews. The charge he brings against them is one of
" frightfulness," of barbarity in their dealings with one

another. In at least one case the cruelty is not perpetrated against the Hebrews ; the Moabites are to be punished because they " burned the bones of the king of Edom into lime " (Amos ii. 1). What, on the presuppositions of ordinary monolatry, has that to do with Yahweh ? Let the god of the Edomites see to it, and avenge the wrong done to his people ! Yet Amos will have it that it has everything to do with Yahweh, and that Yahweh will punish it by sending a fire upon Moab (verses 2-3). Any violation of the common decencies of international intercourse, he affirms, is the concern of Yahweh.

In a later chapter of his prophecy, Amos states that Yahweh not only presided over the destinies of His own people, the Israelites ; it was He who brought " the Philistines from Caphtor, and the Syrians from Kir " (Amos ix. 7). Further, the Israelites are no more the objects of Yahweh's regard than if they were " children of the Ethiopians," i.e., African negroes (verse 7). This must have been a startling and unwelcome doctrine to the contemporaries of the prophet. Whether he thought of Yahweh as the Creator of all things that exist is uncertain. The two passages that seem to imply it (iv. 13; v. 8) are of doubtful genuineness. But we are justified in describing his conception as " ethical monotheism," and it was only a question of time before absolute monotheism should be reached in the explicit assertion that Yahweh created all, and that there is no God but He.

Amos was not a theologian. It was intuition rather than logic that led him to his conclusions. So far as he reasoned the matter out, his argument would seem to be this : Yahweh is a morally righteous God—this conviction had long been becoming clearer to the Hebrews ; righteousness cannot be one thing here and another thing there, but something that has a universal quality ; hence, if Yahweh is the embodiment of the principle of righteousness, His writ must run everywhere. On the other hand, Yahweh is emphatically not a mere personification of an abstract principle of righteousness. He is first and always personal—no Hebrew ever for a moment doubted that—and His personality is a righteous personality. Amos is a master in the domain of conscience, and he grasped the truth that nothing can be good in God that is evil in men.

ISAIAH : THE PROPHET OF THE DIVINE HOLINESS

ISAIAH prophesied from about 740 B.C. to the close of the century. By the middle years of his ministry, the Assyrians, who in the time of Amos loomed only dimly upon the political horizon, were thundering at the gates of Damascus and Samaria, and before his ministry closed they had, unsuccessfully it seems, invested Jerusalem. Isaiah, even more clearly than Amos, is convinced that the whole earth is the sphere of Yahweh's action. Yahweh even uses the heathen Assyrians to chastise his own rebellious people. They are the rod of Yahweh's anger, the staff in whose hand is His indignation (Isaiah x. 5-6). Yet let them take care lest in their overweening pride they exceed the bounds of their commission. If they do, Yahweh will not spare them either, but will " punish the fruit of the stout heart of the king of Assyria, and the glory of his high looks." " Shall the axe," asks Yahweh ironically, " boast itself against him that heweth therewith ? Shall the saw magnify itself against him that shaketh it ? " (*ibid.*, verses 7-15).

The plain fact was that monolatry was doomed to destruction before the advance of mighty empires like that of Assyria. The Assyrians saw that clearly enough, and taunted the Judæans that Yahweh would no more be able to protect them than the gods of dozens of other little kingdoms had been able to protect their worshippers (Isaiah xxxvi. 18-20 ; xxxvii. 10-13). And indeed the Hebrews, situated on the narrow land-bridge between Assyria and Egypt, in a country, moreover, of very slender material resources, could never hope to become a great world-power. It is even difficult to see how they could fail to be overwhelmed by the sheer brute force of contending empires. Yet it was their fortune—whether good or bad fortune will depend upon the way we look at it—to have a succession of men of outstanding moral genius, who insisted that the calamities that came upon them were due to their apostasy from Yahweh.

Their plight, in both its material and moral aspects, excites our sympathy. The prophets must have been uncomfortable people to live with, but their amazing courage and insight turned a stern necessity to glorious gain for all mankind. For them there was nothing for it : Yahweh must either perish, or at best become a fifth-rate god in some empire pantheon ; or the daring conclusion must be drawn that it is He who controls the course of history, using, if need be, the heathen to teach the people who flatter themselves that they are His favourites. This was the conclusion they came to, and when they insisted—as they always did—that they stood in the counsel of the Most High, who shall affirm that they were mistaken ?

Isaiah, following in the footsteps of Amos, moralised the conception of Yahweh's holiness. When, in the Temple, he saw his vision of Yahweh " high and lifted up," he was smitten with a sense of his own moral uncleanness. " I am a man of unclean lips, and I dwell in the midst of a people of unclean lips," he cried (Isaiah vi. 6). He is the first to speak of Yahweh as " the Holy One of Israel," and the phrase is characteristic of him.

JEREMIAH : PROPHET OF INDIVIDUAL RELIGION

JEREMIAH prophesied a century later than Isaiah (from 626 B.C.), and in the interval the little state of Judah, though it was suffered to keep its king, was in reality a province of the Assyrian empire. It was Jeremiah's painful duty to announce the forthcoming dissolution of the kingdom and the destruction of the Temple, which his purblind fellow-country-men believed to be inviolable. During the course of his long ministry the Assyrian empire fell to pieces, and its place was taken by a rejuvenated Babylonian power. Jeremiah's attitude toward Babylon was much the same as Isaiah's had been toward Assyria, only he went further in that he insisted that the Babylonians were commissioned by Yahweh to bring Jewish autonomy to a complete end. His conception of religion left no place for the Temple, nor for the animal sacrifices that were offered there (Jeremiah vii., especially verses 14, 15 and 21–23). He believed that state and temple must come to an end in the interest of a purer and more spiritual religion, in which each man would apprehend God for himself without the assistance of any intermediary, or even of any teacher (chapter xxxi. 33, 34).

In this, if we are to take him literally, he was even more thoroughgoing than a modern Quaker, and such high idealism might be subversive of morality if we attempted to apply it even to-day. It is, however, not unusual for genius to state bluntly, and without qualification, truths which succeeding generations are toiling all their lives to find. No doubt it would be disastrous if, neglecting to teach our children, we trusted to their unaided instinct to find God for themselves, and, having found Him, to order their lives entirely according to the dictates of the " inner light." But we can appreciate the truth of Jeremiah's main principle, that the individual human soul may have direct access to God. It was a truth that had been forged in the glowing furnace of his own experience. Scattered here and there in his prophecy are records of intimate conversations between himself and God which leave us amazed at their daring (Jeremiah xii. 1–6, xv. 10, 11, 15–21, xvii. 14–18, xx. 7–12).

Extremes meet : it is only as religion is individual that it can also be universal in its application. Monolatry is concerned with the nation, not with the individual. An intense national-ism, as we are still reminded, is not easily compatible with a world outlook. But if God is the God of one man, of me here, it is difficult to see how He can be otherwise than the God of all men everyhere. Jeremiah does not say that in so many words ; but he tells the Jews who are exiled to Babylon that if they pray to God even there they shall find Him (xxix. 12, 13). The Jews in the centuries following were slow to draw the conclusion that God cares for all men *as* men. Yet the writer of the little Book of Jonah represents God as moved by a charity and compassion that extend even to infants and cattle in such an execrable place as Nineveh.

IDOLS BECOME THE VICTIMS OF A PROPHET'S SATIRE

" SECOND ISAIAH " is the name given to the anonymous author of some chapters (xl.–lv.) that are now bound up with the Book of Isaiah. He prophesied immediately preceding the fall of Babylon before Cyrus the Persian in 538 B.C., and in him the doctrine of the sole deity of Yahweh comes to clear expression. After the manner of his predecessors he states that it is Yahweh who has raised up Cyrus (Isaiah xliv. 28, xlv. 1 ; cf. xli. 2, xlvi. 11). More than this (in language that will never be exceeded for sublimity, no matter how vast the universe is discovered to be), he extols Yahweh as the Sole Creator, who leads forth the starry hosts—as if they were His martial retinue—by number, calling them all by name, so that none is absent nor lags behind when He commands them to assemble (xl. 26, and the whole passage, verses 12–26). Throughout the prophecy there runs the refrain, " I am Yahweh, and there is none else ; beside Me there is no God " (xlv. 5, cf. xliv. 8, xlv. 21–23). The first Isaiah had described idols as " nonentities " ; the second Isaiah ridicules them. In language that is riotously satirical, he describes how the helpless idols are made, and fastened by nails to their bases so that they may not tumble down (xl. 19, xli. 7, xliv. 9–20). Yahweh carries His people ; the idol-gods must needs be carried by their misguided and disillusioned devotees (chapter xlvi.).

After the Exile the Jews were uncompromising in their monotheism, and their standards of personal purity and probity were very much higher than those of any contemporary people. They were not always popular. There was about them something severe and puritanical, with more than a touch of self-consciousness, and, perhaps, of self-righteousness. They laid great emphasis upon the transcendent holiness of God. His Fatherhood was recognised (Psalm ciii. 13), but He was the Father of His people rather than of the individual Jew. The command to " love Yahweh thy God " (Deuteronomy vi. 4, 5) was, generally speaking, obeyed with a glad abandon, since he was " a gracious God, and full of compassion, slow to anger and plenteous in mercy."

CHRISTIANITY TAKES SHAPE

WHAT has been said of the importance of the historical element in Judaism is even more true of Christianity. It has been remarked that the most serious argument against Christianity is precisely that it is a historical religion. The objection to it on this score is twofold. In the first place, the truth or otherwise of Christianity depends upon whether events that are said to have happened two thousand years ago really did happen, and at this distance of time, it is argued, it can never be definitely proved whether they happened or not. In the second place, it is said that the Infinite cannot in the nature of things be compassed within the finite, nor the Eternal revealed in time ; that it is only as religion is entirely dissociated from the temporal process, or in other words from history, that it can be absolutely true.

DOES IT MATTER WHETHER CHRIST LIVED OR NOT ?

ACCORDINGLY there have been those who, feeling that to relate Christianity to history is to burden it with so much *impedimenta*, have proposed to disengage it from so embarrassing an encumbrance. The important thing is not, it is asserted, whether Christ said or did this or that, nor even whether He lived. What matters is the " Christ-idea," which, it is urged, appeals to the highest in man altogether apart from history. Maybe it does ; but what guarantee is there that the " Christ-idea " is anything more than a figment of man's imagination ? Is there any reality corresponding to it and, if there is, can it ever be bodied forth in this strange complex of good and evil that we call human life ? And if it cannot be so embodied, or, to use the Christian word, incarnated, of what use is it except to remind man continually of his inability to reach the unattainable ? We have seen, from our study of Hinduism and Buddhism, what results when religion has no relation to history, and there is no conception of a divine meaning and purpose in history. Religion becomes " sicklied o'er with the pale cast of thought," a chaotic jumble of what, when all is said, are incompatible ideas.

If the association between religion and history is a difficulty the New Testament certainly shows no disposition to ignore it. " The Word became flesh, and dwelt among us " (John i. 14). Evidently something like the problem we are considering was already encountered, and one writer is at pains to say : " That which we have heard, that which we have seen with our eyes, that which we beheld, and our hands handled, concerning the Word of life (and the life was manifested, and we have seen, and bear witness, and declare unto you the life, the eternal life, which was with the Father, and was manifested unto us) ; that which we have seen and heard declare we unto you also " (1 John i. 1–3).

Moreover, to affirm at the outset that the Infinite cannot be revealed in the finite, nor the Eternal in time, is to beg the question. " Infinite " and " Eternal " are not quantitative measures ; they are qualitative, moral. Without, therefore, prejudging the issue, we should first of all ask what it is that is revealed. It is sometimes said that the only unqualified and fully convincing truth about God would be that which should describe what He is " in Himself." The inference is that man can never know God as He is in Himself, and that therefore there is nothing for it but to take up an agnostic position, and confess that in the last resort we do not and cannot know God. But if the New Testament is right in affirming that God is love, love which by its very nature is self-giving, then " God as He is in Himself " is an unreal abstraction, if the phrase be meant to imply that God as He is in Himself is somehow different from, and superior to, God as He reveals Himself and as men apprehend Him. The God of revelation may not be some second-best, some faint copy of reality, but God in all the plenitude of His redeeming grace.

STORIES OF THE BIBLE VINDICATED BY MODERN RESEARCH

FOR more than a hundred years the New Testament Gospels have been subjected to the most searching tests of modern critical investigation. The result, it is not too much to say, is that their essential veracity is increasingly recognised by all who value their reputation as historians. A century ago it was usual to dismiss as legendary any incident that savoured of the miraculous. To-day the miracles of healing are on all sides acknowledged to be historical. It is generally agreed that this is a universe in which we cannot say of anything that it could not happen ; whether or not it happened is entirely a matter of evidence. We may not understand how five thousand people were fed on five loaves and two fishes ; but that does not justify us in rejecting the story as unhistorical, provided it is early and sufficiently well-attested. Much that was denied by critics in the mid-nineteenth century is now perfectly credible. The conviction grows that given a personality like that of Jesus there is no knowing what He may do.

That Jesus lived there is no question. That He died a death by crucifixion is equally certain. No body of men in their senses would have gone about proclaiming a crucified Messiah in a world where such a " gospel " was " to Jews a stumbling-block, and to Gentiles foolishness." And the apostles were not demented. That Jesus rose from the dead —meaning not simply that His spirit lived on, but that His tomb was empty on the third day—is the only supposition that can account for the birth and continuance of the Church, and the amazing confidence, both in life and in death, of the first generations of Christians. There are those who have doubts about the Virgin Birth, but although this is affirmed in the Creeds the doctrine of the Divine Sonship is not derived from, nor is it even dependent upon it.

The first three Gospels were written within the lifetime of many who had known Jesus, and much of the materials of which they are composed is earlier still than they. The Fourth Gospel is later than the others, and is besides of a somewhat different character. But it can be shown that its author had access to reliable sources, and that he is at pains to correct, in some particulars, the work of his predecessors. If this were not sufficient, the extensive writings of St. Paul, who died before the fall of Jerusalem in A.D. 70, are independent testimony to the extraordinary impression that Jesus made upon His contemporaries. Although there may be uncertainty about some of the details, of the truth of the story as a whole there remains no reasonable doubt. Nearly all that is told of Jesus relates to the last three years of His life, but the picture it presents of Him has all the marks of verisimilitude.

THE DIVINE SONSHIP OF JESUS

WE have seen how some founders of religions, such as Gautama and Confucius, who made no claim to be divine, were later deified by their followers. Such deification has generally been delayed until several centuries after the founder has passed away. Jesus is in a different category in that He was believed to be divine by his contemporaries and by those who knew Him. The epistles of St. Paul were written within thirty years of the Crucifixion, and they everywhere ascribe divinity to Jesus in the most unqualified terms. Properly speaking, Jesus was never deified. There was no time when, from being regarded as human, He became exalted in men's thoughts as divine.

This fact is the more striking when we remember that belief in the divinity of Jesus was first current among Jews, a people who were altogether disposed to be fanatically monotheistic. In Greece or in India the addition of another god or two to the pantheon would occasion no difficulty nor excite any remark. But a rival to Yahweh ! . . . by this time the Jews did not venture to take so sacred a name upon their lips ; they referred to Him as " the Blessed," or " the Name," or " the Lord." Nor were those who perpetrated this blasphemy Greek Christians who managed later on to get their error adopted by Jewish members of the sect. They were men like Peter and James and John—and, above all, Paul, who, although a Jew of the Dispersion, born at Tarsus, was the most thoroughgoing Hebrew of them all.

The thing that convinced the followers of Jesus that He was divine was undoubtedly His resurrection from the dead. Yet it would not be correct to say that the belief in His divinity is, or ever was, based entirely upon the Resurrection. It is not as though, if the Resurrection were disproved or denied, belief in His divinity must necessarily fall to the ground. St. Paul put it that Jesus was " declared to be the Son of God . . . by the Resurrection " (Romans i. 4), as if to say that the resurrection put the matter beyond any possibility of doubt ; but the ultimate reason and ground for the belief lies in the self-consciousness of Jesus Himself.

In some ways the most remarkable saying of Jesus is one which is found in both Matthew and Luke : " All things have been delivered unto Me of My Father : and no one knoweth the Son, save the Father ; neither doth any know the Father, save the Son, and he to whomsoever the Son willeth to reveal Him " (Matthew xi. 27 ; Luke x. 22). The striking similarity between these words and the language of the Fourth Gospel has often been noted. Both the gospels which report them derived them from an early collection of the sayings of Jesus. The context in which they are found shows that they were unpremeditated and entirely uncontroversial : they are part of a spontaneous outburst of thanksgiving at the return of some disciples from a successful mission. There was, if we may put it so, something quite un-self-conscious about the self-consciousness of Jesus. He did not go about trying to prove that He was the Son of God. Yet in many ways, as, for example, when He tacitly assents to the charge that for Him to forgive sins is to claim equality with God, His consciousness of being in a unique relationship to God leaps out.

The word most frequently upon the lips of Jesus when speaking of God is Father. It was characteristic of Him to use language that was picturesque and homely, suggestive of moral values, and at the farthest remove from abstract and philosophical speculation. The correlative of Father is " Son." All men are potentially sons of God. He Himself is " the Son." His conscience is entirely clear from any imputation of sin, or even of sinful inclination.

THE DISCIPLES' FIRM BELIEF IN CHRIST'S SURVIVAL

FORTY days after His resurrection Jesus took final leave of His followers, and ten days later an experience came to them which changed them from the timid, faint-hearted creatures they had once been into men of indomitable energy and courage. Such a " baptism of the Holy Spirit " Jesus had promised them, assuring them that He would not leave them orphans, but would come to them (John xiv. 18). He had even told them that it was expedient for them that He should go away, because only so could He send to them another " Comforter " (so the English Bible—the Greek word, *Para-*

clete, means " one called to the side of another " as an Advocate or Helper).

Whatever may be the explanation of the strange experience that came to the Apostles on the Day of Pentecost, the remainder of the New Testament simply pulsates with their assurance that Jesus was alive and to all intents and purposes with them. Although they no longer saw Him they felt not the slightest sense of loss. The language they employ to describe their experience is perhaps not always clear, nor even consistent. Thus, St. Paul writes in one sentence, " If any man hath not the Spirit of Christ," and in the next " if Christ is in you," as though to have the " Spirit of Christ " and to have " Christ " are one and the same thing (Romans viii. 9-10, and for a similar ambiguity, see 2 Corinthians iii. 17). Yet when he speaks of the " Spirit of Christ " it is to be presumed, if language means anything, that while " the Spirit " and " Christ " are very closely related, they are not precisely the same. And, indeed, Jesus was gone, and they saw Him no more. Nothing, however, was more certain to them than that He was for all effective purposes with them.

THE DOCTRINE OF THE TRINITY

THE purpose of theology is to set forth in reasoned and systematised form the intellectual implications of religious experience. Such " experience " must, if the theology that is based upon it is to command any general assent, be something more than the experience of one individual. It must be shared by members of a community. Even the experience of a considerable group may be largely subjective and illusory. To guard against this it should be an experience that is occasioned by some happening or series of happenings, the truth of which is still capable of verification. In other words, religious experience, and with it theology, is most convincing when it is directly related to history.

Now the religious experience of the early Christians centred round the fact of Jesus Christ—His teaching, His life, His death upon the cross, His resurrection, and His continued presence with them in the Holy Spirit. His teaching gave them a new moral standard. His life was an example and pattern on which to frame their own. Through the cross —however they might explain it—they were conscious of the forgiveness of their sins. His risen life, and the power of the Holy Spirit, which was indissolubly joined with it, brought them life and power such as they had never known before. This rich and complex experience, moreover, did not cease with the first generation of Christians. It has been repeated in countless lives ever since. It is available to-day.

The doctrines of the Incarnation and the Trinity are simply the attempts that the Church has made to explain how it could be that both Christ and the Holy Spirit have the religious value of God. Obviously, Jesus was not God in the ordinary sense of the word. He was a man, and He prayed to God. Yet His relation to God as Son was something that no other sane man has ever been conscious of sharing. Nor is the Holy Spirit God in quite the sense that the word usually conveys, as Creator of the universe. In the New Testament the Spirit is always associated with Christ, and His work is to mediate Christ to the believer. We shall inevitably misunderstand the doctrine of the Trinity if we imagine that certain early Christian Fathers, who had once been pagan philosophers, proposed to themselves that they should invent some mathematical formula for God. They may have been right, or they may have been wrong, in their definitions; but at least they began with the basic facts of a widespread Christian experience—an experience that was occasioned by a unique series of historical events—events which may still be examined and verified.

Those who framed the Creeds naturally employed the language and forms of thought in which they had been nurtured. It was impossible for them to do otherwise. They spoke of Christ as " being of one substance with the Father," and of " three Persons in one God." However unavoidable this may have been, it was, for us at least, unfortunate, since the words " substance " and " person " have somewhat different meanings from those they had 1500 years ago. On the other hand, there is a tendency to-day to exaggerate this difficulty. Except in the Athanasian Creed, ambiguous and abstruse words are few.

SHOULD THE CREEDS BE REVISED ?

FOR the first four centuries of the Christian era, discussion was concerned with vital issues of the faith, and on the whole it is difficult to see how the early Fathers could have come to truer conclusions than those which they formulated. To accuse them of mere logic-chopping is to misunderstand them. They felt themselves to be the custodians of a historical revelation, and they were honestly concerned to guard what had been entrusted to them from the encroachments of error. To say that they disputed about one letter may be true. Nevertheless, there is a world of difference between saying that Christ is *homoousios*, " of the same essence," and saying that He is only *homoiousios*, " of like essence," with the Father. The one word makes him divine; the other makes Him when all is said—a creature.

The difficulty that confronts the modern inquirer is this : the Creeds, even though they may be perfectly true, are to some extent framed in language which he cannot fully understand unless he has made a study of early Christian thought. He needs to be something of a historian, and he naturally pleads that for this he has neither time nor training; or he feels that the controversies of a bygone age are entirely irrelevant to the conditions of to-day. He has a suspicion, too, that those who do understand the questions at issue are continually making mental reservations, repeating the Creeds, but meaning by them something different from the sense that their words convey.

Accordingly he asks that the Creeds should be " brought up to date," framed in language that shall be quite unequivocal and easy to understand. The demand is both intelligible and reasonable. The question is, Who is to redraft the Creeds ? Unfortunately, Christendom is divided. It is true that the controversy between Catholics and Protestants is not about the Godhead or the Person of Christ, and that by all sections of western Christians, except Unitarians, the Creeds are accepted. Even so, a general council to revise the Creeds is impracticable. Catholics see no necessity for it, and Protestants are by no means unanimous that it is necessary.

Another very real difficulty is that to alter the historic Creeds is to run the almost certain risk of spoiling them. No Christian believes that they need to be entirely rewritten, and to tinker with them may result in some very ugly patch-work. When Jesus said that " no man seweth a piece of undressed cloth on an old garment," He was hinting that an entirely new garment was needed. There is no indication that the present need is for a new garment, and the old may be in serious peril if we try to patch it. The old has served very well, and may indeed outlast any new one that could be pieced together in this age of transition and uncertainty. For it is certain that any garment fashioned now would be " a thing of shreds and patches." The probability is, therefore, that the Creeds will remain as they are. They have wrought themselves into the very texture of Christian devotion, and those who feel that their language is cold and detached may use instead the *Te Deum*, the greatest hymn ever written, which says much the same things in language that is warmer and more enthusiastic.

In this summary of Christianity, attention has been almost entirely devoted to the Christian conception of God, but it would not be right to leave the impression that Christianity is mainly a discussion about the nature of the Godhead. Such an impression would be false, even though it is inevitable that in any religion the conception of God will largely determine the complexion of every other doctrine and practice. Christianity is a religion of redemption. Where it differs from other religions is that it has a Redeemer who is a well-authenticated historical person, and that the redemption is wrought by the Cross. Something may in conclusion be said of this aspect of Christianity.

HOW CAN THE CROSS SAVE MANKIND ?

THE Creeds are content to say that Christ " for us men, and for our salvation came down from heaven. . . . And was made man, And was crucified also for us under Pontius Pilate. He suffered and was buried . . ." (The purpose of the curiously precise reference to Pontius Pilate was to emphasise the fact that the crucifixion was an event that took place at a definite time, not the crucifixion of a phantom, as some said who argued that the Son of God could not suffer such an indignity.) It is to be noted that the Creeds do not attempt to explain *how* the Cross saves men. In the early centuries the strange idea was current that the death of Christ was a ransom paid to the Devil, who held mankind in thrall. It was not until the Middle Ages that serious attempts were made to grapple with the problem. Then Anselm argued that the death of Christ was a satisfaction made to the outraged honour of God. The theory reflected the feudal constitution of mediæval society. Sin was thought of as *lèse-majesté*, and it was necessary that reparation should be made to the offended Godhead. This Christ accomplished by offering Himself. Since He was man He was competent to act on behalf of men, and since He was God His offering was of sufficient value.

Other theories have been put forward, all of them reflecting in some measure the developing legal and moral conceptions, or the politico-social relationships of men during the eventful centuries that have elapsed since the Renaissance. None of them is entirely satisfying to-day. On the whole, the present tendency is to eschew elaborate definition, and to seek to interpret the Cross in the light of that living experience of its recreating power which first found expression in the New Testament.

When we come to think of it, the emphasis which the New Testament lays upon the Cross is in itself sufficiently startling. Nothing has so puzzled men, or seemed so flat a denial of the power and love of God, as the ever-present fact of suffering. That " nature is one with rapine " is said to be " a harm no preacher can heal." It may not be so bad as that, and many who can make nothing of Christianity are reverentially silent as they contemplate the beauty of nature. Yet, if ever there was an argument against the goodness and sanity of the universe it is that Jesus, of all men, was crucified.

But Christianity, with perfectly amazing daring, has taken the Cross, that stark symbol of the worst that unreasoning cruelty and hate can perpetrate upon the innocent, and has made it the centre of its gospel, that God is love that suffers to redeem. " God was in Christ reconciling the world unto Himself " (2 Corinthians v. 19). "God so loved the world that He gave His only begotten Son, that whosoever believeth in Him should not perish, but have eternal life " (John iii. 16). That dogmatic theology is unpopular may, for the time being, be no great loss if men are driven thereby back to the New Testament, to rediscover the experience from which any satisfying theology must be derived.

ISLAM : THE DOCTRINE OF KISMET

IF we except Sikhism, which is itself a synthesis of elements from Islam and Hinduism, Islam is the youngest of the world's religions. It shares with Buddhism and Christianity the distinction of announcing a message for all mankind, and, indeed, definitely claims to supersede Christianity. By Europeans it is commonly called Muhammadanism. Muslims never call it so, nor do they call themselves Muhammadans. According to them, Muhammad was not the founder of a new religion ; he was the last of a long line of prophets who, ever since the days of Adam, had preached the same one true religion that he himself proclaimed. The name of that religion is *Islam*, which means " submission " to the will of God, and those who profess it are *Muslims*, " people who submit."

Muhammad was an Arab, born at Mecca about the year A.D. 570. He lost both his parents in infancy, and was committed to the guardianship first of his paternal grandfather, and then of an uncle. In his middle twenties he obtained in marriage the hand of a wealthy widow, and thereafter until his fortieth year was engaged in business. Then as he was brooding in solitude by a mountain in the vicinity of Mecca, he heard the archangel Gabriel bidding him proclaim righteousness and judgment in the name of Allah. Allah is the Arabic word for God, and the burden of Muhammad's message was the unity and sole deity of Allah, who had neither daughters, as the Meccans supposed, nor yet a Son, as the Christians affirmed. The greatest sin that man could commit was to associate other gods with Allah.

THE PROPHET WHO LEARNT THE BIBLE FROM GABRIEL

BOTH Judaism and Christianity were represented in Arabia in the time of Muhammad, and the early preaching of the Prophet had much of the emotional fervour and moral passion of the Hebrew prophets who had been before him. He was familiar with Old Testament story, though he sometimes blundered badly, and he seasoned his exhortations with copious and often tediously long-winded illustrations from it. He was not acquainted with the Bible at first hand, and asserted that what he knew of its contents was supernaturally revealed to him by Gabriel. He claimed that the oracles he uttered were not his own compositions, but so many extracts from a verbally-inspired original, the *Koran*, or " recital," of which God was the author.

The Meccans were, of course, outraged by a teaching which derided their gods, and, besides, threatened to rob them of the profits that came to them from pilgrims to their far-famed city shrine. Converts were made only slowly, until at length Muhammad was fain to emigrate, together with his followers, to Medina, about two hundred miles distant to the north. There he gradually established himself as despot, raiding the caravans of the infidel Meccans, and he so gained the upper hand in the wars of attrition that followed, that he was able, in his sixtieth year, to re-enter Mecca as a conqueror. Two years later he died somewhat unex pectedly, by which time he was acknowledged as the prophet-ruler of most of Arabia.

The character of Muhammad has been more hotly discussed than that of any other great religious leader in history. By Muslims he is acclaimed as a paragon of all the virtues. By Christians, until modern times, he has generally been arraigned as an arch-villain. On two main counts his life is open to serious moral criticism. He could be ruthlessly cruel, as witness his extirpation of the Jews from Medina, and a quite gratuitous attack upon them elsewhere. In his later years it is difficult to acquit him of being sexually indulgent: he had ten wives at once, " a privilege for thee above the rest of the faithful," (*Koran*)—other Muslims were allowed but four—and the modern apology that he was actuated by pity for defenceless females will not bear examination. There is no reason to doubt his sincerity. He was an Arab, and Arabia in the seventh century had very little background either of culture or religion. That he raised the standards of morality and religion in Arabia is unquestioned. The tragedy is that what was an advance for seventh-century Arabia has been acclaimed as God's last word for all mankind.

"THOU SHALT OBEY THE LAW"

ISLAM is frankly a religion of authority. It has nothing corresponding to the Christian doctrine of the Holy Spirit. Muhammad had, indeed, heard of the Holy Spirit, but for him the Spirit was only the archangel Gabriel, who communicated the *Koran* to him. If we may use language analogous to that of Christianity, when Muhammad died his followers had no consciousness of a " living Muhammad," nor of the " Spirit of Muhammad," still present with them. They had the *Koran*, which, they believed, was the very word of God ; and on the basis of it they were left to work out an elaborate system of faith and practice that should be an infallible guide in every eventuality of personal and communal life. The Muslim has often had to " do or die " ; it is not his business to " reason why." He is not concerned with motives. All that is required of him is that he should obey the law. If he does not know what the law is, he must consult the expert legist who does.

It soon became apparent that the *Koran* by itself was an insufficient rule of faith and practice. Occasions arose in which it afforded no guidance. Recourse was then had to the example and to what we may call the "table-talk" of Muhammad. This, it should be remarked, was something quite different from what the early Christians meant by the "Spirit of Jesus," and it need hardly be said that in the search for precedents traditions were extensively fabricated. In course of time the necessity of the situation was accepted, and Tradition came to be accorded equal authority with the *Koran*. If the *Koran* and Tradition together failed, analogical deductions might be made from either of them ; for example, if the *Koran* forbade the use of a specific intoxicant it was presumed that the use of all intoxicants, as well as drugs, was illegal. By the end of the third century of Islam four schools of law had grown up, and any doctrine or practice upon which the four agree is binding upon all orthodox Muslims.

It may be felt that this method was not really very different from that followed by the Christian Church, and that, given any set of initial data, the results by either method would have been much the same. There is, however, a vital difference. Islam makes logical deductions from a revelation that ceased with the death of Muhammad. No doubt there has been a development of Muslim theology. Nevertheless, the Muslim conception of religion is static, not dynamic. It knows nothing of a "progressive revelation." The Christian believes that Christ is the full and final revelation of God to man. He does not expect that anything better will ever be given to the world, or, indeed, that there is anything better to be given.

But he does believe that the Holy Spirit of Christ is continually interpreting and reinterpreting the revelation to the Church, so that there is a progressively fuller understanding both of its meaning and of its implications for human life. The initial data are, as a matter of fact, different in principle in the two religions. Muhammad is dead ; Christ lives. The results are different also. Islam has for centuries been stagnant, and it is difficult to see how it can be otherwise without going back upon its initial premises. That is why the Turks have practically abjured Islam.

A GOD BEYOND THE IMAGINATION OF MAN

THE emphasis in the Muslim doctrine of God is upon His power and transcendence. Allah is quite beyond the ability of the human mind to conceive. Indeed, whatever conception the mind of man can frame, that God emphatically is not. Yet Allah has attributes—of Life, Knowledge, Power, Will, Hearing, Seeing, and Speech. The attributes must, however, be accepted " without asking how " they function.

Further, so much emphasis is laid upon the divine omnipotence that the freedom of the human will is obscured, and even frankly denied. The most that can be said is that God wills the actions of a man, and then gives him the power to do them, and then, if the actions are evil, condemns him to hell for doing them. Also, good and evil are what they are, not by any intrinsic quality that they possess, but simply because God has decreed them so. If He were to enact that good should be evil and light darkness, it would be so. The believer will go to heaven, the unbeliever to hell. Neither can escape his portion. Allah wills it, and there is an end of the matter.

Concerning Jesus, the *Koran* teaches that He was supernaturally born of the Virgin Mary, and that He performed miracles, even speaking while yet in His cradle. He was a very great prophet, and some of the language used of Him, language that had evidently filtered through to Muhammad from Christian channels, puts Him into a class by Himself to which not even Muhammad is admitted. On the other hand, the *Koran* is emphatic that He was not crucified. Probably Muhammad was following an apocryphal tradition to the effect that it was Judas Iscariot, or, as another story had it, Simon of Cyrene, who was crucified instead of Jesus. But no doubt in his heart he was scandalised by the very suggestion that so exalted a prophet could have been treated so ignominiously.

THE PATHS DIVIDE

THE great majority of Muslims, say 230 out of 250 millions, call themselves *Sunnîs*, that is, followers of the *sunna*, or " custom," of Muhammad. Opposed to them are the *Shias*, or " party " of Ali, who are found principally in Persia. Shi-ism illustrates a very interesting development of religion. Ali was the fourth Caliph, or " Successor," of Muhammad. The Shias maintain that he should have been the first, by virtue of the fact that he was the son-in-law of the Prophet, and the father of his grandchildren. (The only children of Muhammad who survived him were daughters.) From

Ali the succession should have passed, they say, to his descendants. These *Imams*, or " Leaders," as they are called, were deprived of their rights—so the theory goes—by usurpers, and one of them, Husain, the younger son of Ali, was cruelly butchered by officers of the Caliph Yazid I.

It is supposed that before He created the worlds Allah created the " light of Muhammad." This in due time became incarnate in the Prophet, and then passed from him to his lineal descendants, the Imams. The Imams thus come to be infallible and semi-divine beings. Moreover, it is felt that so exalted a person as Husain need not have died the death he did. He must have died voluntarily, as a vicarious sacrifice for his people. In this way there developed a doctrine similar to the Christian doctrine of the Death of Christ. It seems to have been an independent development, not one borrowed from Christianity. If that be so, it is important as illustrating what is perhaps a fundamental necessity of the religious consciousness when faced by the problem of redemption.

Another very remarkable development of Islam is seen in the mystical movement known as *Sufism*. The early Sufîs were ascetics and mystics. Later on they elaborated a pantheistic monism not unlike that of the Hindu *Upanishads*, coupled with a doctrine of the absorption of the finite human soul into the Infinite Reality that is strikingly similar to the Buddhist conception of Nirvana. How the starkly monotheistic doctrine of Islam could develop into pantheism may not seem very obvious. Yet there is a real connection between the two. The Muslim Allah is so transcendently aloof that the creature man is dwarfed into insignificance.

THE NEXT STAGES IN READING

A HANDY and inexpensive introduction to the subject is Estlin Carpenter's *Comparative Religion*, in the Home University Library, Thornton Butterworth Limited. It does not deal with the several religions separately, but arranges the materials under such chapter-headings as " Religion in the Lower Culture," " Spirits and Gods," " Sacred Acts," etc. A book similar in method but fuller in treatment is F. B. Jevons's *An Introduction to the History of Religion* (Methuen). The sacred scriptures of the higher religions fill many and expensive volumes. Not all, perhaps, have access to the *Sacred Books of the East*. But it may not be superfluous to remind the reader that the Bible is an indispensable source-book for Judaism and Christianity. An excellent and not expensive one-volume commentary is Peake's *Commentary on the Bible* (T. C. and E. C. Jack). Simpler but a little more expensive is the *Abingdon Commentary* (Epworth Press). The best translation of the *Koran* is that by Rodwell, in Everyman's Library ; while the genuine teachings of Zoroaster are translated in Moulton's *Early Zoroastrianism* (Williams and Norgate).

Of one-volume introductions to the higher religions five may be mentioned. Cave's *Living Religions of the East* is excellent and inexpensive (Duckworth). *The World's Living Religions*, by Hume (T. and T. Clark), tabulates the materials in a way that makes them easy to see and remember ; but its discussions are perhaps less penetrating. Some readers may feel that this is an advantage. More advanced are two volumes of five and six hundred pages each by G. F. Moore, entitled *History of Religions* (T. and T. Clark). More recent are *Religions of the World*, edited by Carl Clemen (Harrap), a beautifully illustrated book ; and Gowen's *A History of Religion* (Society for the Propagation of Christian Knowledge), written from the point of view of one who believes in the Incarnation. These last two deal with the primitive as well as with the higher religions.

The latest series of single-volume studies is that published by the Epworth Press under the general title of *Great Religions of the East*. Each is about the same length as this section of the present volume, and they take for granted no previous knowledge on the part of the reader. The subjects dealt with are *Hinduism* (F. Harold Smith), *Buddhism* (C. H. S. Ward), *Confucianism and Taoism* (B. H. Bonsall), *Shintoism* (A. C. Underwood), *Zoroastrianism* (J. W. Waterhouse), *Islam* (by the present writer), *The Religion of Israel* (C. Ryder Smith), and *The Dawn of Religion* (E. S. Waterhouse). All the books mentioned in the above paragraphs contain further bibliographies.

INDEX AND PRONOUNCING GLOSSARY

Compiled by WINIFRED E. PAINE

How to use this Index.—In order to facilitate immediate reference to the principal entry on a particular subject, the page number for this entry is set in italics, thus : *258*. Subsidiary references to the subject which occur elsewhere in the book are indicated by numerals in roman type, thus : 387. References to illustrations are indicated by numerals in roman type surrounded by square brackets, thus : [156]. Cross references given in the index refer only to the index pages.

The pronouncing glossary.—Where the pronunciation of proper names and technical terms is not immediately understood from the spelling, or where the spelling may be misleading, a separate pronunciation is given after the first index entry. In simple cases a hint may be considered sufficient ; in all doubtful cases a complete phonetic re-spelling is given. The word is broken into syllables as it is spoken, and an accent mark (′) follows the syllable on which the stress is placed. The notation used for the phonetic re-spelling is as follows :

ā	*mate*	è	*there*	th	*thin*
ē	*mete*	å	*father*	TH	*thine*
ī	*mite*	ẹ	*her*	zh	*leisure*
ō	*mote*	aw	*awl*	ch	*church*
ū	*mute*	oi	*oil*	g	*get*
ōō	*boot*	ow	*owl*	j	*jam*

The French nasalised *n* is denoted by italicising the vowel and the nasal concerned, thus : *un*, b*on*, v*in*.